To Jen

a token of friendship

HIDDEN LIVES

BY

Charlotte Johnston

Jo Bishop

Published by Lulu.com

ISBN 978-0-9559806-0-2

For my family,
past and present

The Callow Family

Ann Fricker 1844-1869	m. 1862	Arthur Milsom 1840-1869

Richard 1863-1911 m. 1884 **Iris Ware 1864-1930**

Charlotte 1866-1936 m. 1886 **Thomas Callow 1860-1930**

Mary 1892-1927 m. 1923 **John Beer 1882-1942**

Lily 1897-1978 m. 1915 **Walter Besant 1895-1987**

Our Arthur 1901-1960

Jack 1888-1929

Bert 1890-1917

Ethel 1893-1960

Will Shepherd 1890-1950 m. 1911

Harriet b. 1919

Ann b. 1921

Thomas b.1924

Ruth b. 1916

Jo b. 1925

The Bristol Cousins

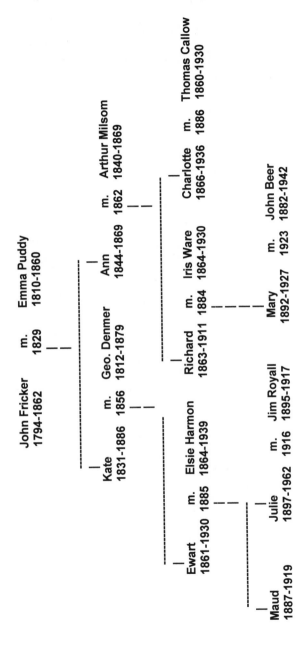

CONTENTS

FOREWORD   09

PART ONE

1   Growing up   1869   23
2   Bristol   1880s   33
3   'not fit to bring a dog to'   1907   47
4   Cuckoos in the nest   1909   55
5   Everyday life   1909   67

PART TWO

6   Lily at home   1909   77
7   Ma Morgan's   1910   93
8   Dic Awen   1911   105
9   Ancient History   1910   117
10 The Cambrian Strike   1911   133
11 Penmaen   1912   147

PART THREE

12 Enter Walter   1913   169
13 Dancing at the Dairy   1913-1914 191
14 War with Germany   1914-1915 213
15 Till death do us part   1915   229
16 Hillside   1916   243
17 'Gwell angau na chywilydd'   1917-1918 265

PART FOUR

18	Public peace private war	1919	289
19	A game of bluff?	1919	311
20	Managers and Men	1921	321
21	Nothing but a gamble	1922-1923	339
22	To see something of the world	1923	357
23	A new beginning	1924-1925	371
	AFTERWORD		389

FOREWORD

"O! Call back yesterday, bid time return"

(Richard II)

Foreword

As I stare in the mirror, my mother's face looks back at me. Greying hair above a high forehead marked, though not deeply, with uneven lines. Thickish dark eyebrows shading deep-set eyes, cavernous in this harsh morning light. Rather a snub nose. Pale cheeks, rounded by the line of contour from the nose to the corners of the mouth. The once-familiar, never-forgotten face of my dead mother.

The resemblance disturbs me, so that I search for the distinguishing marks of my own identity. She had grey-green eyes, cats' eyes. Mine are light-brown, tawny, more like lions' eyes. All her teeth had been taken out by the time she was thirty, so that the lower part of her face looked hollowed. As yet, my teeth are sound, my jaw still firm. False teeth - we never called them "artificial teeth", much less "dentures" - she couldn't get used to, although at first she would try to keep them in whenever there was Company or when she was going Up the Road. But the patent fixative which promised "Comfort for Denture Wearers" with "No More The Embarrassment of Slipping Teeth" made her gums feel sore, so that it wasn't long before she gave up putting them in altogether. Instead, whenever she was talking to "tidy people", she would shield her mouth with the back of her left hand in a self-conscious gesture of concealment.

My father had no such inhibitions. He "never bothered with getting they false teeth", and would talk and laugh open-mouthed, "like a frog. Exactly the same as a frog" my mother would say, her tone at once scornful and resigned, "but he don't care a bit." It was she who felt uncomfortable on his account, for he himself never considered outsiders to be of any importance. It may be that he had a natural confidence which made him indifferent to the bad impression he might be making on others, or perhaps he cared nothing for the opinion of other people because he knew that the one person whose approval he craved would never show pride in him in company or feel affection for him when they were alone. Of outsiders he would say, in the broad Bristol accent which unlike his wife he never lost, "They can bloody well please theirselves, the whole damn lot on 'em. Take I or leave I." He was outspoken with everybody, with my mother's family, with the colliery bosses, even with that lifeline to gentility, the vicar.

"No wonder I'm on pins every time he opens his mouth" she used to say, "afraid to my heart of what he's going to say next."

From an early age I shared her anxiety, for I identified myself with my mother, even as I wished I was more like my sister Ruth, who would laugh and say "Oh, what's the odds? That's just our dad, that is." But both Ruth and I saw him through our mother's eyes. She had married beneath her. We accepted it without question, for to us it was self-evident that she was superior. That it might not have seemed so to others never occurred to us, so it was with disbelief that after her death I overheard a neighbour's "He deserved better". *He* deserved better! But by then it was too late for re-appraisal, and far too late to try and build a different relationship.

My mother dominated my childhood and, by that

early supremacy, much of my adult life. I loved her, and would not willingly have caused her a moment's pain. But by the time she died, the link between us had become too weak for me to feel any of that grief which is the price we pay for love. In old age she had become sour, and now that I see myself daily growing to look more like her, I feel a compulsion to prove that between us there is no more than an outward resemblance. My physical inheritance is unmistakeable, not to be discounted or disclaimed, and I know, because I heard it said so often when I was a child, that my mother "favoured" her mother, so that I suppose, if I live that long, I shall come to look like my Granny Callow, Charlotte, who lived near us and who died when I was twelve.

All my mother's family lived near us, her mother and father and unmarried brothers a few doors away from us, her married sister a little way down the same street. Their lives constantly touched ours, but hardly ever in an approving, much less an affectionate, way. I liked none of them except my Aunt Ethel, though I could see she was no favourite with my mother Lily. My mother cared only for my Gran and my Uncle Jack.

Jack was the clever one of the family. He was censorious and sardonic, severe on himself and on others and by the time I knew him, he had become gloomy and embittered. I used to wonder why my mother thought so much of my Uncle Jack when he was such an unlikeable man.

Bert, the second son, was the son most like his father. Next in age to Jack, he was seven years older than

Foreword

Lily.   Easy-going by temperament and unthinking rather than thoughtless, he was a peace-lover and a peace-maker. In my mother's eyes he was significant only when he threatened to monopolise Jack's time; otherwise to her he was a good-natured non-entity. I never knew my Uncle Bert, "our poor Bert", except by the sepia studio photograph on the wall opposite Gran's bed.

Our Arthur, never just Arthur, was neither good-natured nor a non-entity. He was the youngest of the family, thirteen years younger than Jack the first-born and, to his mother, always "a poor little feller". She insisted that he was "delicate", too delicate to become a miner like his father and brothers, and instead, apprenticed him against his wishes to a cabinet maker, a training which he never finished. Arthur never had a regular job of any kind, and lived all his life at home on Sickness Benefit, so that he must have had some physical weakness even though to look at, he was like the other boys in the family, tall and powerfully built.

"A wasted life" my mother would say mournfully. "Our Arthur's just wasting his life."

"Aye" my father would fling back. "And who be wasting it for him? Lazy bugger. Job o' work ud tickle him up a bit mun, gurt strapping feller like that."

My father was five feet four inches tall, and had no love for any of his brothers-in-law, except Bert. It was only loyalty to my mother which stopped me from sharing his dislike; as it was, I could feel at best indifferent. Arthur was like Jack, but not so formidable. Running errands up the Road I would often meet Arthur coming away from the

Library with an armful of the books he had both the leisure and the inclination to read, but he would stop for only the briefest of greetings, hardly more than he would have given to a neighbour's child. Down Gran's, as I realised, they were all more fond of my sister Ruth than they were of me, although Aunt Ethel couldn't help liking me because I was a child.

My Auntie Ethel was nothing like my mother, neither in nature nor in appearance. She was tiny in stature, plump, with surprisingly thin legs, so that when she darted about she looked like an overgrown sparrow. She had dark brown inquisitive eyes and a sharply-pointed nose, almost like a beak. But her voice was gentle and her laugh was soft like the cooing of a dove. My earliest memory of Auntie Ethel was of the scent and feel of her fur-backed gloves, significant, although I was too young to realise it then, of her "passion for dress". My mother could accept Ethel's fascination with clothes, even though she would say scornfully "all that dolling up and yet she never had the boyfriends I had and could have had". But she could never understand Ethel's obsession with children, not only her own, but anybody's children. "Dull on them" was my mother's verdict.

When we called in to Auntie Ethel's house I never wanted to go home. I wanted to sit with the others on the old bus seats which were their dining chairs and share their supper of home-made chips. Auntie Ethel would make a game of serving them out. Instead of piling them on to plates, she would take orders as if we were in the chip shop. "A pennorth my lamb?" and to me "like some, my love? Don't look at your mother!" This last because I would instinctively seek my mother's permission by a glance even though I longed to say "yes". The orders taken, she would put each portion on to pieces of newspaper and wrap them up in return for the pretend money we were eager to place in her hand. We ate them noisily, greedily, without forks, licking the salt and vinegar from our fingers and asking for more. I would feel my mother's disapproval but in that safe atmosphere I could be bold enough to ignore it.

On the way home she would criticise: "What a way to live. Our Eth dolled up to the nines always, dirt and dust everywhere in the house, kids pulling everything about...those three kids rule the roost there. Talk about spoiling children, our Ethel ruins them, and Will Shepherd not lifting a finger."

I had no habit of thinking my mother to be wrong in any of her judgements, but I couldn't help being guiltily aware that I didn't like our own clean and quiet house half as much as Auntie Ethel's dirt and noise, and that if spoiling meant being called "darling lamb" and eating chips out of newspaper then I wouldn't have minded being spoilt myself.

My mother would never spoil children. When people asked her, as they did sometimes, how many children she had, Lily was perfectly serious in her reply. "Two," she'd say "and that's two too many." Two children, and both girls. If there had to be children, as Lily told her daughters, she would prefer them to have been boys, so we had been a disappointment from the beginning. Lily was like Jack in looks and in temperament, but with the added biological disadvantage of being a woman. "So much better to be a man in this world" she would say, even though she recognised that it was the woman who was the most important member of our family, as of all the families we knew. In our world the man brought home the money, money hard earned by work underground, but it was the woman who decided how it was to be spent.

We lived in South Wales, in the Rhondda, the most Westerly of the four roughly parallel valleys which stretch crookedly like the open fingers of a hand northwards from Cardiff between Pontypridd and the Brecon Beacons. In my childhood, our horizons were limited, literally, by the mountains which surrounded and enclosed us. Once in a while we'd take the red Rhondda double-decker bus down to Pontypridd and on to Cardiff for a "jaunt" and maybe shopping. Cardiff was twenty miles from home, and the bus took an hour and twenty minutes.

Northwards we knew Treorchy. It had big shops, much bigger than in Gelli, and it had the Cemetery. Treorchy was within walking distance, not more than three miles or so, Tonypandy a little further, but a more pleasant walk because of the woods bordering the New Road.

That was the extent of my knowledge of where we lived. I would watch my sister write in her Tiger Tim Annual our name and address by street and town, Gelli Pentre, Rhondda Valley, Glamorgan, South Wales, Great Britain, The World, The Globe, The Planet, The Universe, but our universe was strictly bounded. Beyond Treorchy was unexplored land, the Brecon Beacons, always "The

Beacons", gateway to the rural Wales of Brecknock and Cardiganshire, and stretching Northwards as far as Anglesey. But in our family our gaze was directed South to the Bristol Channel and to England, for both our parents were born in Bristol and we had learned from them and from Gran and Grancher that Bristol was "up 'ome".

The wider society in which a child grows up has an abiding influence, but it is on the small circle of the family that her happiness or unhappiness depends. My mother not only held the financial reins but she also regulated the emotional temperature of the family. Lily's two daughters grew up knowing they were at best only tolerated, and that the affection they could expect from their mother was conditional upon their not causing her worry of any kind. Their father would have been indulgent, especially to his younger daughter. But he was capricious, and worse, weak-willed, so that he allowed his feelings to be dictated by Lily's reactions, and his conduct towards both his children to be governed by her decisions. He outlived Lily by nine years, and during the whole of that time he followed exactly the patterns of behaviour she had set down, nor did he change from the attitudes of mind she had taken up for him.

Her influence, on him and on her daughters, was profound. One mark of its strength is my own reluctance to accept my outward physical legacy, and my desire to be different. I know that her life was not easy, that her potential for good was unfulfilled, and that she suffered a cruelly hard death. It is this knowledge which makes me accept that her failure to love her husband and her children was not her fault or theirs, but rather their misfortune.

I observed them all with the clear myopic gaze of childhood, this family, some of whom had lived more than half their lives before mine had ever begun. But those past years of theirs were not unknown to me. I grew up hearing the same stories over and over again, memories of early married life, accounts of quarrels brought to mind, old scores long settled, hardships suffered, and the nostalgia for Bristol which passed for conversation Down Gran's.

My father had no patience with 'Raking up the Past". It was an essentially Callow activity, pointless and tedious. "There baint no need of any on it. Morbid I calls it."

But I was a listener, and their talk with its Somerset phrases and Bristol accent served to feed my imagination and to confirm my intuitive grasp, common to all solitary children, of the intent which lay beyond the words themselves.

My sister was nine years older than me, and we were never close. She was a rebel by nature, provoking and revelling in conflict, whereas I was the conformist seeking peace.

I would sit at the top of the stairs when I should have been in bed, hoping that the angry voices, Ruth's as loud as my father, would soon stop. I was glad when she left home, although I missed the good times when she didn't come sobbing to bed, and we played dangerously with the lighted candle, putting our fingers more and more slowly through the flame.

Foreword

I became virtually an only child, with Ruth an insignificant part of my life and my mother glad of me as a listener. Lily was only ten when they left Bristol, so her Somerset memories were mostly variants on Gran's stories, but she seemed to have total recall of their early days in the Rhondda, and of her feelings and fears she would tell me more than I wished to hear.

The Callows lived through "interesting times" and of these times the events are well documented, history as public property lying in collective memory. But the history of a family living through these events depends for its telling on the viewpoint of individual members, subjective and biased as it must be.

This is my telling of their story, beginning with my great grandparents Ann and Arthur Milsom. They died in 1869, leaving their two young children to be brought up in Ann's sister's family. The girl, Charlotte, was my grandmother. Her brother, Richard. I never knew.

They are long gone from this earth, but I hear their voices in my head, sharp and clear. My grandmother's is querulous with pain, "Whatever be she writing now, Lily?". My father as so often taking my part against the hostility of all "they Callows", "Let 'er be, mun, she bain't doing no harm", and my mother's warning "Mind not to let too much go outside this house, remember".

I have let some things go outside that house, but there is much more which remains untold. Hidden lives, hidden secrets.

PART ONE

CHAPTER ONE

GROWING UP

1869

"Cousin: A collateral relative more distant than a
brother or sister"

O.E.D

Chapter One

It had been a fitting day for a funeral, sleeting rain glistening on the backs of the horses and the top hats of the drivers, mud from the carriage wheels spraying almost up to the glass sides of the hearse.

At the graveside, the wind spattered the newly-turned clay with leaves, the rain muffling the vicar's words of committal and drumming heavily on the coffin lids with their engraved brass plates. "Ann Milsom 1844-1869". "Arthur Milsom 1840-1869". Just two among the many victims of typhoid fever, leaving as their pitiful legacy the children Richard and Charlotte, too young to realise their loss.

Charlotte at three had no memory of that day, no memory even of what her mother and father had looked like. She kept only the faint impression of a warm hand enclosing hers long ago, yet all her life there were times when an unheralded sense of emptiness would overwhelm her and make her day dark.

Richard the big brother three years older felt more bewilderment than sorrow. Their Aunt Kate and Uncle George were strangers who were about to take him and Charlotte away from their Bristol home. They were to live in Wells and be part of the Denmer family, to be brought up with Ewart, almost exactly Richard's age.

Kate's grief for her only sister had spurred her into immediate action. "No Mullers Orphanage for they two, for all it's cracked up to be", she said. "No, not while we got a roof over our own heads".

Ewart begrudged the attention so willingly given by his mother and father to his cousins. When in the beginning Charlotte would ask "When are we going home?" he was quick to remind them "You got no home to go to. You got no father and mother".

Richard seeing his sister's tears would begin a fight which, however it ended, would put Richard in the wrong and earn him the undeserved reputation of being the one who picked the quarrel. Richard was the taller and stronger, which gave Ewart the chance to complain that Richard was a bully.

Everything was a cause for disagreement between them, every outing a clash of wills, so that Aunt Kate in exasperation would say "I declare, I never will bring you two boys out ever again, and if I do go out, it shall be on me own or else with Charlotte".

Charlotte looked forward to the outings but not to the boys falling out as they always did.

"All this quarrelling and argufying," said Aunt Kate. "It fair makes me head spin."

Richard would beg her to take them again into the Cathedral to look at the astronomical clock in the North transept, "that picture clock and see the tourneyment".

"Silly old clock," said Ewart under his breath, "and a boring old building."

But he would wait with the others for the hour to strike to see the knights in armour ride out from behind their doors and knock a knight off his horse every time they went round.

"Tourneyment," said Ewart, "that be no tourneyment, knights riding round. Takes more than that to make a tourneyment. You be wrong again Dicky Know-All. Dicky Dullard more like."

It was no better when they went to watch the swans in the moat around the Bishop's Palace, stretching out their necks and catching hold of the bell rope in the wall to ring for food. Ewart would dare Richard to throw sticks at the swans, and then call him namby pamby when he refused.

If Richard was namby pamby, Charlotte was a timid cry-baby, an easy target for Ewart's so-called teasing. He did not always succeed. When he tried to frighten her about the old books kept in the Cathedral library fastened to the shelves with great chains, he tried too hard.

"Them books be dangerous. They breaks them chains at night and they comes after people."

This was not to be believed, especially when Richard was nearby to assure her that it was all nonsense.

"Better they two boys be kept apart" Uncle George, seeing the hostility between them, would say with a sigh. They were too unalike in temperament and in outlook ever to agree, too different in what they thought important and interesting.

Richards's passion, even when he was very young, was for buildings, houses, cottages, churches, asking "What is it made of? How old is it?", and Aunt Kate always declared that Richard taught himself to read by looking at the inscriptions on tombstones. Reading "sleeping", "at rest", Richard had to reassure Charlotte that the people underneath the stones would not suddenly wake up, refreshed, and rise up out of their graves.

Chapter One

When he was older he would go by himself to the Cathedral, walking the cloisters, examining the stonework and getting to know the structure and the different styles of building long before he learned the meaning of the word "architecture". Sometimes he would take himself off for the whole day exploring the countryside, on foot to Glastonbury, hitching rides to Bath and once, all the way to Bristol. He would go inside the churches and the abbeys, noticing where their fabric was in need of repair, seeing how the features of the gargoyles could be restored, and all with a dedication which was almost religious in its fervour.

Uncle George could not share or understand such enthusiasm, but he could see the practical use of Richard's interest. "I'll gladly pay for the lad to be 'prenticed to the master stonemason hisself. I reckon as how the boy will have a trade in his hands and a skill as will keep 'en from being beholden to anybody. Seven years, a long time but worth it in the end."

George and Kate Denmer had never consciously made any difference between the children, and had no wish to deepen the sense of obligation which both Richard and Charlotte could have felt.

But Ewart lost no chance of reminding them of that obligation, and that they were not even adopted but just taken in. His only interest in Richards's apprenticeship was in making sure that Richard never forgot that it was Ewart's father who was paying the premiums. He could not share his parents' pride when near the end of his apprenticeship Richard was chosen to help restore the carvings on the West front of the Cathedral, and he was irritated to see how eagerly they and Charlotte listened to Richard's outpourings about "all they saints and martyrs, made of Doulton limestone they be, lovely white stone, but going crumbly in time. Hundreds of years old and like to stand for a hundred more. A man's work's never done with they 'postles and martyrs. Doulting stone, still from the same quarry today, and not far to bring it".

Ewart's plan for himself was simple. He would go into the family business, the carrier trade which George had begun with just a handcart in the Whiteladies Road, and had built up into a flourishing concern.

There was the heavy-duty haulage cart pulled by two dray horses, and the lighter one-horse delivery cart, each with the Denmer name and address painted in white on the sides.

Once in a while George allowed Ewart to take the reins while they delivered parcels and foodstuffs, mostly to little places like Dulcote and Chewton and Upper Godney, though sometimes as far afield as Cheddar and Midsomer Norton. Ewart's delight was in looking ahead to the time when not two but a dozen or so carts would bear his name and be known right throughout Somerset. "Ewart Denmer Haulier. Goods large and small".

George did not live to see his son's dream realised. When in 1879 his father died, Ewart was barely eighteen, but he was used to being in charge of the business of "Geo. Denmer and Son, Hauliers".

Ewart was hard-working and shrewd; in less than five years he was well on the way to fulfilling his ambition to replace his father's country carrier's carts with long-distance wagons. His nine carts had become a familiar sight in Bristol, Bath and Exeter, while his drivers were soon delivering as far afield as Plymouth in the South and Gloucester in the North.

Even Richard had to agree with Aunt Kate that Ewart had "a good head on his shoulders" as far as money-making was concerned; from his new base in Bristol Ewart was planning further expansion, regular services to all the big cities in England as well as to the coastal towns of South Wales, and it was not an impossible goal. Far from it. When his side-line "wagonnettes and landaus for hire" proved a success, Ewart's confidence in himself felt justified. He was gaining a reputation for reliable though pricey service, and as his reputation grew, so did his money.

Ewart was going up in the world and now that he had something behind him in the bank, he could think of getting married.

He was irked that Richard and Charlotte were still sharing his mother's house, even though Richard was out of his apprenticeship. Behind Kate's back he could be blunt:

"Moving out into lodgings yet Richard?"

"Thinking of paying your way at last thanks to my father?"

And to Charlotte:

"Found yourself a place of service yet then?"

Or "When's the wedding to be?"

Chapter One

There was to be a wedding, but not Charlotte's and not, for a while, Ewart's.

"Richard's the first to go off" said Aunt Kate sadly.

Richard had been courting ever since he began earning a steady wage as a skilled and fully trained mason, and in May 1884 he and Iris got married. The wedding was in St Luke's Brislington, the church where Iris' widowed father, the Reverend Frederick Ware, had been vicar for ten years.

Ewart was glad that Richard had got himself a place out of his mother's house, but he was not pleased that Richard could afford to get married eighteen months before him, although it was only to "a nonentity from a family as poor as church mice".

That was a mistake Ewart was determined to avoid.

With Richard gone, "living out at Knowle of all places", and Charlotte keeping house as unpaid servant, Ewart looked about for a suitable wife. He was not going to marry for money, but certainly where money was, for Elsie was the only daughter of Harmon the Wine Merchant, whose business was said to be the equal of John Harvey's.

"A stuck-up mommock" was Charlotte's verdict when finally and reluctantly she and Elsie were brought face to face. It was a judgement she never altered.

Ewart had taken a house ready for his bride in St Michael's Hill, furnished in the best of taste by Elsie with money provided by Robert Harmon.

"Not exactly Great George Street" said Elsie, "but good enough for the time being."

Chapter One

It was more than "good enough" to make Charlotte feel out of place the few times she went with Aunt Kate to Clifton to visit the newly-weds. She would never have warmed to Elsie. Aunt Kate in time might have become fond of her daughter-in-law, for she was accustomed to liking people. But that time was not given to her, for in January 1886 Aunt Kate died of pneumonia.

"And I know what brought it on, too" said Charlotte. "That cough. I know when it started."

She was thinking of the bitterly cold November morning of Ewart's wedding two months before.

St Mary Redcliffe was icy, hardly warmer than the air outside, and the service was impossibly long, with vows, anthems, hymns, exhortations and a sermon lasting a full three quarters of an hour.

"Wasteful with the time, like with everything else" said Richard. "Although" he added "it were a bonus to get a good look at that lierne stone vaulting and measure up in anybody's mind the length of that nave and the width of them transepts."

Charlotte grieved for the aunt who had taken the place of the mother she had hardly known, and was sorry to leave the house where she had been brought up.

But Ewart was business-like. By Kate's will the house was to be sold and the proceeds divided equally among the three "just like as if they belonged to our family and had our name, which they aint got" said Ewart in disgust.

He was the executor, and had put the house up for sale even before the funeral. Charlotte was in the way.

Chapter One

"Vacant possession attracts buyers", and Ewart was anxious to increase his capital.

It was just as well for Charlotte that Richard and Iris were eager for her to share their home, and she was only too glad to move with her few possessions to their rented house in Wells Road.

Those months in Knowle were to be the happiest of her life.

CHAPTER TWO

BRISTOL

1880s

"What is your name?

Charlotte Milsom

Where is your home?

Bristol."

A Child's Catechism

Bristol, an ancient commercial and industrial city and a great sea port with an old Cathedral...City of churches and charities..."

Baedeker Bristol

Ewart was outraged when he heard the news.

"Never did think much on her, nor Richard neither but 'er might have had a bit more sense. Or shown some respect for my family. Mother and father takes them in and gives them a good life, more fool they, and this is the thanks you get. Thank God Mother aint here to see this day. Married to a hulking brute, seven feet tall, voice like a fog horn. Thrown herself away completely."

Elsie was cool: "Nothing you can do. She's found her level by the looks of it. Old enough to know her own mind, nearly twenty."

"I blame that Iris, her influence," Ewart persisted. "All on us equal in the sight of God and all that. Well there's equal and equal, and with all respect that Thomas Callow aint my equal though I says it myself. No farm hand's my equal and that's flat...Living from hand to mouth".

Elsie sighed. "Poor relations. What a bore. I only hope they keep their distance, otherwise it'll be a drain on our income."

Iris was more idealistic and romantically inclined to think the marriage would somehow turn out alright.

"He's a rough diamond" she said "and he knows she's a cut above him. He dotes on her...see the way he looks at her. And he don't smoke, he don't gamble and I lay my oath he's not one to run after other women."

Richard nodded. "Maybe it's wrong what they say, marry in haste and repent at leisure."

But he couldn't help wishing that Charlotte had known Thomas longer. She had been swept off her feet he reckoned, the good looking farm hand who had spent so many hours tending the church grounds of St Luke's, summer and winter alike. Iris' father had encouraged the hard-working lad. But then, he supposed, so had Charlotte.

"Well, if he makes her happy..." he said.

"And," said Iris, "many a couple have set up home on as little money."

Home for Charlotte and Thomas, their first home, was in Luckwell Road, not a bad part of Bedminster. For 4/6 a week they had the use of the scullery and two rooms besides for themselves. As 'partments go, it was homely, and at first they were happy.

Here in May 1888 Jack was born, closely followed in July 1889 by Bert.

It was time for Thomas to think of leaving Court Farm in Longwell Green. A farm labourer's wage was not enough to support a family of four, soon to be a family of five.

By the time Ethel was born in April 1893 Thomas had made the move. Work as a loader on the docks at Avonmouth was hard, but the pay was good, enough to justify their move from Luckwell Road to a house on Nursery Lane. The rent was six shillings a week, but for the time being, affordable.

"Now you got the girl you wanted" said Charlotte. "And that's the last on 'em, God willin'."

For a time it seemed that God was willing, but there were to be two more children before Charlotte could reckon herself "finished wi' all that sort of thing", another girl four years later, and the last, Our Arthur in 1901, the apple of Charlotte's eye and yet another cause of friction with Thomas.

Ewart and Elsie's first daughter, Maud, had been born in 1887, within eighteen months of their marriage, but it was ten more years before they were pleased to announce to all and sundry via the Births column of *The Morning Post* the safe arrival of another daughter Julie Elizabeth Mary.

It was in that same fruitful year 1897 that Lily Callow made her largely unnoticed entry into the world, May the 29th, "Oak-Apple Day", ten days after Miss Julie.

Ewart had looked forward to having a son to carry on the Denmer name and eventually inherit the business, but Elsie made it clear that twice was more than enough to have one's figure and social life ruined for the best part of a year. And besides what guarantee could there be that a third attempt would result in a boy.

Ewart could not expect his lady-wife to make such a sacrifice for such an uncertain outcome. But it was galling to see Charlotte's family, boys and girls, not good-looking of course but obviously healthy. He suspected that Richard was slipping money Charlotte's way because she must be finding it hard to make ends meet.

Ewart was right in one thing. Money was becoming a worry. Thomas had long been considering pay day his hard drinking day and been lingering behind in the "Hen and Chicken", enjoying the company there and putting off as long as possible the return home to face Charlotte's tears and reproaches.

Chapter Two

When he was in a good mood, Thomas became boisterous, easy to like, so that Charlotte would recognise in him the attraction she had once felt for him. The children all remembered how he would amuse them by singing and shouting "Here we go, all of a row, down to see Joe Baker's show," clapping his hands and dancing about.

But he was sometimes savage, picking violent quarrels with the boys, finding fault with the girls. Usually he was wary with Charlotte, but when his mood was malicious, he would peer into her face and try to stroke the fine hairs on her upper lip, saying "Thee'st need a shave old lady". Then, looking up and raising his hands in mock despair he would sigh "O my, O my, O my Lord", not stopping until Charlotte made some response. It was usually only "Oh stop that damned nonsense" but it was said with such venom that his glee would vanish.

Our Arthur would run from the room when his father came home in a quarrelsome mood; he would sit in the stairs, his fingers in his ears, willing the angry voices to stop.

But Lily feared the days of sulking silence more, when Charlotte and Thomas would communicate only through the children. "Tell your father dinner be on the table if 'er wants it." Our Arthur, as the youngest the natural go-between, had early learned enough diplomacy to translate Thomas' angry reply into "'Er don't want none, mother". Charlotte's face would harden, but all she ever said was "all the more for them that does, then".

Lack of money was only one source of conflict.

Even more bitter were the quarrels over their family. Thomas still cared for Charlotte, and craved her affection. Instead he had to see that all her love was lavished on the children neither of them had wanted, and especially on Jack the first-born, and Our Arthur, after whose difficult birth Charlotte had become a semi-invalid.

Charlotte had no secrets from either her brother Richard or Iris his wife, and it was with them that she shared her greatest disappointment about Jack's schooling, all the greater because success had seemed within her grasp.

Jack and his father had always been at loggerheads; with Jack, "Damned little know-all", Thomas felt out of his depth.

He knew that Charlotte's ambition was for Jack "to make summat of hisself different from us" and it was clear that Jack had ability.

Charlotte was proud to tell Richard that Jack had sat the examination at the Elementary School and had won a scholarship place to Queen Elizabeth's Hospital, the City School.

"All fees paid, but of course the uniform and that to find. But" said Charlotte, "I been putting aside bit be bit and 'er can have 'er chance."

Jack would be one of the Blue Coat boys and wear the long blue cloak and yellow stockings and make his family proud, despite Thomas' hostility to the idea of Jack being educated above his station.

Thomas' hostility was not only in his mind. He had it in his means to stop Jack having his head stuffed with useless book learning; it was easy to find where Charlotte kept her not so secret hoard, and easier still to pocket it.

"For the lad's own good."

Thomas was prepared to make a virtue out of what Charlotte called theft, and to squander without remorse the money Charlotte had hoped would pay for Jack's board and lodging.

"No call for the lad to leave home, only twelve years old. No, what were good enough for I be good enough for any lad o' mine."

Useless for Charlotte to hope that Thomas would agree to Jack's being a day boy. "Over my dead body. I says no more."

Jack left the Board school at the end of the term in which he turned twelve and started as a day-labourer at Cottles' Farm in Long Ashton.

But to Charlotte it marked a further stage into what was to become permanent ill-health.

In the early days she had been well enough to walk across Victoria Park to visit Richard and Iris and be surprised to find that her dislike of children had not included Mary, the little girl who was getting to look more and more like her father Richard. In later years she would make her way to the tram junction for the 208, which stopped almost at their door in Wells Road. But the "pain in me insides", an unexplored benign tumour, had become sometimes almost unbearable, so that she would be unable to stand, let alone walk.

It was to Lily, young as she was, that Charlotte turned for help in the house. Ethel had begun work at

Wills' Tobacco Company and the hours were long. She was earning, "aye and spending too" said Thomas, noticing that beer money was no more forthcoming now than before Ethel left school and Bert joined Jack at Cottles' Farm.

Thomas who had been the main wage-earner had become a drifter, never staying long in any one job, out of work more often that not, and threatening to throw everything up and leave Bristol, perhaps to leave England altogether and to emigrate to America. One of his drinking pals, Joe Totterdale, had left his job beside Thomas at the docks at Avonmouth and taken his family, not as far afield as America it's true, but far enough away, across the Bristol Channel to South Wales, to find work in the coal fields of the Rhondda valley.

Charlotte had never liked Joe Totterdale, but she had, through feeling sorry for her, become friendly with his wife Lizzie. Now Lizzie had gone to join Joe and their two sons who had all found work underground at the coal face. According to Thomas, everyone who went to the Rhondda quickly succeeded in making their fortunes. It would be almost like joining the gold rush in America. Charlotte had learned to be suspicious of any scheme that Thomas was enthusiastic about and, as always, she turned to Richard for advice. To her surprise, he was cautiously optimistic.

"You see, Charlotte" he encouraged her "there's plenty of work in the pits, and good money to be earned. By all accounts, people are flocking there from all over. Jack and Bert'd be in regular jobs."

"And Thomas?" Charlotte couldn't think that any change of place would transform her unreliable husband into a steady worker.

Richard had no good opinion of his feckless brother-in-law, but he said "Well, Jack's nineteen, and Bert gone seventeen, and they can soon bring in a man's wage. Of course the boys have never been underground, but they're strong willing lads and they do say that boys pick up the skill in no time."

"But underground" protested Charlotte "it 'ud be dangerous work."

There were coal pits not far away, at Ashton Down and at Bedminster, and she had not forgotten the explosion a few years ago where four men had been killed. Due to "fire-damp" they'd said.

"Accidents do happen everywhere" Richard reminded her. "On the farms, in the docks. And them newer pits be safer, I'll be bound."

Richard had no idea of what the conditions in the pits of the Rhondda were like, but he knew that Thomas was determined to make the move, and that Charlotte would have to go with him. He saw it as his task to smooth his sister's path as far as lay in his power, and if by his words he could make her less reluctant to leave, then he was prepared to make any number of unsubstantiated statements.

All that Richard knew about coal-mining in South Wales was that there was good coal down there, and that people were anxious to buy it. He knew nothing of the twenty-four new pits which had been sunk between 1870 and 1884, where the deeper seams of smokeless steam coal were far more dangerous than the shallower bituminous coal mines,. He had no idea that they were being intensively worked by miners without the aid of mechanised tools.

The demand for Welsh steam coal for ships' engines had raised the price of coal and fortunes were being made. But not by the miners. They worked with pickaxe and shovel for twelve hours at a stretch, with the ever-present danger of explosions, subsidence, roof cave-ins, falls of coal at the face. And for their labour they were paid two shillings a ton, with, at that time, no guaranteed minimum wage.

Had he known more, Richard would have felt less confident in urging Charlotte, "Now's the time to go. Ethel will find something, and with Lily and Arthur still at school, they won't mind being uprooted. And for Jack and Bert, farm-labouring isn't much these days. They're ready for summat different."

Lizzie Totterdale had written from somewhere called Gelli Pentre to say that houses were scarce with all the newcomers arriving all the time but that there was a house to let in the very same street, and should she "put in for it" for them.

Number 11 Railway Terrace. It was so quickly arranged, all fixed, all settled, all packed. Some of the furniture had been sold, clothes and china stacked into tea-chests and, the only part of the move that Our Arthur ever remembered, the grandfather clock had been put on top of the big feather mattress and covered with blankets.

During the first few unsettled weeks in the Rhondda, Our Arthur would be begging "Put the clock back in the bed, mother, and we can go back home". But he was more excited than any of them at the prospect of leaving Nursery Lane and seeing all their goods loaded onto Uncle Ewart's cart - at a discount price - on their way to Temple Meads Station. A train journey, and such a long one, through the Severn Tunnel under the Bristol Channel made him at once anxious about all that water above them and yet eager for the move.

Lily, boasting at school about the riches soon to be theirs, took it for granted that The Move was welcomed by all the family. So when Ethel said casually "Mother don't want to go", it was her own certainty as much as Ethel's reputation which made her quick to say: "Liar. Bigger liar'n Tom Pepper. 'Course 'er do."

But Ethel was well-informed. Of all the family, only Lily and Our Arthur failed to realise the depth of their mother's unwillingness to leave Bristol.

Charlotte knew it would be a wrench to leave the shabby familiar streets of Bedminster, where she had spent all the twenty two years of her married life. But she hardly realised how difficult it would be to leave that other Bristol, the city common to all its citizens, the second city in England, whose foundation could be traced as far back as Alfred the Great. Historians could point to the city in the Civil War as a key to the West, whose recapture by Cromwell put an end to the King's Cause; they could chronicle the persecution of the Puritan dissenters during the Restoration, and their mass emigration to America; they could list the trail of "Bristols" and "Bristows" from New York State to Oklahoma in the wake of Bristol traders looking for new markets, and could call the Bristol of the Seventeenth Century the "gateway to the New World".

But to Charlotte and Thomas, as to others with their lack of education, this was all hidden history. They were unaware of their city as the living legacy of the past, ignorant of the lives of her churchmen, statesmen, merchant venturers, philanthropists, educators and industrialists.

But they could see the elegant houses on Clifton Down, in the Paragon, in Worcester Terrace, in Royal York Crescent, all homes which proclaimed the depth of the merchants' purses. They saw the well-built almshouses and the ancient charity schools with Jack's Blue Coat School one of them, all monuments to the benevolence of the Fosters and Colstons amongst those same merchants. And they saw the many city churches, from the Cathedral and St. Mary Redcliffe, down to the smallest, St. John's Gate, which bore witness to past ages of faith.

Like all Bristolians, they took pride in their spectacular Avon Gorge and Brunel's new suspension bridge thrown across it, although for Lily it was spoilt by Charlotte's story of the poor girl who had thrown herself off the bridge. Her skirts had billowed out, wafting her safely to land on St. Vincent's Rocks, but in Lily's imagination she was always there in mid-air, falling, falling, and never landing.

Charlotte would look back to their days in Bristol, and it was through sharing Charlotte's memories that Lily felt throughout her life that the city was part of her experience too. She would feel superior to Our Arthur who

Chapter Two

had left it when he was "too young to remember *anything*".

But Lily felt no pang at leaving, only a sense of importance that they were going across the Bristol Channel to another country where people spoke a different language, and where the Callows were going to be rich. Only Charlotte wondered whether it was going to be worth it, and whether Jack and Bert would take to being miners. Of one thing she was certain. Our Arthur was never going underground in any colliery.

It would not have comforted her to know that at that moment her fears were being shared by many, that men and women from England, from North Wales, from Mid and from South Wales were facing the challenge of making a new life in the Rhondda valleys.

But for Charlotte, it was exile, a life-long exile which began on that raw day in October 1907 when the train steamed out of Temple Meads Station and through the Severn Tunnel to Newport and then to Cardiff. She was forty one, and was never again to see her brother Richard alive.

CHAPTER THREE

'NOT FIT TO BRING A DOG TO'

1907

"Dylifa bechgyn ffolion
I'r cwm o hyd yn gyson
O wlad yr Haf hwy ddont yn scryd
Fel ynfyd haid o ladron"

"The stupid fellows flock in day by day,
From Somerset they make their foolish way,
Like idiot gangs of thieves no man can tally,
The hordes pour in to overrun the valley"
A Rhondda Valley traditional verse form 'Triban'.

"Us'll not go back for she
For her does not belong to we"
Somerset local rhyme c. 1888

Chapter Three

Number 11 Railway Terrace. How Charlotte hated that street and that house.

Crammed into the narrow valley floor, Railway Terrace was one of the many rows of streets following the line of the Taff Vale Railway which ran alongside the river Rhondda. The small houses, not yet twenty years old, but their walls already black with coal dust, rose in monotonous tiers half way up the hillsides on both sides of the valley.

All exactly alike, they were shoddily built, put up in a hurry to house the flood of immigrants attracted by the lure of the great King Coal.

Dark and north-facing, Railway Terrace was unfortunate in being sandwiched between the workings of Bryn Colliery and the railway line, so that the houses trembled with every Up train to Treherbert, shook with every Down train to Cardiff, and were hardly ever free from noise and coal dust.

Our Arthur, who still had his truckle bed in his parents' room, was both fascinated and repelled by the trains and by the colliery trucks, heavy and slow when they were loaded with coal.

At first, when he wasn't very well, and he was often not very well, he would call out querulously "Mother! These trains be making I thin!" But he loved to run out when it got dark to watch the lighted windows of the passenger trains or, if he was already out playing in the street, he would rush to climb the steps of the nearby footbridge. If he was very quick, he could reach the middle just as the train was passing underneath, and then he would feel the warm white cloud of steam engulf him, leaving his hair damp and his face chilled as it evaporated.

It was one more worry for Charlotte. "Oh the poor little feller. 'Er'll catch er death. Straight on to the chest, and then the fat'll be in the fire…"

Thomas his father had no patience. "O give over fretting theeself Charlotte! No call for thee to go on fretting theeself. Whining mommock. He be right as rain, gurt babby…"

But Charlotte was refusing to admit even to herself that Our Arthur, like the rest of the family, was settling quickly and becoming happy in their new life.

The Callows had come to a boom town where the population had more than doubled in the previous twenty years and was still increasing. Where so many were newcomers, in that brash, close-knit lively community, it was easy to be accepted. But Charlotte prided herself on keeping herself to herself, and except for Lizzie Totterdales's, she never went uninvited into any neighbour's house, nor did she encourage any to come into hers.

Amongst her neighbours, Charlotte could not help but establish herself as being "different", "not belonging", because she felt herself to be so. It was a self-imposed alienation which was to last throughout the thirty years of her life in the valley, and it had begun on that first journey up from Cardiff Queen Street.

At Pontypridd they had to change trains and as they waited on the cold crowded platform for the Treherbert train to take them up to Rhondda Fawr, she heard her first words of Welsh spoken. "Shw mae, Ianto?" They were called across to an old man who looked cheerful enough, but who replied in a melancholy drawl, "O weddol, wir". The first speaker by his tone and look seemed to want to sound reassuring. "Da iawn, bachgeni." But the uncomprehended words fell disagreeably and threateningly on Charlotte's ears. It seemed to her that everyone was speaking Welsh on that Pontypridd platform, Welsh with now and then words or whole phrases thrown in in English.

To Charlotte the journey seemed endless, and yet in distance the whole length of the line up the valley from Cardiff to where the trains stopped at Treherbert was less that twenty-three miles. And from Pontypridd as far as Ystrad Rhondda was only some seven or eight miles.

The Rhondda Fawr, the Big Rhondda, to which the Callows had come, was Big only in relation to the Rhondda Fach, the Little Rhondda, from which it diverged at Porth. Both Rhonddas, Big and Little, were narrow steep-sided valleys running parallel to each other and separated by the thousand-foot high Rhondda Ridge, the Cefn y Rhondda.

The Little Rhondda was almost as long as the Big Rhondda, but it was narrower and more steep-sided and with fewer collieries. Charlotte's future acquaintance with its people, as with its places, was to be limited to hearsay and to the common knowledge that one of its townships, Maerdy, had come justifiably by its notorious nick name of "Little Moscow".

But on that first journey, Charlotte had no thoughts, only feeling, feelings of apprehension and dismay. They were coming no great distance from Bristol but to Charlotte it was an alien country.

From Pontypridd the train snaked its way up the narrow valley floor, stopping at stations whose names she never learned to pronounce – Trehafod, Porth, Dinas, Tonypandy and Trealaw, Llwynypia, and at last Ystrad.

Dinas was the worst place. Here the first levels had been opened and in 1812 Walter Coffin sank the first colliery. His name bore a grim prophecy.

When the train stopped at Dinas it was dusk. But Charlotte could make out the remains of the original wooden huts built for the miners, as well as the stone houses which clustered too closely round the pit-head workings. Thomas was pointing out to Our Arthur the wheel and girders of the pit winding gear and stack outlined against the sky, and showing him the trucks in the railway sidings, full of coal and ready to start their journey down to Barry Docks.

Those loaded trucks were being transported in ever greater numbers, for the Welsh steam coal which had fuelled the Mauritania on the Blue Riband crossing of the Atlantic was in demand, not only by all the main steamship companies and the Admiralty, but also by the newly-built railways of South America, India and South Africa.

All the Rhondda pits were working the deep steam-coal seams; Charlotte was to recognise their names, the Maendy, the Parc, the Dare, the Eastern, the Pentre, the Tynybedw, the Gelli, the Lady Lewis, the Cambrian, Tydraw, and on the sides of the coal trucks, the names of the companies owning those pits, Cory Bros,

Chapter Three

Ocean Coal Co, Powell Duffryn. Especially Powell Duffryn, "P.D. – Poverty and Death".

By 1909 the Rhondda valley, the most intensively mined in Great Britain, was supplying the largest coal exporting port in the world. For the few who owned the mines, the profits were generous; for the many who worked them, the rewards were meagre and the perils great. No one, capitalist or workman could have foreseen how soon and how disastrous would be the decline in that demand.

But the valley had already suffered sixty years of outrage. When Charlotte looked out of the grimy train windows she saw a squalid man-made landscape, a far cry from the valley once described as "the gem of Glamorgan", with its glorious hills, green meadows and wild flowers, even though here and there stretches of woodland kept company with the river and the railway, with unfenced fields sloping down to the very tracks.

And where the river looped away from the railway, dense woodland linked Gelli with Llwynypia, for the New Road opening a second route down to Glyncornel was not to be built for another decade and more.

But all Charlotte could see was that the river flowed black and evil-smelling over its pebbly bed, and that the black slag heaps, pyramids of waste, were thrown up threateningly behind the houses.

Richard had painted a rosy picture. But he had never travelled outside Somerset. He had not witnessed the rape of the land.

And he had never set foot inside 11 Railway

Chapter Three

Terrace "Nor never will, thank God" said Charlotte. "Not fit to bring a dog to, much less a poor little feller like Our Arthur."

"We're *all* here, mother," Jack reminded her. "And others before us have made out. If Totterdales can scratch a good living, so can we."

"Aye", said Charlotte. "Us'll have to, I reckon."

CHAPTER FOUR

CUCKOOS IN THE NEST

1909

"The people who lived between the Rhondda hills...generated a unique humour, fortitude and goodness, a currency not recognised at the bank."

Gwyn Thomas

Those who came flocking first to the coal field were miners from the vale of Glamorgan and from Monmouthshire. The Callows' next-door neighbours on either side in Railway Terrace were Welsh-born and Welsh speaking, and had been in the valley for twenty years. On the other side of the street lived families from Cardigan and Pembroke, who had joined in the coal rush in the mid eighteen-fifties, when the railway line was extended as far as Llandyssul. When Lily and Our Arthur started school, they sat next to the children of former lead-miners from Anglesey, and slate-quarry workers from Bethesda and Ffestiniog, as well as the children, like themselves, of farm labourers from Somerset and Devon. At school they were taught in the official language, English, but at home many of them spoke Welsh with their monoglot parents, who had been settled in the Rhondda for thirty or forty years.

Those first Welsh words on Pontypridd station had convinced Charlotte that an awful lot of people would be speaking this language she would never be able to understand. She was not to know that in fact the Welsh language was rapidly giving way to English, helped by families like the Callows and Totterdales who spoke no other language, and of these families, most came from Somerset. Their nickname, given to them by the Welsh speakers who came originally from East Glamorgan was "Cuckoos".

"Cuckoos?" said Charlotte. "Cuckoos indeed. *They* be the silly cuckoos, not we."

"They cuckoo-birds comes from England way though, mother." Our Arthur was always ready with an opinion, right or wrong.

"No, 'taint that" said Charlotte, "us all knows about cuckoos. Foolish birds and a nasty habit of laying their eggs in other birds' nests. Cuckoos got a very bad name, theest know. Oh aye, we be unwanted here, like they birds. We got no nest of our own, more's the pity. We been and left ourn in Bristol."

Bristol was Home. How could the Rhondda ever be 'ome? Everything was different in this new community of which she was so reluctant a member. There was so little variety in the jobs people could do that the kind of life they led and the standard of living they achieved was much the same for everybody.

Although Charlotte had known of wretchedly poor people in Bedminster, worse off than the Callows had been, yet she had seen too the households of the comparatively well to do. Her brother Richard, as a skilled stonemason received a meagre enough wage, but he and Iris lived in a house which was comfortable and roomy, with a garden back and front. Ewart Denmer of course, was wealthy. Even before the Callows left Bristol, his 'haulage concern' as he called it, was growing so rapidly that Elsie Denmer was talking grandly of a place in Dowry Square. "Lower Clifton, off Hotwell Road". Yes, Charlotte knew of it, an area far beyond the means of families such as the Callows.

But in the Rhondda, there seemed to be no such areas. She could see only people like themselves, living cheek-by-jowl in narrow terraces of dingy houses, each one exactly like its neighbour. And go where you would throughout the valley you saw only houses, institution-like schools, and the big bleak-looking non-conformist chapels. Only a handful of "proper" churches, Church of England churches, and a few managers' houses. Certainly no medieval castle ruins, no eighteenth century squares - hardly room for squares in the narrow valley - no arcades, no architectural follies, no Corn Exchange.

In Bristol, Ethel had worked in Wills' big tobacco factory; boys and girls she had been at school with had jobs in Fry's chocolate factory, in glass and pottery works, in the warehouses of wine merchants, as servants to wealthy families. There was work to be had in the docks, on the railway and on the farms. And although there were three times as many people in Bristol as there were in the Rhondda at the time of the 1901 census, yet there was far less over-crowding in the individual houses, and the houses themselves were scattered over a wide area North and South of the River Avon.

In the narrow valleys of the two Rhonddas there were few jobs for women, and most of the men worked in the mines. Families were crowded together and, as was to happen with the Callows, they often took lodgers in as well, so that beds were hardly ever empty, day or night.

Coal dominated all their lives, for the colliers and their families far outnumbered any other workers. Of course there were shopkeepers, bakers, blacksmiths, ministers, doctors, teachers and even a dentist. But most of their customers, their flock, their clients, were miners, most of the pupils, miners' children. For without the pits there would have been no community. And that homogenous community, brash, unrefined, close-knit, warm-hearted, lively, struggling as it was, would have accepted and absorbed Charlotte as it did the rest of the family.

Charlotte's "we be unwanted here" echoed her own personal feeling, although there had been antagonism in the early days, when English boys and men had come to work alongside the Welsh-speaking miners. But much more than their difference in language, it was their lack of skill which provoked the Welsh miners' hostility; inexperienced men in a mine not only put a brake on the earning capacity of the skilled miner but also, in such a dangerous job, added to the possibility of accidents. It is the stupidity of the Somerset gangs, those foolish youths, "bechgyn ffolion", stressed in the verse of the Rhondda Triban.

In all their years in the pits, neither Thomas, Jack nor Bert, found prejudice against them solely because they were English. When men worked underground, danger drew them together. Literally stripped of the outward trappings of dress, the status of a man depended on his character.

A man's life depended on his trust in his workmate, in his "butty", and that dependence created a fellowship which flowed over into life above ground. Men who worked alongside each other by day would sing in the same chapel choir, or drink in the same dingy pub at night. Their wives and families too shared a rich communal life, a life from which the fear of accident or death was never far away. It was a society which excluded no-one, and even Charlotte had to admit that she had no positive grounds for feeling that her neighbours resented her. But she was too old, at forty-one, to put down her roots again. To the end of her days, she regarded herself as a Bristolian. And she sounded like one.

"The little varmint!" she would exclaim. The noun was a corruption of *vermin*, but her tone would show her affection, unlike her use of *mommock* and *nesh* (finicky), which were usually terms of abuse.

Our Arthur was only five when the Callows came to the Rhondda, and when he started school in Gelli his broad Bristol accent and shaky sense of standard grammar was a subject of correction, if not of secret amusement, for Miss Thomas-the-Infants. He saw nothing wrong in saying "Her gives it to I".

"No, Arthur," said Miss Thomas-the-Infants, "you mean your mother. You should say 'She gives it to me'."

"No, Miss," said Our Arthur, "I means my father and her don't give it to thee Miss. Her gives it to I. Her *do* do, Miss." Our Arthur was not to be moved.

He knew that at home "Her was a good father" was as grammatically acceptable as "Her be a good mother", and that whatever Miss Thomas-the-Infants might say, "He be a big house" was normal usage.

He was accustomed to hearing Charlotte and Thomas using *thee* instead of *you*, and *cass, cuss* and *wuss* instead of *can, could* and *would*; all intelligible to Somerset families but an initial source of bewilderment to their Welsh-speaking neighbours.

Charlotte would call out "Where bist going Tom?

Cass dap thee hand on that mossel o' fancy work for I?" or, scolding Lily, "Rouse theeself from that book! Theest be sitting there like Queen Victorial 's know!"

Vanw-next-door never did get used to that *I* tacked on to words ending in a vowel, though she quickly understood that *on Mary's shelf* meant *on the floor*, and *a picked rook* was Thomas' scornful description of a very thin neighbour. "All outside show like the crows", "done up like a fourpenny hambone", "I'd sooner their room than their company", "I'll speak my mind, affront or please", these were phrases she often heard in the burred speech which became so familiar to her in every cry of "Arrthurr! Our Arrthurr! Pay heed, Varrmint!" Vanw herself had clearly articulated vowels, fewer elisions, a quicker pace of utterance and the sing-song intonation of the South Walian.

That intonation Charlotte and Thomas never acquired but over the years they became familiar with Welsh words in common use. When Lily had a septic swelling on her thumb that had to be lanced and stitched, Bopa Williams diagnosed a "ffelwm", and by that time they had been long enough in the valley for even Charlotte to accept that "felum" it was, even though "back 'ome" everybody would have recognised it as being a whitlow.

When Our Arthur begged for a halfpenny to buy *lossins* for him and Lily, Charlotte knew it was for *sweets*, and by the disgusted face he made when he said *achyfi* she recognised that it was yet another foodstuff he refused to eat, although he seemed to be using the word for pretty nearly everything at times.

Chapter Four

And from somewhere or someone, he kept picking up words, Dammo, Diawl, Mawredd, Duw Mawr, Iesu, Munifferni, which made Granny Thomas two doors down frown "shame on you boy,.. and you from a tidy family".

Charlotte too would have scolded had she understood, and Thomas threaten to wash out his mouth with Vim. Swear words were never permitted, let alone blasphemy.

"Our Arthur be running wild and our Lily worse than he."

But though it went against the grain she had to recognise that they were happy.

Lily and Our Arthur were free to roam through Gelligaled woods, gathering great armfuls of bluebells which drooped in their hands and died overnight; they could roll down the side of the Lady's Field, clamber up the grassy tips and come home "looking like rodneys". Especially Lily, whose thick wavy hair looked "like a besom in fits", her ribbons long lost.

Lily was proud of her chestnut-coloured hair. "I could sit on my hair when I was young, it was that long", she would tell her daughters in years to come. But washing and drying it was always an ordeal, not helped by Ethel's "mother can't get a brush through your hair, Lily, let alone a comb". It was an accurate but unnecessary comment. Lily was only too well aware that Charlotte's struggles to bring order to the damp tangles only succeeded in bringing tears to her eyes. She would shout angrily "Better than your old rats' tails anyway, just like a bit of string in the water", which usually brought a sharp

"Mind your words Lily" from Charlotte. That temper of Lily's hadn't changed, thought Charlotte, even if everything else seemed to have.

Lily was always bringing a gang of children into the house or else hawking Our Arthur off with them up the mountain and gone for hours. Or, worse still, going into neighbours' houses and coming back with "Bopa Jones says this" or "Bopa Davies did that"...

"Bowpurr?" said Charlotte when she first heard the word. "That woman's name's Gladys, not any Bowpurr."

"Well, she said for me to call her Bopa", Lily insisted. "Like 'Auntie' I think."

"You ain't got no aunts here, Lily, as well you know. Your Aunt Denmer's in Clifton and your Aunt Iris Milsom down at Knowle." But when Ethel broke in with "Mrs Morris Top House is Bopa as well, mother", Charlotte decided she had better let well alone.

They was funny women, though, in her opinion, wanting other folk's children to call them "Bowpurr" or summat. And as for the menfolk, she could make nor head nor tail of some of their nicknames. "Billy the Milk" and "Evan the Bread" and "Fairy Feet" for the dapper little husband next door were all straightforward enough, and so was "Piping Bill" for Bert's friend Billy Pritchard, as soon as you heard him continually trying to voice his opinions in his reedy little treble. But it needed Lizzie Totterdale to explain that every member of the O'Malley family of ten children was known as "one of the Tulips" simply because their mother's response to a neighbour's kindly "Another baby I see, gel", was reported to have been "Yes, they just come in the spring".

It was not only the names that puzzled Charlotte. It was the attitude of mind. "All that laughing and cracking jokes, Lizzie, and singing all the time, like as if they was going off to the Hippodrome instead of to their place of work".

Charlotte was to change her opinion, but only after she had lived through the hard times which were to make her appreciate such qualities, and to make her glad to be among such neighbours. When they first moved into Railway Terrace she felt nothing but scorn for the other wives. She would note disapprovingly how they would come out on their doorsteps to call across the street to one another, and how they lingered in Maggie May's front room corner shop long after they had made their purchases. "Bain't they got nothing better to do than to stand gossiping?" she would mutter, priding herself on having "summat better to do wi' my time".

She would see them standing in the street, little knots of three or four, all day as it seemed, with their babies in their arms. They carried their babies in big heavy Welsh wool shawls, draped over one shoulder, the ends brought round in front to wrap the baby against the mother's breast. "Cwtch in now, cariad" they would murmur if the baby got restless, cuddling the little body in a closer embrace.

"Far better that child was lying in its bed to sleep" was Charlotte's opinion, though she had to admit that such babies were remarkably contented, and that the toddlers, tugging at the long fringes of the shawl for attention or holding on to them for comfort were, even in her book, "good little souls". Some of the women too, she realised, were making their shopping trips last a long time because they had a husband or son on night shift who had to get his sleep during the day. If like Jack they were light sleepers, the least household noise or baby's cry would disturb them. The clatter of cooking and cleaning had to be left until the men had gone to work, that was only common sense.

But she still considered them to be idle. "Nary a bit o' sewing nor knitting in their hands the livelong day, only chat, chat, chat". She was exasperated by what she called their "come-day, go-day" attitude, and roundly denounced their neighbourly interest in her affairs as "nosy-parkering".

"What do they want to know about I for? I don't meddle wi' they and their concerns. I got enough to do to keep track of me own."

She would have been even more irritated to know that the first question of "they Nosy-Parkers" Bopa Jones and Bopa Davies was invariably "Well, Lily, and what's your mother doing today?"

Charlotte never really understood her neighbour's delight in vicarious living, for her own concern in anything or anybody outside her home was slight. Jack was to be passionate about the struggles of the Miners' Federation to wrest a minimum wage from the coal owners, with their resistance to Unionism. But although such struggles were to have a lasting effect on the Callows, as on every mining family in the Rhondda, yet Charlotte was as if cocooned. Until, that is, the Cambrian Strike, when the very name

Chapter Four

Cambrian became synonymous throughout the valley with bitterness and defeat.

CHAPTER FIVE

EVERYDAY LIFE

1909

"Workshops and Workplaces in Gelli

1 blacksmith

10 barbers

9 carpenters

13 fried fish shops

17 dressmakers

3 glaziers

2 jewellers

5 milliners

3 picture framers

2 plumbers

1 sweetmaker

5 tailors

9 quarries"

Rhondda Urban District Council
Report of M.O.H. 1913, p.89

Chapter Five

The Callows had come to the Rhondda at a time when it was about to become the focal point of unrest in the South Wales coalfield. The Cambrian strike of 1910 was just over the horizon, a strike which lasted for eleven months and which brought defeat to the miners, even though it resulted in one of the most momentous Acts in Trade Union history.

As momentously for Charlotte, it was to influence her whole attitude towards her neighbours. In sharing their adversity, she was to feel a sympathy and sense of belonging to a close-knit community that in prosperity would have been forever denied her. It was in hardship that Charlotte learned to value people whose concern for their neighbours outweighed their concern for themselves, so that she never afterwards condemned their interest for being "nosey-parkering", nor mistook their friendliness for "meddling in other folks' affairs".

But before prosperity had turned to hardship, Charlotte's world was bounded by her family, a world where the important thing was to be a "good manager", to be able to set something aside after the four and sixpence rent had been paid and the food and clothing bills met.

The food bills were always high for, apart from the men, there was Lily, Ethel and Our Arthur, whose appetite was too finicky to be cheap, and they together were enough to "eat anybody out of house and home". Sometimes Charlotte would travel up to Treorchy and back as far as Carter's Corner, on one of the new open-topped trams that ran their electrified way right through the valley, braving the speed, the clanging, the swaying and the overhead sparking. But as she told Thomas "I'd sooner the old Morris Brothers brake any day. Dear enough at a penny, for matter how short the distance, mind, but give I the horses for preference."

"Horses is on the way out, mother. They be too slow."

"Listen to Our Arthur, Thomas, like a boy twice his age".

"Aye", said Thomas to himself. "He be getting like Jack, ought to bite his tongue a bit. Too damn forward, made too much on."

Horse-drawn brake or electric tram, neither was an issue. It was mostly walking everywhere.

When she felt well enough, and in the first few years there were times when she was free from pain, Charlotte would go as far as Pentre to buy groceries, stopping to look in the windows of the big Ystrad Road shops, so much more enticing than the smaller shops in Gelli. Charlotte hardly ever patronised the little shops, particularly not the one in the middle of Railway Terrace kept by an elderly husband and wife. Every so often, they would close the shop, propping a scrawled note between the window and the drawn-down yellow paper blind. "Shop here never no more. By order J. Williams." But in a few days, the blind would go up, the note fall down unheeded amongst the jumble of sweet jars, fly papers and boot laces on display in the window, and the front door would be held open again with the sack of potatoes beside the cast-iron weighing scales.

"There's no reliance on such folk," Charlotte

grumbled as she made out a long list of groceries for the 'Co-op'.

Charlotte was never tempted by the big double-fronted stores, the International Stores, Peglers, Thomas and Evans, the Home and Colonial, Liptons, the Maypole, nor by the smaller single windows of the Calcutta Tea Stores where you could exchange their tea-packet stamps for clothes-baskets, china dogs and swans, scrubbing boards or even one of the iron hoops which Our Arthur had been coveting.

She bought most of their things from the Co-op, for the dividend was a useful source of income. Jack had explained to Lily how at the Co-operative Stores you were a shareholder, and all your purchases went towards your dividend, and although she had no clear notion of how this could be, Lily could appreciate Charlotte's jubilation when the "divi" went up to one and ninepence in the pound. She would watch the shop-girl enter the details of all purchases in their blue-covered "Co-op Book", and help Charlotte calculate the amount of divi payable when each page was full. You could have the goods on credit. "Mam says, please to book it" was a sentence most Railway Terrace children were quick to learn, but although Lily was often sent to buy a pound of sugar or a quarter of tea, she was always given the money to pay for them. So Charlotte's divi never had to go towards paying off any debts and, unlike many of her neighbours, she was never in a panic at the End of the Quarter when the books were called in to be "made up", for her book was always clear.

It was not only food stuffs that she bought at the

Chapter Five

Co-op. Charlotte was not a keen needlewoman, but there had to be occasional visits to the Drapery and Haberdashery Department to buy the yards of white calico, the white linen buttons, the hooks and eyes, and sometimes the lace trimming needed for school petticoats and pinafores.

Lily would admire the deft fingers of the assistant as she parcelled up the material, made out the bill, then screwed both bill and money into the little wooden cup suspended on the railway above her at arm's length. A pull on the handle, and away the cup would go, whizzing along the overhead wire to its terminus, the glassed-in office of the cashier at the far end of the shop. Sometimes if the shop were busy, several cups would be travelling from different departments at the same time, and having to take their turn for the cashier's attention. When it came back to the waiting assistant and her customer, the cup contained the receipted bill and the reckoned change.

This was sophisticated Emporium practice, found only in the Co-op in the Ton and in one other shop, Howells, the big General Drapers set back from the road in Pentre. Here Millinery, Mantles and Haberdashery were spread over two double-fronted floors, with separate departments for Children, Youths and Maids. There were wax models dressed appropriately in each department, looking so life-like you could fancy they were blinking their eyes, except that they were betrayed by the price tickets hanging from their hat-bands and half hidden on the sleeves of their jackets.

Charlotte was not impressed. "Think o' Lewises in

the Haymarket before thee'st crack up summat like this",
she pronounced. "That there Lewises in the Haymarket
had *nine* floors. Thee cuss fit the whole of this lot into *one*
on 'em!".

But Lily had no memories of Lewises in the
Haymarket. To please Charlotte, she sometimes
pretended to remember more about Bristol that she really
did, and to be interested in hearing about the shops in
Wine Street and Castle Street, where Charlotte had picked
up the bargain cheap prints which had been the equal of
Aunt Elsie Denmer's grosgrain any day.

There were few such bargains to be picked up at
the Co-op, and none at all at "Avon House", the little
drapers shop on the corner opposite the Co-op, where
Miss Jenkins, dressed in her own creations knitted from
wool in stock, sold material-by-the-yard and a few, very
dear, ready-made clothes.

"A scandal to charge all that!" said Ethel, outraged
by the price ticket (4/11½) on a baby's bonnet. "Nearly five
shillings for a baby's bonnet! I knew a girl, a milliner she
was, in the workshop of Fricker's warehouse down
Anchor's Road, and she got paid ninepence for making a
dozen of them bonnets, round hats for little boys and the
bonnets for baby girls, silk and trimmed all round with
swansdown."

And yet somebody bought the bonnet at four
shillings and elevenpence halfpenny, for when wages were
high, people spent. As Charlotte said, "They got no
thought whatever for the morrow. And if they got childer,
nothing be too good for them. Them childer be spoilt little

critters."

Not many of the Railway Terrace women bought at "Avon House" though. Hers was a high-class shop, patronised by what the rougher women called "crachach, the snobs who think themselves *it*", when they went to buy "something nice".

There was no booking it at "Avon House". Miss Jenkins had written a notice on a card in very neat characters "Please Do Not Ask For Credit. Refusal Often Offends". But she was willing enough to "put wool by" for customers, who then bought it one or two ounces at a time, going back for more when they had finished knitting up what they had taken. With wool so dear, twopence and more an ounce, you couldn't expect people to buy outright and all at once the amount they needed. Besides, they might have over-estimated. Miss Jenkins would split a four-ounce hank and sell just the one, but she was unwilling to take back any single unused hanks. Odd ounces mounted up, and there was a limit to the number of multi-coloured jumpers and cardigans her wardrobe could absorb and still allow her to look tidy behind the counter.

No, Miss Jenkins was "not very obliging", people agreed, acting as if she didn't really want to sell anything. And as for giving change! Charlotte tried to have the right money if she bought anything at Avon House to avoid the embarrassment of seeing Miss Jenkins flinch as if she were robbing her own till. But with so many goods priced at one shilling elevenpence three farthings or tenpence farthing, there was no dodging it. Miss Jenkins solved it, for the farthing, by handing out, reluctantly, a paper folder, pink, yellow, or pale green, stuck with five or six rows of small-headed pins.

Charlotte had amassed quite a pile of these folders, and it irritated her for, though she had never refused the pins, which often enough came in handy, yet she would have preferred the halfpennies and farthings. Not that money was particularly tight during those first two years, with Jack and Bert as well as Thomas working underground and Ethel in Evans the Shoe-Shop on Gelli Road. The Callows were more comfortably off than ever they had been in Bristol, even though you never knew when the pits would be on short time or, worse, on strike.

They could not have foreseen how soon the mining boom was to come to an end, and the miners' standard of living collapse.

PART TWO

CHAPTER SIX

LILY AT HOME

1909

"Don't expect too much from human life, a sorry
business at the best"
   Sidney Smith to Lady Georgiana Morpeth 1820

Chapter Six

Lily seldom slept through the long, mournful blast of the seven o'clock hooter, even after more than a year in Railway Terrace, and never through the heavy tramp of the colliers' hob-nailed boots ringing on the paving stones, although just beside her, lying diagonally across the bed, Ethel would sleep on undisturbed.

The only time Ethel had not slept "like a dead man" thought Lily was their very first night in number 11 Railway Terrace.

They had all been awakened by Our Arthur's cries. "Mother! Mother! Quick! These flies be on my face! They be crawling all over I!"

The candle had been lit, revealing the flies to be bed bugs swarming out of the hole in the wall where the lath and plaster was showing through. Our Arthur's bed was moved away from the wall, the hole re-plastered and tins of Keating's Powder applied in liberal layers. As a final deterrent, every week the coil springs of the mattresses were brushed with paraffin. The high turnover of Keatings and paraffin in Rees the Ironmonger on Gelli Road showed that it was to these two remedies that everybody looked. They must have been effective, or maybe it was that the beds were constantly being disturbed, but certainly, after that first dreadful night, bugs were never high on Charlotte's list of worries.

She had soon got used to the big black cockroaches which came out at night and covered the floor of the kitchen, rustling and disappearing as soon as you shone a light on them, though she never felt as calm about accepting them as the Picked Rook, Vanw-next-door, who assured her "in every house they do be, Mrs Callow fach. Black pats we do call them by here, see."

What caused her more distress was the noise and dirt from the colliery on the other side of the wall. When the wind was blowing from the North West, fine coal dust would settle on the furniture indoors, and would make it impossible to hang out the washing in the back yard. "They all calls it the back garden, but it be only a dirt patch, nothing like the back garden your Uncle Richard had down at Knowle. That was summat like a garden and thank God he aint here to see us now, the way we be living, and dirt everywhere, nothing decent."

Charlotte was failing "to keep things decent" but with Lily's help "us might keep on top o' things ". Not that Lily ever minded doing housework. "Our Lily knows how to work" was one of the few approving comments which Charlotte allowed her, and it was praise well-earned. For Lily tackled the dirtiest of jobs, cleaning the kitchen range, emptying the slops, the contents of the chamber pots, as well as the lighter work like turning out the front room.

Small and north facing, this was Lily's favourite room, the first room on the right off the narrow passage, which was never called the hall. It had a square of Axminster carpet, a cast-off from the Denmer household, hardly worn except in one or two patches, and all the best furniture, the two horse-hair stuffed armchairs and matching sofa. There was hardly any space to walk round the mahogany table covered with the dark red chenille cloth fringed with bobbles, even when the six chairs were pushed in underneath it, and the four-tiered whatnot in the corner by the window projected so far out that it was almost impossible to water the aspidistra in the jardinière without drenching the ornaments crowding the lower three shelves. These were only fairings, little china ornaments, jugs, bells, trays, hats, thimbles, cups and saucers, boxes with lids, some with coats of arms, some inscribed with their place of origin, none of any intrinsic value.

Back in Bristol, when drink had made him both belligerent and reckless, Thomas had threatened to sweep "the whole lot of they damned dust-gatherers" into the grate. But the real target of his irritation was what he had sarcastically christened "the Heirloom", given to them by Ewart and Elsie Denmer as a wedding present.

The Heirloom took up the whole of the top shelf of the whatnot, a big glass dome protecting six delicate cut-glass goblets and a decanter with silver lid and handle, all resting on a base of dark blue velvet. Its fragility symbolised for Charlotte a leisured, unattainable, wholly enviable way of life, but for Thomas its uselessness represented all that was patronising and pretentious about the detested Denmers.

Lily thought it the best thing in the room, better than the big Bible with its brass clasp, where their names and dates of birth were recorded on the flyleaf, better even than her favourite "Daniel in the Lion's Den" and its companion picture "Moses Surveying the Promised Land", taking up nearly the whole of the long wall facing the window.

Daniel radiated contentment. Oblivious to the bleached bones on the den floor, he stroked the nearest lion, whilst the others turned their handsome golden faces in homage towards him. Moses, though, had a sour face, and was prodding the Promised Land petulantly with his long staff, disappointed with the unyielding earth that God had chosen.

Far better, thought Lily, if mother had left Moses behind in Nursery Lane, so that Jack's lovely drawings of dogs and horses could have been put up instead of having to be stacked in the boys' room where nobody, including Thomas, could see them. But there was no room for Jack's paintings anywhere in the house, for all three downstairs rooms as well as the three bedrooms were overcrowded with furniture.

The middle kitchen leading off the passageway overlooked the back yard, and the backs of the houses in the next street. Except for the view, it would have been a pleasant room, for it got all the afternoon sun. In this room, Charlotte was to spend both her days and nights, never leaving her bed, but in the early years, it served the family as a dining and living room. Here, around the big deal table under the window, the family sat for their meals, though it was not often that all seven ate together, and here the men sat to read or talk in the so-called easy chairs around the big open fire kept alight summer and winter. The girls and Charlotte sat here too, but always with some knitting or crocheting or mending in their hands. They never just sat, and reading was only when there was nothing better to do.

There was nearly always something better to do, even if it were only seeing to the papers for the Dub.

Chapter Six

The Dub stood outside in the back yard opposite the coal house. It was enclosed by a stout wooden door with five holes bored in two rows near the top. Beneath them somebody had painted in white the letters WC, the water closet, "the Dub". Inside was a long wooden plank with a too-large hole in the middle; above it a water-tank, with a short chain attached, rested on a pair of rusting iron brackets fixed to the white-washed wall.

At first Our Arthur had refused to go in on his own: "Don't make I go in there, mother. I beg of 'ee. Don't make I."

(as if, thought Lily, mother would ever try to force Our Arthur to do anything he didn't want to do)

Even when he had conquered his fear of falling down the hole and drowning, Lily still had to go with him, partly for company and partly because he was not tall enough to reach the chain to pull after him. And if he stood on the seat...

It was Lily's job every Saturday to scrub the seat and the stone flagged floor and to see to the supply of newspaper pieces hung on the nail behind the door.

She would begin by cutting old copies of the *Rhondda Gazette* and the *Christian Herald* into squares and threading them with one of Charlotte's darning needles neatly, with matching holes, on to a length of wool.

But all too often her eye would be caught by some item of news, and it would take Charlotte to remind her to finish the job and not waste her time reading. And then Lily would abandon the scissors and tear the pages roughly into jagged-edged pieces and thread them higgledy-piggledy.

So in the end Ethel decided she would take over that task and leave Lily to help in the back kitchen where the heavier work was done.

The heaviest job Lily found was not the washing, the ironing, or the cooking, but the cleaning of the iron range which filled the whole of the far wall.

In the centre the coal fire with iron bars in front and the box for ashes underneath burned summer and winter to heat the room, the hobs and the top and bottom ovens.

On the high mantelpiece, a clock and, Charlotte's pride and joy after The Heirloom, two china dogs red and white with gold collars, not thought at that time to be of any monetary value.

The whitened hearthstone was bounded by a wide steel fender where Charlotte kept an extra kettle of hot water until the day Ethel nearly scalded her leg by brushing against the spout. Ethel had been rushing into the back kitchen "like a mad thing" said Our Arthur, but only to escape Lily's clutches. So that while Ethel got the sympathy for the effect, Lily got the blame for being the cause.

It was a long job even to prepare to clean the range. The laying of newspapers round the hearth, the raking out of the ashes and cinders, the sweeping out of the grate, the getting rid of the grease with newspaper, all this was just the beginning. There were still the iron parts to black-lead, the steel parts to clean with bathbrick and the hearthstone to wash and whiten with pipe clay. When Charlotte did the cleaning, the black-lead tin of Zebo never seemed to get empty, but Lily used too much and brushed it off too vigorously, so that on cleaning days she never got rid of the black under her fingernails nor the ingrained grime from her hands. But the grate gleamed like ebony – until frying the food and raking the fire made it spotted and dull again.

On the hobs at either side of the fire grate, Charlotte kept two big iron kettles boiling for the men's baths when they came in from work covered in coal dust, the whites of their eyes showing up starkly bright against their anonymous blackened faces. Charlotte found it hard to get used to this daily ritual, the bringing in of the galvanised tin bath kept hanging outside on a nail against the kitchen wall, the filling of the kettles, the washing and drying of the towels, to say nothing of the "pit clothes" themselves.

The bath would be put down on the brightly coloured rug Charlotte had made from scraps of material, and the men would kneel and wash the top half of their bodies, asking Charlotte to wash their backs. Then left to themselves in the kitchen, they would step into the bath and "finish off". The emptying of the bath would have been too heavy for the girls, but the men would each take a handle and carry the bath full of dirty water with ease to the outside drain, for there was no sink or wash basin inside.

There was a tap, a cold-water tap, in the kitchen and under it, an enamel bowl standing on an upended orange box. The wooden orange box was divided by a partition, which served as a shelf for the soap dish, shaving mugs and brushes, and on the wall above the tap Charlotte had agreed to a mirror so that Thomas and the boys could see to shave. But to stare at your own reflection was asking for trouble.

"I don't hold with looking glasses Lily. Theest know what'll happen, sure as eggs is eggs. Devil'll come and look over thee shoulder. I be sick and tired, Lily, of thee looking at theeself. Boys have got to see theirselves o' course..."

Charlotte was always having to scold or warn Lily about something or other and to urge her to be more like Ethel who, even at Lily's age, had kept herself "like a bandbox" whereas Lily, the tomboy, was always tearing her clothes. Instead of sitting at home knitting or sewing, Lily would join the roughest children in Railway Terrace to slide on pieces of board down the tip on Gelli mountain or even to play down by the forbidden territory of the river. No wonder Charlotte counted it a waste of time to sew new clothes for Lily. Instead she was the one who had to wear the cast-offs sent in parcels from Bristol.

Cousin Julie Denmer was almost exactly Lily's age, though only very approximately Lily's size and Aunt Elsie Denmer was generous in sending clothes for "poor Charlotte's girls". Such good quality clothes, they would be outgrown long before they were outworn. Aunt Denmer had sent a particularly scratchy navy blue serge dress bought for Julie, and Charlotte had read aloud the letter that accompanied it.

"My Lord!" was her outraged comment. "It's brand new, and the little hanimal wouldn't wear it!" Lily could not refuse to wear it, but she was rebel enough to see that it got shabby and torn in record time, even though the calico pinafore protecting it was hardly soiled.

It was lucky that Thomas never even noticed the dress. Every parcel from the Denmers had to be hidden, and the things brought out bit by bit.

"Damn nerve, as if we be in need. We baint in need of their cast offs, no fear. Burn the whole damn lot I say. You and Our Eth keeping up with that lot, drives I mad."

No. Lily was not like her sister. "Lily, thee bissn't fit to tie our Ethel's shoe laces" or "fitter theest take a leaf out of Our Ethel's book. Her was never like thee". No wonder Lily thought of herself as "the black sheep of the family".

Within the family, there was little affection, though they were clannish and suspicious of outsiders. Jack was the only man Lily ever cared about, just as her mother was the only woman, but they were both incapable of giving her the demonstrative love she pretended to despise. Jack was fond of Lily but he seldom showed it, while Charlotte gave what affection she had to the boys, and especially to Jack and Our Arthur. Lily she never understood, nor could she return Lily's love for her.

Because Lily found so little response at home, she looked for affection from outsiders. When she was older, she would strike up instant, ephemeral friendships with people she met on trains or buses or on a day's outing, and would be gentle, animated, sympathetic, so that what she would report later, with a sort of boastful wonder, was nothing but the truth: "they said what a charming woman I was". Strangers she found attractive because they had done nothing to make her unhappy. With strangers, she could play a more exciting role, a solo role, and become for a while the sort of person people liked, the sort of person she felt she could have been.

But in their first few years in the Rhondda, there was no need for Lily to play a part. She was happy. She loved the friendliness of the street life, for every house in Railway terrace where there were children, was open to every other child, and even though it meant braving Charlotte's disapproval of hooligans, Lily was one of the street gang who were in and out of the neighbours' houses.

At home Lily never thought of herself as being "put upon"., and she would have been surprised had she known the depth of pity which lay behind the kindliness she was offered in every house. Nothing could be hidden in that enclosed community, although everything was open to misinterpretation.

Vanw-next-door was not the only one to notice Lily "scrubbing through" on Saturdays and helping out with the washing and ironing after school. Mrs Callow (no one ever called Charlotte by her Christian name) was unpopular in Railway Terrace. She was shy by nature, unhappy by circumstance, and increasingly in pain, but it was easy for outsiders to interpret reserve and physical discomfort as disdain and bad temper. Lily in these early years had little insight, and unwittingly helped Charlotte's isolation by being herself so ready to accept and be accepted.

At school, Lily found lessons easy and she knew she was a favourite with my-teacher-Miss-Richards. Even the Welsh lessons, twice a week, were not a burden, for by learning to pronounce the words properly, Lily could sing with confidence. And as Miss Richards remarked to Miss Davies ("Davies-Thumper" to her pupils) who played the piano in the hall, Lily's soprano voice was as clear as a bell. "It would really take training Miss Davies."

Not that the Welsh words were easy – those lls and chs came with some difficulty. And for Marco who sat behind her and pulled her long ringlets, they were an impossibility. Marco was "the Bracchi boy", although on his father's newly opened café-cum-sweetshop on the main road the name 'Granelli' was plain to be seen. But the first Italians who came to the valleys twenty years before the Callows and opened ice cream parlours were the Bracchi brothers from Bardi in Northern Italy. And all who followed them were known as Bracchis, no matter what their own surname might have been.

There were very few cafes selling ice cream, sweets and coffee that were not owned by a Granelli, a Sidoli or a Figoni family. "Like gypsies, exactly" Charlotte would say, her eyes taking in every detail of the women, with their lustrous hair, their olive skins, their gold earrings, and the skirts of a colour brighter than her own usual grey or black alpaca,

Lily's main interest was in singing and when on their first St. David's Day she won the solo soprano competition in the school Eisteddfod, even Charlotte was pleased. She was less pleased when in a few years time Lily would be spending hours out of the house, so-say practising for singing Festivals ("- it's for the Bethel

Gymanfa Ganu mother") and getting up to Lord knows what mischief.

Her other love was reading, and she was allowed to go by herself to the workmen's library, only a short walk from Railway Terrace. But she liked it best when the shift Jack was working allowed him to go with her, especially if it was evening and getting dusk. They would go through the Gothic-arched doorway and up the wide staircase with its polished brass handrail to the halfway landing, and here Lily would pause to look through the long barred window at the lights in the houses on the other side of the river reflected brokenly in the murky water. Beyond the dark shapes of the houses loomed the darker mass of the mountain, and above that again, the inky blue-black of the sky.

A left turn and a shorter flight brought them to the two Reading Rooms, the Adults' and the Children's, way past the Billiards Room. Sometimes the door of the Billiards Room would stand ajar, and Lily could glimpse the dark-green baize tables bathed in pools of light and hear the soft insistent click of the balls. Lily would feel the concentration of the players and the tenseness of the spectators in the silence of the crowded room, and she would creep past the open door as noiselessly as she could to gain the shelter of the Reading Room.

The Reading Room, with its heavy glass-fronted bookcases and solid polished wood tables breathed an aura, which Lily was to recognise later, when she was in service at Penmaen, as the hallmark of wealth. Money had been lavished on the library when it was built, not ten years before, and it showed. It showed in the carved doors with their gleaming brass knobs and fingerplates, in the pitch pine easy-rise staircases, in the moulded ceilings and in the brilliant chandeliers. Even the massive nonconformist chapels Nazareth, Bethesda, Jerusalem, Bethel, were not built on a more splendid scale, while the two Anglican churches, St. John's the Parish church near the station, and St. David's, nearer Railway Terrace, were both unimpressive.

Yet, however unremarkable their architecture, the churches, the chapels and the Workmen's Libraries were opulent in comparison with the miners' dwelling houses. The contrast between the grandeur of the public buildings and the squalor of the private houses had struck Jack keenly from the beginning, but it was one which Lily at eleven was too young to appreciate. She was too absorbed in herself to adopt any of Jack's radical ideas about the inequality of society, too concerned with her family to be affected by the disparity between coal-owner and coal-miner.

Lily was contented with her world especially when that world included Jack's borrowing for her from the Adult Section, books like *The Channings, A Peep Behind the Scenes, The Wide Wide World,* and *Queechy,* for she was an avid and uncritical reader. Jack's books she never read, though she was sometimes tempted by a title to look inside the cover. She felt sure that *The Idler* would be a Good Story, but a very few paragraphs were enough to disappoint her. Usually she got no further than simply noticing the names – *The Wealth of Nations, An Essay*

Chapter Six

Concerning Human Understanding (a big book for just an essay she thought), *Discourse on Method, Rasselas, The Canterbury Tales, Tom Jones, Amelia.* She marvelled at what a lot of books Jack borrowed, and what a lot he knew.

Jack was an intellectual by nature, and now for the first time in his working life, he met men who were thinkers and debaters, and who shared his interests. Engaged in the hardest of toil underground, they still had energy and curiosity enough to read and discuss the books on economics and politics, and the classics of English literature they found on the shelves of their new workmen's libraries.

When he was at home, Jack was happy to paint, to draw, or to read, but Bert was like Thomas, and was eager to see what Charlotte judged to be "vulgar peepshows" at the Theatre Royal in Tonypandy or to gamble on the Scotch coal company horseracing at the Partridge Field in Llwynypia. Jack would sometimes go with them to see the boxing and wrestling at the Judges Hall in Trealaw, and was as keen as any to follow the rugby matches in Cardiff Arms Park and further afield, on cheap rail excursions to London to Crystal Palace and to Belle Vue in Manchester.

But despite the nine years difference in their ages, it was to Lily that Jack felt closest. They were alike in character, and their friendship, born of mutual respect, lasted unbroken till Jack's death.

Like Jack, Lily was given no chance of education beyond the Elementary School, but at that time in her life, she would not have wanted to go against her parents' wishes. It was taken for granted that she would leave

Chapter Six

school when she turned twelve. Miss Richards had learned of a suitable position, and recommended her favourite pupil, though with some misgiving, and so Lily started her first job of work, in Service.

In the summer of 1909, Lily went as maid of all work to Mrs. Elizabeth Morgan, the widow who, with her spinster daughter Edith, kept the Sub-Post Office on Ystrad Road, just over the bridge from Railway Terrace. "Maid of all work" was an accurate description.

CHAPTER SEVEN

MA MORGAN'S

1910

"Which of us is to do the hard and dirty work for the rest - and for what pay?"

(Ruskin, Sesame and Lilies)

Chapter Seven

There had been no competition for the job at the Post Office, which was hardly surprising, considering that the wage was so small and the employer so unpopular. But Lily had left school with pleasure, and was prepared to enjoy doing the housework she could do well.

She was supposed to be "helping out with the rough", though it would have been more accurate to say that she did it all, since Mrs. Morgan kept no other help, and never soiled her hands herself.

It was Lily alone who scoured with whitening stone the window sill and the three outside steps up to the front door, Lily who cleaned the brass, which meant the door knocker, letter box and the wide threshold, as well as all the inside door knobs and finger-plates, together with the huge pairs of candlesticks with snuffers which were part of the ornaments on the parlour mantelpiece. It was Lily who scrubbed the brown diamond-patterned oil-cloth which covered the floors of the passage and of the front-room Post Office. It was Lily who ran the errands, Lily who blackleaded the kitchen grate.

It was all done under the watchful eye of Mrs. Morgan and the concealed scrutiny of Miss Edith, and for a wage of one shilling and sixpence a week, and her dinner and tea every day. For a lively twelve-year old with a sense of fun like Lily, the household was dreary, and the work heavy. But Lily thought herself lucky. She was glad to be contributing to the family income, and in being thus openly set apart from Our Arthur. It was as much this consciousness of status as her own high spirits which would have made her hum and sing aloud as she worked, except that Mrs. Morgan had lost no time in checking her with a disapproving "No more noise of that kind, if you please, Lily".

Elizabeth Jane Morgan was the widow of the late Mr. Moses Morgan, staunch Rechabite, bass soloist in "Judas Maccabeus" in Nazareth Chapel, and "Deep Moss" to his fellow choristers. As relict of so respected a figure, Elizabeth Jane Morgan imagined herself to be entitled to a measure of deference. Universal esteem she was confident she commanded. She would not have believed that she was known to all as "Ma Morgan", sometimes with the distinguishing title of "Ma Morgan the Post" and, amongst the most disrespectful, as "Mother Morgan". She would have been equally unbelieving, though infinitely more horrified, to know that her daughter's colourless complexion and hairy face were suspected of being the result of an unspecified but definite interest in her own bodily waste products. She was happy in her ignorance.

Ma Morgan was the kind of woman who would have crushed the spirit of a girl less resilient than Lily. She was not uncharitable, but she was forbidding, both in face and manner. In her youth she had possessed a dainty dignity, but now that she was past sixty and overweight, she had become prim and imperious. In her own mind, she was sure that she looked exactly like the late-lamented sovereign, Queen Victoria. Not the very slim young Victoria perhaps, for she was conscious that her figure had become pleasantly rounded. But not the aged sorrowing widow either. More like Victoria in her prime, just before the death of Prince Albert. Her Moses Morgan had been near about Albert's age when he died, so that she too had had a long and solitary widowhood, though in Edith she was thankful to see a constant reminder of the dear departed, as good a husband and as fine a singer as any in the land

Ma Morgan's self-image was not one which outsiders would have recognised. The sharp pointed nose and bristly grey hair, half hidden as it was under the white lace-trimmed cap, would have made them see the justice of Charlotte's comparison: "Her puts I very much in mind of an 'edge'og, 'snow."

"Well", said Lily "she do creep about more like a mole than an 'edgehog, mother, poking 'er long nose into everything."

But Ma Morgan was not as prickly as she looked, and she had no fault to find with Lily's work, poke and pry as she might, for Lily had been used to Charlotte's more exacting standards at home. Lily was doing for money the work she had done for years at home without any payment, hardly any open acknowledgement, and seldom any praise

"If a job's worth doing, Lily, it be worth doing well." Charlotte's usual comment never varied, but by her tone Lily was never in any doubt as to her opinion of that particular job. When she said it firmly, as if inviting her statement to be challenged, Lily knew it was a reproof. The expected standard had not been reached, and the job might have to be done again. When she said it gently, and as a statement of fact universally acknowledged to be true, then Lily recognised that she was satisfied.

But Lily craved encouragement and, although she had learned not to expect Charlotte ever to give it, she was still resentful when she saw Ethel more highly regarded. Lily was never given that approval, however hard she worked to earn it. To the end of her long life, Lily never accepted that love was a gift, to be given freely and not according to desert. Her own affection she gave in proportion as she felt the recipient deserved it, never uncritically, and never unconditionally, at least to her husband and daughters.

She felt insecure in her own mother's love; perhaps it was inevitable then that when she became a mother herself she held out to her daughters the threat of withdrawal of love or even complete rejection. "I shan't love you if you..." was a warning which her elder daughter was not afraid to provoke but which made the younger girl guilt-ridden and anxious to placate. Lily was aggressive, partly in an attempt to gain her mother's attention, and partly from dislike and jealousy, especially of Ethel.

Charlotte was fond of saying: "Theest could rely on Our Ethel, never on Our Lily," remembering the time "Her left Our Arthur to play in the street all on his own and she gallivanting off with that gang, boys and girls, from Smith Street. Catch Our Eth doing summat like that?"

Ethel would never play truant so often from Sunday School, much less spend the half-penny collection money on lossins the following day. Ethel felt it her duty to report to Charlotte as many of Lily's misdeeds as she knew about, especially the larking about instead of Sunday

Chapter Seven

School, and there were enough such reports to make Charlotte sigh and say "I be at my wits end wi' thee, Lily".

Lily felt remorse, for she was sensitive to reproof from either Charlotte or Jack, but it was a feeling of repentance short-lived compared with the anger she vented on Ethel for "telling". "You better shut your big gob, Our Ethel, or I'll shut it for you", a threat which was realistic enough to make Ethel feel it might be wiser to turn a blind eye now and again. Only of Lily could Thomas say in exasperation, "Telling she off be like pouring water on to a duck's back. Thee'st got too much old buck Lily".

Lily was the most boisterous of all the family, the most lively and the most noisy, and when she came home at night from the Morgans, "it were just like Bedlam" according to Thomas, who would have preferred Lily to have a "live-in" job. But Lily would have accounted it a wasted day if she had not seen her mother and Jack, and the idea of sleeping under a strange roof, in a bed all on her own, was not to be entertained at any cost. To be under the same roof as Miss Edith especially! Miss Edith Morgan was the reason why people trailed all the way in all weathers to the main Post Office in Ton, even just to buy a half-penny stamp. Her way of looking up wearily from her paper work at intruder customers, and her peering suspiciously over her gold-rimmed pince-nez before she boomed out "*Yes?*" made an errand to the sub Post Office something to be avoided.

Miss Morgan would not have thought of herself as fearsome, and yet it was only after they moved up from the Infants to the Juniors that nervous children, Our Arthur among them, would drop the habit of crossing over to the other side of the road on their way to school lest they should accidentally catch a glimpse of her head through the barred window.

It was not only the way she sounded, but also the way she looked which made Miss Morgan an object of childish dread. Edith Morgan had inherited her father's physical characteristics, his large frame, his sonorous voice. But Lily had never known Moses Morgan, and she had decided that Miss Edith was very like one of the pictures in Jack's *Illustrated British Birds and their Habitats*. It was her Roman nose and dark moustache that did it, together with her long gaunt neck and gleaming black hair piled high and untidily secured with loose hairpins. As soon as Jack had pointed out the black and white picture of The Raven on page 81 and had read the paragraph describing it, she had thought of Miss Morgan:

"Large and thick-set, with a longer neck than other crows...glossy black with heavy black bill...loose feathers give a shaggy look..." And the final phrase, which had set Lily off giggling and made Jack slam the book shut in irritation, "omnivorous and a scavenger".

With Miss Morgan's likeness lying between the pages of Jack's book, Lily could not feel intimidated, despite Our Arthur's expressed fears for her safety and his relief at seeing her home at night. In any case, Lily had found that if you were bold enough to look into her face, not fearing to be turned to stone, you saw that the dark eyes were surprisingly gentle. Not so much like The Raven ("wary and aggressive", page 82) after all, Lily thought, especially since she was safely behind her counter cage most of the time.

From behind her wire grille, Lily could feel Miss Morgan's eyes upon her as she wrung out her cloth over her bucket or reached carefully into the corners when she washed the Post Office floor each morning. Hers was a silent vigilance, for during all the eighteen months Lily was at Morgan the Post's, Miss Edith exchanged hardly a word with her, and never varied her expression.

"I don't know why she do always look like that, though", Lily reported.

"Like as if in pain?" suggested Our Arthur

"More like something nasty-smelling under 'er nose", which was enough "to set they two off laughing and sniggering fit to bust", much to Charlotte's irritation. "Our Lily's laugh!" Charlotte used to say. "If they was to kill her for it, 'er wouldn't be able to stop."

Lily's laugh was well-known for being as infectious as it was uncontrollable. When they heard it, even Ethel would join in, while Our Arthur would laugh till he cried, sometimes without even knowing the cause of it all, until Jack would slam shut his book to ask more in resignation than anger, "is there any peace to be had anywhere in this house?"

That was always the signal for Charlotte to warn Lily to "draw her horns in".

Lily had enough of peace and quiet in the drab household of Mother Morgan, but even so she was content to be her "girl" for more than a year and a half, before "my-teacher-Miss-Richards" gave her a character which was to take her as housemaid to Penmaen, the big house on Ystrad Road.

When she first started at Ma Morgan's, Lily spent most of her evenings at home, and one of her pleasures was in hearing Jack read aloud. Jack was an avid learner, and an instinctive teacher, and in Lily he had, if not an ideal pupil, then at least a willing listener. She was the one and only listener.

Ethel had found herself "a decent enough feller" in Will Shepherd, and was spending much of her time up in Ton Pentre with her future in-laws, while Bert and Thomas would be "out" somewhere together.

Our Arthur would be in the back kitchen tormenting the cat by dressing it up in the little baby cap and petticoat he last wore as a baby, pulling its front paws through the sleeves and tying the ribbons at the back of its neck. He would wrap it in a duster, English-fashion, to nurse it, until it leaped from his arms to flee with a screech and outstretched claws under the couch out of harm's way.

Charlotte would be in the middle kitchen, mending the clean pit clothes, a never-ending task, for pit clothes were always getting torn, especially since they were only taken on for work when they were 'ripe' anyway. Or else she would be reading the latest *Christian Herald*. Jack would join her, book in hand, and would draw a chair up to the table to read aloud to Lily.

At first Lily would busy herself with the plain sewing or piece of knitting which Charlotte provided so as to foil Satan's mischievous intent where idle hands were concerned. But if Jack's choice interested her, she would drop her work and sit silent, her eyes never leaving Jack's face. She never fidgeted through *David Copperfield* or *The Mill on the Floss* but when Jack tried to teach her industrial history or economics according to Marx, she would become confused and bored. She would bend her head over her work and make a great show of being attentive, nodding her head when he paused, or looking up with a half-smile as if she were about to interrupt with an intelligent question which would prove she was not only keeping up with the argument but even seeing the difficulties ahead.

Jack was never taken in, and he would soon close the book and suggest a game of cards. If Thomas should unluckily return while they were playing, they would scurry to get them all hidden before he came into the room, for Thomas was convinced that playing cards were "Devil's cards", and as far as he knew, he was harbouring none in *his* house.

Jack would normally have scorned any subterfuge, but experience had taught him that in "things indifferent", it was more expedient to keep the peace. Thomas was still liable to explode with unforeseeable anger, but the move to the Rhondda had changed him no less than it had affected the others. He couldn't help noticing that Charlotte was often in pain, and that she was becoming an invalid.

Thomas had never lost his affection for Charlotte, and as he grew less boisterous and more openly tender towards her, so Charlotte's tongue lost some of its sharpness. They had found a common source of anxiety in their children, or more specifically, in Jack and Lily. In a family which was generally so conformist in its attitudes and so prudent in its actions, Jack and Lily could not help presenting a contrast of which they themselves were most painfully aware. They were different from the others, and they knew it. But Jack could always rely on his mother's uncritical affection, whereas Lily knew that she was looked on disapprovingly by both parents. They felt they had cause for their disapproval, for Lily had a reckless, impulsive side to her nature which was showing itself as defiance, and Charlotte was observing it with unease.

"Mark my words, Lily, thee'st be going to come a cropper one of these days". If only she could see how easy it was for a girl to be thought "forward". Why couldn't she be more like Ethel? The neighbours were noticing that Lily was "getting into a lovely girl", that her eyes were bright, and that she had a smile for everyone. Jack, too, might have commented that she was spending more and more time out "at choir practice" or "down Olive's house, you know mother, Olive from Gelli crossing". But Jack was seldom at home himself these days, for he had become caught up, first with pit politics, and then with the Rhondda Labour Party.

CHAPTER EIGHT

DIC AWEN

1911

"The workmen desire to get as much, the masters to give as little, as possible".

(Adam Smith, The Wealth of Nations)

(Chapter 8, Of the Wages of Labour)

Jack's involvement with pit politics had begun on his first day in the Garth, when he met Dick Jenkins the Federation. Thomas and Bert had found places in the Bryn Colliery, the other side of the wall from Railway Terrace. But Jack had gone further afield. Thomas had started at the Bryn because it was natural that he should go where he knew Joe Totterdale, his friend from the docks at Avonmouth. But it was equally natural that Jack should want to go somewhere away from his father. Garth Colliery was bigger, and some twenty years older than the Bryn, and was two miles or so away from Railway Terrace. Jack, like the other Gelli miners who worked there, walked there and back, savouring the air in summer, but wishing in the dark winter months that they lived nearer the pit.

When he looked back, Jack considered it his good fortune to have been taken on in the Garth, although at their first meeting he had not been favourably impressed with his butty. Richard Jenkins looked older than his forty-four years, even though his slight figure was firm and upright. He was almost bald, and very short-sighted, with a face marked with the tell-tale accident-blue scars characteristic of miners. His expression was unfathomable, and the dryness of his greeting not particularly reassuring: "A bit old for a tyro, boy bach, but we'll soon lick you into shape. It's kill or cure down here, like, see." But before the ten-hour-long shift was over, he and Dic Awen as he was often called, had taken each other's measure. Jack had found his father figure and Dick Jenkins had enrolled Jack in his mental register of Federation men.

Chapter Eight

Dick Jenkins had been a farm labourer in Pembrokeshire, but he had been working underground in the Rhondda for over twenty years, and was a skilled face worker. He had earned his nickname Dic Awen (Dick the Muse) because of his poetic successes at local eisteddfodau, though neither Bardic Chair nor Crown were ever to mark him a National winner. He was a devout member of the Welsh Baptist Church, one of the deacons who sat in the Sêt Fawr (the Big Seat) on a Sunday, and who could recite whole verses together of the Old and New Testaments, both in Welsh and in English. Not that Dick was a Sunday Christian only, for he took his religion into his daily life. He was an idealist, an ardent socialist, and he lived in Hillside, a few streets away from Railway Terrace, with his wife and father-in-law. A keen debater, he was, as Thomas scornfully assessed him, "just Jack's type o' man, never any cussing or swearing, not normal".

He was as eager to instruct as was Jack to learn, and like all the other 'foreigners', Jack had everything to learn.

The cage had dropped them over a thousand feet straight down the shaft with heart-stopping speed, slowing down only when it got to within a few feet of the pit bottom. The first few times Jack feared they were not going to slow at all, but would go on hurtling down until they crashed, though he soon learned to gauge the depth they had covered, and even to feel exhilarated by the sudden descent.

Dick had noticed the look on Jack's face. "No need to worry about the cage, bach. The winding-man got his depth-indicator there in front of his eyes, big arrow on the wall. It do tell him exactly when to put that brake on."

"And if he forgets to look at that arrow?" Jack was only joking.

"He don't forget," said Dick. "But in case of emergency, there's always the over-winder. 'Dead man's pin', Jack, the copper pin half inch thick. It's fixed to the top of the cage and it gets cut if the cage is over-wound. Acts like a brake then, locks the two cages, the one going up and the one going down. Automatically."

"And that over-winder is always set in position I suppose?" said Jack.

"Always," said Dock. "Well, except of course when they're loading timber into the cage. They got to lift the gate fence then, high enough above the pit top to get the lengths through the folding doors. And to do that they got to put the over-winder out of action. Just for loading. As soon as they finish, then back goes the dead man's pin into its working position again. Always replaced at once. So that's what I say, Jack, you're as safe as houses on your way down the pit. It's when you get there you got to look out. More chance of being blown up or burnt alive or maybe crushed by falling rock than being in a cage accident."

But he couldn't resist adding "mind you, if you are in a cage careering out of control, make sure you're in the one hurtling down. In the one going up you don't stand a chance, except by a miracle. Flung up over the Big Wheel you are, then. But going down, well, it do crash below the bottom and you might get off with just broken bones.

Unless, of course, others fell on top of you and flattened you."

Jack was silent. His introduction to the pit was sobering enough to make him glad that Dick expected no comment. But more than a decade later he was to remember those words.

As they walked in single-file carrying their Davy lamps the mile downhill along the cold main heading, Dick was explaining:

"Nowhere to wash the dirt from your hands, and only the gob for the calls of nature...life in the raw, bachgen...watch them journey ropes now... lift your head a bit by here...here's our stall..."

Dick Jenkins knew all the ways of the pit, and could sense if the top was good or whether the place was on the move, long before they heard the creaks and groans of the timber pit props, or felt the ominous dribble of small coal on their backs. The pit-bottom was never silent, but was alive with noises and echoes, with every now and then a louder rumbling in the distance. Dick would listen. "That's safe enough", he'd say. "For now, anyhow." Or warningly, "You got to be careful today, Jack. Be on the alert, bachgen. She's lively today."

Dick had had three or four lucky escapes. "He didn't want me Up There just yet" and so many minor accidents "only just taps, like" that he had lost count of them. And, like all miners of his age, he already had enough coal dust on his lungs to ensure that, in a few years' time, every painful breath would be a reminder of his working life.

Chapter Eight

Everybody knew Dick Jenkins to be a powerful worker, despite his age and small physique. He never seemed to notice the heat in the stall, even though Jack felt the sweat pour off his own forehead and nose and run in rivulets down his back. Dick walked as steadily back through the heading at the end of the shift as at the beginning, even if they had spent hours crouched in a two-foot seam.

"What has that wife of yours been putting in your snap box then, Dick?" the others would ask, conversationally as if they expected a factual reply. Or from across the heading from another stall would come the earnest shout, "Hey Dic! Dic Awen! What you got there in your jack, boyo? Cold tea *we* do be drinking. You got elixir of life by there, or what?"

"Aye aye, sure to be, mun, sure to be" Dick would answer, his thoughts far away from his surroundings as they sat for their twenty minutes break, letting the stream of joking talk flow over his head.

At work underground, men were fluent in swearing and blaspheming, whether in Welsh or English or a mixture of both, but not when they called across to Dick Jenkins. Everybody knew that Dick never used such words, out of respect for God-given language itself. Not that he was anything like those victims of the Religious Revivals which had swept through both Rhondda valleys at twenty-year intervals since the eighteen-fifties. Those were generally flash-in-the-pan conversions, where the converts advertised their Newness of Life by their unnatural piety of speech and exaggerated gentleness of action. Even tolerant souls such as Dick were heard to murmur against the transitory nature of such dramatic changes, while the majority condemned the "daft buggers" as being more nuisance than they were worth, especially considering their effect on the pit ponies.

"Them animals dunno what the 'ell to do when them soft sods of hauliers give over shouting and swearing at 'em. Stop dead in their tracks they do, mun, waiting for the usual choice words of command. And by damn, they don't stir till they hear them, neither."

But Dick's abstinence from irrelevant adjectives and inappropriate descriptions was not temporary. He was known to be consistent, whether he was "Mr Jenkins, Noddfa deacon", "Dic Awen, Bard", "Richard Jenkins the Federation", or, in the pit, "Dick boyo". Dick respected every man because he had respect for himself.

He could see that Jack was finding the work underground more punishing than he had expected. He understood the ache Jack felt in his arms and shoulders from swinging the mandrel and shovelling the coal on to the dram. He knew the heavy numbness in his legs, the strain on his knees, and the pain of straightening his back. He knew why Jack left his bread and cheese untasted in his snap box but drained the cold tea in his tin jack. The fine coal dust in the air irritated their eyes and clogged their nostrils making their throats as rough and dry as sandpaper.

Jack marvelled at the high spirits of the other men on the shift, even when they were working inches deep in water or lying cramped on their sides, and he wondered how they could sing and joke, knowing that injury or death gave little warning. But as his muscles became hardened, he realised that his own attitude to the job had changed. The pit was a place of danger, but not a place of fear. He became more adept at hewing the coal, following Dick's "sometimes, boyo, you got to coax your way, not smash your way"; he found that he had banished from his mind all thought of the weight of earth which threatened the roof only inches above his head; he could dismiss those images of cloud and sunlight on the mountain tops which had made him feel that he would suffocate trapped in the foetid world of the pit bottom; most of all he savoured the fellowship born of shared labour and fostered by the philosophy of life which Dick described as "simple, bach. It's simple. St. Mathew's words. That's what we do go by. 'Digon i'r diwrnod ei ddrwg ei hun.' 'Sufficient unto the day is the evil thereof.' That's it, isn't it? We know not the day nor the hour when we shall each of us be called to account for our lives. So, live for the day and take no thought for the morrow. Tomorrow, see Jack, well, the morrow may never come. Just one shift at a time, that's enough to worry about."

Jack nodded. He would never share Dick's metaphysical beliefs, but he knew that one shift had been more than enough for him in the beginning, when he had been as ignorant of the language of the pit as of its workings. From Dick he had learned that the 'gob' was the space left after they had taken out all the coal, that it was to be packed with stones and rubbish and left to shore up the roof.

Chapter Eight

"First though, you do saw your timber into three or four foot lengths. That's your cogs. Then you do put your cogs on top of your gob. And you do leave it."

He had helped Dick to 'moil the dram', upsetting the truck on its side for the haulier's horse to get past the narrow place. He had heard Dick describe how to put a brake on the full 'journey' of trucks if, as sometimes happened on an incline, it was gathering speed and going wild downhill.

"You do throw a sprag in the wheel, Jack."

And he had seen that the sprag was a wooden bar, about a foot long, to be thrust into the spoke of one wheel of each truck of coal in the line or 'journey'.

"If your sprags are in short supply, and they always are, then, Jack, of course you'll use your broken bits of pick handles. Anything to stop the old journey when it's runaway."

From Dick he had learned how to conserve his strength, how to use the pick and shovel so as to fill the drams and still have breath and energy enough to talk. If the seam was good, they could fill in a day as many as six or eight drams, each holding a ton and a half of coal. Before the haulier took them to the coal-shaft, Dick would chalk his number on the side of each dram, so that the check-weigher would know to whom the full drams belonged and could calculate their wage. The size of their wage depended partly on the market price the owners could get for their coal. When the selling price was high, miners could earn as much as five or six pounds for their six-day week. If the rate paid to the miners was two shillings per ton, then if they could produce fifty-four tons, the wage shared between the collier and his butty would be as high as five pounds eight shillings. Two shillings per ton was a good rate, reflecting a high selling price. But the selling price of coal was not constant. When it dropped, the rate paid to the men at the coal face for every ton also dropped. Owners' profits were kept high by cutting the men's wages. There was no guaranteed minimum wage by which at least a bare standard of living would have been safeguarded.

Even if the market price and therefore the cutting price, were high, wages could still be low, for the amount of money each miner brought home at the end of the week depended on the number of drams he had been able to fill. To be paid by piece-rate in a difficult seam or in an 'abnormal place' was labour ill-rewarded.

"It's not too bad if the old seams are workable" said Dick, "and believe me, those seams by here are the best seams of steam coal in the world, Rhondda coal."

"Best," said Jack thoughtfully. "Best. Best quality. Best for selling. Best for burning. But not best for working."

"Aye, that's just it," said Dick. "Very dry and fiery, the steam coal. Always the danger of explosions in the steam pits. And the trouble is, though, that any seam can have a stone band running through it. And any seam can have a fault crossing it. I've seen a displacement then, Jack, of hundreds of feet. And any seam, even a thick nine-footer can thin out. Hardly any warning, mind, and then it do disappear altogether. "Wash-outs" those are. What a job then, to pick it up again."

Many times Jack was to hear men describing in far more colourful language that job of picking up the seam again after a 'wash-out', and dwelling luridly on the attitude of managers and under-managers to the time the men were taking and the coal production lost.

"Them bloody bosses do call it 'time-wasting'. 'Time-wasting' by damn! I dunno what the 'ell they do call time well spent then. They ought to come down by here and give it a try theirselves..."

No pit was proof against wash-outs, nor against water-logging or low head-room, places where men would be lucky to fill even two drams in a day. Their wage then would be a shamefully low return for six days of work each ten hours long.

The men were resentful of the low rate of pay decreed by the coal owners, but they were more bitter at the indifference shown to the conditions under which they worked, conditions which had changed all too little since 1855, when Her Majesty's Report had declared 'I can imagine no refinement of cruelty more worthy of the annals of Roman African or Siberian crime than compelling men to work in places where virulent though insidious poisons defraud them of their strength, their health, their lives.'

That a man could work underground in the pit and still keep his humanity was surprising enough, thought Jack. That he could develop his rationality, his love of music and of debate, was almost unbelievable. And yet Jack knew that there were many like Dick Jenkins, whose cultural and social life was as rich as their working hours were arduous. For every miner who spent his spare time in gambling and drinking away his family's carefully-budgeted money, there was at least one other whose delight was in the chapel choir and in the workmen's library. Jack had met his intellectual equals where he would least have expected it, and in Dick Jenkins he had not only discovered a man of like mind, with whom he could discuss his political ideas and share his social ideals, but he had also found a friend.

CHAPTER NINE

ANCIENT HISTORY

1910

Major fatal accidents in Rhondda collieries

				Killed
15	July	1856	Cymmer Porth	114
9	Nov	1867	Ferndale	178
10	June	1869	Ferndale	53
24	Feb	1871	Pentre	37
13	Jan	1879	Dinas	63
10	Dec	1880	Naval	84
24	Dec	1885	Maerdy	81
18	Feb	1887	Wattstown	27
12	Aug	1892	Trehafod	58
28	Jan	1896	Tylorstown	57
18	Aug	1899	Llest Garw	19
10	March	1905	Cambrian	33
11	July	1905	Wattstown	119

Chapter Nine

"We don't never see our Jack these days" Charlotte grumbled. "When he baint working nor sleeping, he be off wi' that there Jenkins feller, out of the house at meetings or summat."

The 'meetings' were usually the District Lodge meetings of the 'Fed', which Charlotte never knew by its full title of the 'South Wales Miners' Federation'. But there were sometimes, if shifts allowed, the tutorials in industrial history which Jack and Dick went down to Tonypandy to attend even though neither ever became members of the Plebs League which organised the classes. Most often, though, they would meet with others in the back room of the Temperance Bar, the local Bracchi shop near Bwllfa Bridge, to drink coffee and to talk.

Questions of ethics, psychology, religion, social conditions and above all, politics, were absorbing to Jack, but of no interest to Thomas or Bert.

Thomas and Bert were members of the Conservative Working Men's Club on Gelli Road, but their commitment to the philosophy of the Tory party was in name only. The Conservative Club was the nearest place where they could buy their beer, nearer than the King's Arms, and much closer than the Labour Club, nearly three-quarters of a mile away down in Ystrad.

In the early days, Jack had tried to interest Bert in becoming a 'union man', but Bert had been swayed by Thomas, whose opposition was not so much to the union as to the officials.

"All they cares about is their £4 a week and their travelling expenses, and that's a damn sight more than I get for working my guts out, day in, day out. I tell thee this, Jack, I'm not working to keep them collar and tie men on top of the pit."

He would have been surprised to know how dissatisfied Jack himself felt with the paid miners' agents, the professional leaders of the union, because of the use, or misuse, of their power to negotiate terms with the coal owners.

Jack was not alone in thinking that keeping in with the coal owners meant more to the Federation officials than winning from them better pay and conditions for the working miners, but he knew that Dick, a founder member of the Federation, and a member of the Garth Lodge Committee, did not share his views.

Sitting in the middle kitchen of number six Hillside, where Annie May Jenkins had lit the fire even though it was a fine evening in July, Jack realised, not for the first time, that to Dick the very existence of the miners' Federation was a continuing triumph.

"When we started, bachgen, that was in 1898, we numbered less than fourteen thousand. And now, in this year of Our Lord, nineteen hundred and eleven, well, how many would you reckon we got now?"

Before Jack could answer, remembering that there were over twenty Lodges in the Rhondda Number One District, Dick had gone on: "I'll tell you. Over thirty-one thousand, all fully paid-up members. Not bad going, eh?"

Jack had to admit that in numbers that wasn't at all bad going. "But tell me, Dick, what is the Fed doing for us? Conditions in the pit are just about as bad as they could be, and as for wages, I'm getting less now than when I started."

Dick looked thoughtful. "Well, there have been improvements in conditions compared with fifty years ago..."

Jack burst in: "So there damn well ought to be, mun. But no thanks to the Fed."

Dick had started along a well-worn path, and was not to be side-tracked. "My father-in-law, Wil Ifan, could tell you what it was like in the pit years ago, when there were no safety measures at all. He was working in the Tynewydd Colliery down in Porth, and he remembers the explosion in Cymmer Old Pit. In 1856 that was. Tuesday the fifteenth of July, 1856. A hundred and sixty of them, men and boys, working underground, and a hundred and fourteen killed. And those few who came out alive had terrible injuries, terrible burns. Young men a lot of them, Jack, young boys, *children* Jack. Door boys, all children the door boys were of course, nine year olds and eleven year olds, suffocated, all suffocated. Aye, a pitiful day, that."

Jack was silent. This was the kind of industrial history in which no Rhondda miner needed lessons. Dick was going on: "That was the worst explosion that had ever been, not just in England or here in Wales with us, but anywhere, in any country in the world. And all as a result of neglect, neglect of safety precautions by the Manager and the Overman. That's what came out at the coroner's inquest. Manslaughter, caused by the negligence of the

Manager, the Overman, and the Fireman. And so it was, Jack. They went to trial of course..."

"Eventually, yes" said Jack grimly.

"They went to trial," said Dick slowly. "But what happened? The Swansea Assizes cleared them of blame. Cleared of legal blame. No personal default. That was the verdict of the law. No legal blame. Cleared. But you know, Jack, two years before that explosion, *two years*, mark you, Her Majesty's Inspector of Mines had sent special rules to the owner of that Cymmer pit, James Harvey Insole. Insole and Son it is now, of course, aye, Insole and Son."

The Mackworth Recommendations, the first set of rules sent to a Rhondda coal-owner about enforcing safety precautions in a particular pit. Jack knew their drift only too well, and he nodded as Dick went on:

"Yes, a set of rules, set out all detailed, nice and tidy. Sent to that pit, to that particular pit, and relating to *that* pit, sent by Her Majesty's Inspector, Herbert Mackworth. And what were they? Things like having a qualified mining engineer at Cymmer, examining the work places every day, seeing that there was artificial means of ventilation, getting to use Davy Lamps. Commonsense, *important* things like that." He looked at Jack, his matter-of-fact tone masking the depth of his feeling.

"They were still using naked lights in that place, Jack. Naked lights! When everybody knew that there was gas in that pit. It was notorious for it. Not enough air going through them new workings, not nearly enough air headings, see. Lighted candles they had to work by.

They'd see the cap, as they called it, the cap on the candle. That's the ignited globule of gas, Jack. They'd see that cap standing half an inch high at the end of the candle flame. As much as *two inches* high sometimes. Nobody said anything. Nobody complained. It wouldn't have been news to the manager! And they'd have been out on their neck. And the manager would see that they never got a job in any Rhondda pit again. Trouble-makers, see, Jack."

Managers and men, thought Jack. Nothing had changed.

"Jabez Thomas the manager was." Dick had never forgotten the details. "Not a mining engineer he was. That's what he said at the inquest. And his duties, *above ground* altogether. And yet, see, Jack, he was the one to say yea or nay to the opening up of the headings or the airways *underground*. And he was the one who saw to it that those underground managers who complained about the lack of ventilation didn't stay in their jobs very long. That was the man who had been Insole's manager. For twenty six years he had been Insole's manager. He was the master in that pit. Insole left it all to him. Insole said as much at the inquest. Because Insole, you see, was only the owner of the pit, only took the profits, had no say in the running of it at all. Didn't want to have anything to do with the managing of it."

"Well no," said Jack. "Of course not. A typical coal-owner. Concerned only with the money to be made, and how fast it can be made. Why should he concern himself with the men who are making it for him? He doesn't know them. He'll never have to see them. They don't exist as human beings for him at all."

Dick had scarcely heard him. "The manager was the one who received the Mackworth Recommendations. Yes, he was the one who received them. And he was the one who ignored them. Jabez Thomas. That was his name. You know yourself Jack, that there were well-known rules about safety lamps, about gas, about fire-damp, and those rules were in use in other collieries. But not in Cymmer. No, not in Cymmer. And after they had all been cleared, the officials, cleared of legal blame, then, of course, you got the victimisation. There weren't many survivors but some of them had given evidence that would help implicate the management and after that they found work was refused them, week after week. Never mind that they had shown courage at the time of the explosion, and tried to rescue others, oh no. Their evidence might have convicted the guilty men. And that wouldn't do."

"No," said Jack. "The bosses must never be seen to be at fault."

"And for years after the Cymmer explosion", said Dick quietly, "nothing was done about using safety lamps there. For years. More than forty years on from Cymmer, in the Garw disaster, the Llest, nineteen suffocated because of the gas explosion. And how did that explosion happen? Naked lights. Still using naked lights they were, and the manager happy to let it go on. Known to be a fiery pit, the Llest, danger of working without safety lamps officially pointed out".

Chapter Nine

"And the verdict there," said Jack, "equally well known. The sternest reprimand only along the lines of 'unfortunate error of judgement in not introducing safety lamps.'"

"Too true bachgen. And 'not introducing safety lamps' sounds a lot more acceptable than 'Allowing naked lights to be introduced into a gas-filled atmosphere'."

"Might as well have issued their death warrants along with their naked lights."

In the pit, every miner accepted that there was danger. Fire, explosion of gas, flooding, falls of coal from the face, falls of rock from the roof, all these were familiar hazards. Disasters were always possible. But when there was total neglect of the commonest measures of safety, disasters were more than possible. They were inevitable.

"And why were those safety rules ignored, Jack? Greed. Greed of gain by the owners. A lot of them holding their mineral rights on short leases, of course they had to see to it that the coal was brought out fast."

"Aye, get as much money as you can now," said Jack, adding "And to hell with the poor devils bringing out the coal. Examining the working places every day! Good God, they might find the roof was loose or that there was fire-damp, that it was dangerous to work there and that work would have to stop for a bit..."

Jack was getting heated and it was only partly the glowing banked-up fire which was responsible. A pity, thought Dick, that Jack saw fit to take the name of the Lord in vain. He broke in quickly "Take the Tynewydd back in '77. Fourteen men trapped, nine survivors. Some rescued after eighteen hours, but five of them trapped down there by the water for nine days. Nine days. The water rising, and the rescuers in danger of being swept away themselves. Wil Ifan had left the Tynewydd, to come up by here. The Garth had been opened a few years, see. But he knew all of the four men who were drowned, and he knew the other one as well, the one killed during the rescue...the rush of compressed air..."

He paused. "The Albert medal for bravery they got, twenty-five of the rescuers, pictures in all the papers and that. No more than their due, mind. The first time that medal had been awarded for bravery on land. Heroes they were, Jack, heroes, acknowledged heroes. But a pity that the owners hadn't seen to the old workings of the Upper Cymmer. That's what did it, the water from those old workings flooding through to the Tynewydd. All before your time Jack, and mine too, for that matter."

"Aye," said Jack. "Past history. Ancient history. But what have they learned from it? Damn all if you ask me. Think of 1905. *That's* in your lifetime in the pit, Dick. Very nearly in mine, only six years ago."

Dick shook his head slowly. He took off his glasses and laid them on the table in front of him, looking straight ahead. He passed the palm of his left hand up over his forehead in a weary gesture to his hair-line and down again. Then he reached for his glasses and put them on. When he spoke again his voice was as steady as ever, but resonant with deep-felt emotion and still unburied memory. "1905. Thirty-three killed in the Cambrian in Clydach in March. In July, a hundred and nineteen killed in the National in Wattstown. A hundred and twenty two working there, and only three survivors. One of Wil Ifan's uncles was killed in the National. Wil was walking in the funeral procession for the National boys. Five miles long it was. When the horses were pulling the first of the hearses through the cemetery gates in Trealaw, the Llethr Ddu cemetery, the last carriage was just leaving Wattstown. The whole valley mourned that day, Jack. Not just the widows and the children and the parents who had lost their sons, but the whole valley."

Pit disasters, thought Jack. To the outside world, just a catalogue of statistics of so many killed and injured, but to every miner in the Rhondda, a roll-call of honour of the dead they had known and whose loss they mourned. Dick seemed to have read Jack's thoughts: "'Gwyn eu byd y rhai sydd yn galaru,canys hwy a ddiddenir.' That's what we are told in the Sermon on the Mount, isn't it. 'Blessed are they that mourn, for they shall be comforted." But indeed, they will take a lot of comforting, too, the father and mother of a lovely boy of fifteen crushed in a roof fall."

Jack was as familiar with the works of John Donne as Dick with the Gospels. The words came unbidden into his mind. "'Every man's death diminishes me.'

But Dick had become brisk again. "Anyway," he was saying "look on the bright side, isn't it? Things could be better, of course, but there have been some improvements. We've got our Davy Lamps for one thing, and a fireman to see to ventilation and that. And no boys under ten working underground, and no women or girls either. That's something. Not like in the old days."

Chapter Nine

"That's true Dick, but it's still not good enough that boys of twelve are working with us underground."

"Well, it's only eight hours at a time now remember. Not so long ago, it was ten hours."

"Yes," said Jack. "Only a year ago it was ten."

"Two more hours, Jack, when you can lift up your eyes unto the hills, from whence cometh your help."

Jack smiled. "That's all very well for you Dick. I'd like to think my help was a bit nearer at hand though. That's where the Fed comes in, I reckon. Take those eight hours. The owners still expect us to get out the same amount of coal in that time as we used to in the ten. They think we are machines, wheels that can be set to turn faster. They are paying us for eight hours and wanting to get ten hours of work out of us. What kind of improvement is that? You got to face it, Dick, the coal owners don't care a damn how they make their profits so long as they're raking in the money. Who are the owners anyway? Who sees them? Faceless men, only names to us..."

"Most of them, Jack, it's true, yes, only names to us. One or two, though, well, Edward Davies for one... A lot of the workmen know him, and he knows them and their wives and children..." Honesty made him pause before he added "Well, those who go to the same chapel anyway."

"The exception that proves the rule, then. How many others live in Treorchy or Gelli? How many of them come near to see the conditions we got to work under and the houses we got to live in, much less listen to us asking for a better deal? No, they are all too busy building their mansions in Cardiff and in Brecon. Too eager to invest their profits, buying country estates where they can live like lords and claim to be gentlemen."

"The Fed speaks to them for us Jack."

Jack was scornful: "Aye. And in a whisper too. The Exec. isn't behind us, Dick, that's the trouble. They sold us out on the Conciliation Board when they agreed to the sliding scale. Who wanted the sliding scale? Not *us*. No, the owners wanted the sliding scale, to safeguard their profits. The selling price of coal drops, they dock our wages. So their profit margin as they call it, is still kept up. We can go on risking our lives, but they mustn't risk their money, oh no. And the Exec. agreed with them."

Dick was reluctant to join in that criticism: "Oh, I dunno about that Jack..." he began.

Jack let him get no further: "Well, *I* do."

The fire was dying down, and the clock on the mantelpiece showed that Jack had already stayed what Charlotte would consider to be too long a time in somebody else's house, but he had got into his stride: "What the Fed ought to be fighting for is a guaranteed minimum wage. And another thing. There ought to be enough extra pay for difficult places, abnormal places - as if any place underground can be called normal! - where we have to work twice as hard to fill only half the number of drams. So you know as well as I do that at the end of the week you don't bring enough home to live on. The extra they give us for abnormal places is laughable.!

Dick knew what Jack was going to say next: "Take the new Bute seam at the Ely now that there's so much trouble about. That seam's going to be a devil to work, with that stone running right through it. And what have the management offered? A penny a ton extra! Derisory, Dick. A penny a ton, irrespective of the thickness of that stone when they get to it."

Everybody knew that the dispute at the Ely was about the rates offered for the working of the new Bute seam, and that the men were in a mood to fight for better. Dick nodded as Jack went on. "And that makes a price list of one and tenpence. One and tenpence a ton, and the men are sticking out for two shillings and sixpence. So what's the Fed going to do about that?"

Dick trusted the Executive to convince the owners that the men deserved a better rate of pay. "Surely the owners will see this time that our cause is just. 'Teilwng yw i'r gweithiwr ei gyflog' - 'the labourer is worthy of his hire' Jack. We read that in Saint Luke."

Jack wondered how such an intelligent man could be so naive. Surely he could see that justice and greed were incompatible concepts. You'd think his long experience would have taught him that. Yet he was still talking about negotiation, still affirming his faith in fair play.

"They'll negotiate, Jack."

"Aye", muttered Jack. "Aye, negotiate and come up with another Conciliation scheme."

Dick was repeating, "Yes, they'll negotiate. It's the only way. The Exec. will win a decent rate for the Ely boys. And then they'll be pressing for the minimum wage, not only the rate for abnormal places. We're in the vanguard here, Jack. We'll carry the Miners' Federation of Great Britain with us in getting a minimum wage, not just for Welsh miners, but for every miner in the land. But it starts here, Jack, here with us in the Rhondda. Nearly a third of all the miners in the South Wales pits, that's us in the Rhondda coalfield if you count all the Rhondda Districts together. Our voice will be the loudest."

Jack could bear it no longer. "No Dick. Our voice won't be heard at all. We haven't got a voice. Even if we had hundred percent membership of the Fed, we still wouldn't have a voice. What we *have* got are paid officials on the make, acting like catspaws for the owners."

Dick's "Steady on a bit boyo", was lost in Jack's vehement "What we want are representatives who go to the owners knowing the strength of our case, and knowing our mind, knowing it because we've told them, through the ballot box. We got no power now, none at all. It's the ballot box that ought to decide our policy, Dick, not the President and General Secretary. You can bet your bottom dollar - except of course you don't bet! - that the Exec. won't do any pressing. They won't press for the Ely boys. There'll be no pressing for the minimum wage..."

Dick got up restlessly from his chair. The President, William Abraham, 'Mabon' had no greater supporter than Dick. "Well, Jack, I am positive sure that Mabon has done his best for us. Been at the head of us from the beginning. A good man, Jack. We can trust him to deal with the owners. Yes, Mabon will get the Cambrian Combine to budge a bit from the one and tenpence. Depend on it."

Jack wound his white silk muffler round his neck and reached for his cap. Dick had never lost his trust in his

Chapter Nine

fellows, he thought, always judging others by himself. When he spoke, Jack's words were more gentle than he intended. "I hope you're right Dick. Otherwise it'll mean a fight this time, and we'll all be in it."

Jack was right. The dispute which began with seventy men, over payment for working the new Bute seam at the Ely pit, ended with a strike involving the twelve thousand men of the pits of the Cambrian Combine. It began on the first of November 1910, lasted for ten desperate months and was to bring riot and bloodshed, misery and defeat. The defeat was only in the short term, for it paved the way for an historic victory, the granting of a minimum wage for all miners. But it was a triumph won at an exorbitant cost to the few, and in the Rhondda it left a bitter legacy.

CHAPTER TEN

THE CAMBRIAN STRIKE

1911

"Through all the long dark night of years

The people's cry ascendeth

The few shall not for ever sway.

The many toil in sorrow.

The powers of hell are strong today,

Our kingdom comes tomorrow."

(Cambrian Strike Manifesto 16 June 1911

"Thomas Morgan (19) collier of Tylorstown was summoned for stealing coal. PC Hall said that while on duty at the National Colliery Wattstown he saw the defendant take a piece of coal off a tram. It was his first offence and he was fined 15 shillings."

Rhondda Gazette, 23 February 1924

Chapter Ten

"Thank God our Eth's married and out of all this lot," said Charlotte. "'Er'll never have to go through it neither. Will Shepherd be one of the lucky ones with his being on the railway. Not much money of course, but coming in regular as clockwork. Not like Thomas and the boys, and nothing whatever to do wi' their pits..."

Even Charlotte had not been able to shut her ears to the talk about the Ely men before the strike began; even she had known about the difficult new Bute seam (which she heard as *Beaut*, short for *Beauty*, a most unsuitable name she always thought), and the refusal of the Cambrian Combine to give more than a penny a ton extra for working it. But when on that Tuesday, the first of November 1910, the boys and Thomas had been called out on official strike, her first reaction had been indignant unbelief:

"But it baint nothing to do wi' your pits" she had protested. "Yourn be the Bryn, the Garth. That there Beaut where they be having all the bother baint up here. It be down the valley baint it?"

Jack had tried to point out to her that the miners' strength lay in their unity with their fellow workers, and in their loyalty to an interest and a policy which was understood and worked for by all, but Thomas spoke a language she understood: "See here, old lady. It be like in a family. If Our Arthur was to be picked on by some bully-boy, all on us 'ud rally round 'en, and try to fight for 'en. Us miners have got to stick together."

Sticking together in the family was a gospel truth with Charlotte, but it was a revelation to her to see how that could be extended to take in whole streets of families. For the first time she recognised that behind the 'nosy-parkering' lay concern for another's welfare. Never again was Charlotte to feel alienated. She would always be in exile, but it was exile in a friendly country, the inhabitants united by the bonds of privation and hardship.

The Callows were comparatively well-off even without Ethel's money coming in, for Charlotte was able to draw on the money she had put by and, unlike Vanw-next-door, they never sat down to bread and marg and potatoes. Aunt Elsie Denmer enclosed packets of tea and tins of biscuits with the parcels of clothes she sent for 'poor Charlotte and her girls', and Charlotte's brother Richard was generous with gifts of money, sent only on the lawful occasions of Christmas and birthdays, so that Thomas could hardly take offence.

Richard had read with horror the accounts the Bristol newspapers had given of the November riots in Tonypandy, how Winston Churchill the Home Secretary had had to send in not only reinforcements of police but also soldiers, how there had been casualties on both sides in days of clashing, how there had been looting of shops and criminal damage. His letters had been anxious. Had his nephews been involved? Were they safe? Would Charlotte bring Arthur to stay with him and Iris at Knowle until the troubles were over?

Richard's concern for his sister was compounded by the memory that he had encouraged Charlotte to go with Thomas...but what alternative had there been... "I don't know how I be going to answer your Uncle Richard's letters" said Charlotte. "What to tell 'en? He be worriting hisself sick about us. 'Er baint well be all accounts. Your Aunt Iris put in a note to say that 'er's had to be off work for a week..."

"Tell him the truth" said Jack. "See if he can understand our side of it. Not many outside the valley can see the need for what we are doing. Tell him that the owners were putting in strike-breakers to keep the pumps and ventilation going at the Glamorgan in Llwynypia, and that the police were lying in wait on the colliery to see to it that those blacklegs got through. Tell him that we stopped them. And tell him that the next day we packed the square in a peaceful demonstration, and that the police charged us with truncheons. Hundreds of police. Tell him that his nephew Jack was there and nearly got his arm broken, and that what he saw of violence sickened him. Tell him it was civil war. And don't forget to tell him that the troops who were sent in to help the police to crush us were armed soldiers, trained and armed soldiers, and that their names will never be forgotten - The Lancashire Fusiliers, the 218th Hussars and the West Riding Regiment. Let him know that General Neil Macready's men may have all the artillery, but that we've got the guts. Tell him that it's not the moon we're asking for, but a decent wage. God knows, we work like slaves, and a lot of us die like animals. Don't we deserve a wage that will let us live like men?"

Charlotte was well-used to Jack's impassioned speeches, but she had neither the wish nor the language to use any of his words in her letters. She wrote as best she could, little knowing how few were the letters left to be exchanged. There was no warning, no preparation for the news which came at the end of April, that Richard had died of a heart attack. He was forty eight.

"No age", mourned Charlotte. "There was so much I wanted to say to him, so much..."

Her grief was long-lasting, and all the more deep for having to be unshared. Richard's widow Iris was too far away for her to offer and receive comfort, and of her immediate family, Charlotte felt that only Ethel and Jack would have understood and so lessened her sorrow.

But Ethel was wearing the happiness of a newly-wed, an armour protecting her from feeling outside ills, while Jack was absorbed in the misery of those around him. When he was not attending meetings of the Cambrian Combine Strikers' Committee, he was exhausting himself in organising strike relief for the extremes of age, the young and the old, who were dependent on others, so that he was seldom at home. Every day that the strike dragged on, into weeks, into months, he could see people becoming more desperate, the valley like a town under siege. Once he came home with the news that Tom Phillips, Top House, had been caught scavenging coal from the tip above Bryn Colliery and was going to be prosecuted.

"But they all does it," Charlotte protested. "Lizzie Totterdale do swear 'er seed Vanw-next-door t'other evening, helping Fairy Feet to carry down a bag. And it be only waste-stuff, bain't it? Like mountains theirselves, big black mountains."

"Yes mother," said Jack. "But you must remember that those great mounds of waste belong to the owners, and whatever good coal is embedded in them belongs to them as well. So of course it's stealing for a man..."

"And his wife" Charlotte put in.

"....stealing for a man to try and salvage a bit of coal that's been thrown away and that he dug out in the first place."

"Aye", said Bert. "And of course he might have the nerve to sell a bit of it to some other poor devil who's not quite so badly off..."

"Oh," said Jack bitterly, "they'd think that was showing a true speculator's spirit no doubt, probably want to turn a blind eye to that."

"Trying to keep body and soul together, that's all they be doing," said Charlotte, shaking her head in pity. "Little 'uns got to be kept warm and fed."

Charlotte was having to revise her opinion about the idleness of the women. Nobody in the strike-bound valley was idle, least of all the women. While the men repaired the shoes of their own and other families, their wives patched and mended the clothes, ate sparingly themselves and tried to make meagre dishes into appetising meals and, hardest of all, kept a cheerful face.

There was barely enough money for the necessities of living, but time and to spare for things which needed only energy, enthusiasm and talent. Choirs rehearsed and gave concerts, eisteddfodau were organised, the chapels held their annual Anniversary services, discussion groups flourished. And, two noticeable effects, washing could be hung out and taken in dried, free from coal smuts, and miners' faces lost their pallor. Outwardly, there was cheerful bustle. Inwardly, there was gnawing anxiety. Those who themselves had little to give, shared with those who had even less, and whenever she spoke of those months, Charlotte would say "People were so *good* to one another."

Had she but known it, 'people' were thinking the same thing about Charlotte. Whereas in the early days she had frowned on Lily's bringing 'all they dratted childer into the house all the time', she had become tolerant of Our Arthur's 'Railway Street Gang' and no longer held out against his pleading for "bread and jam, and some for Ianto, to eat outside in our hands, mother". What she had condemned as "a slovenly habit, not sitting down at table like Christian folk" had become a way of ensuring that Ianto and Hywel and whoever was with Our Arthur at the time needed less to eat when they went home.

The Callows were able to 'manage' better than many families, and 'Freely have ye received, freely give' had become a text close to Charlotte's heart. She had never been so poor, not even when the family had been young, back in Bristol, but she had never felt so enriched. Charlotte was seeing the courage and compassion which lifted men and women above the squalid struggle to keep alive, and she was marvelling at the buoyancy and strength of spirit which turned despair into black comedy. Not that Charlotte savoured irony, any more than did Lizzie Totterdale. Lizzie had taken to calling in most days, especially after Richard's death, "just to see how theest be keeping", and to keep Charlotte informed about the gossip.

"What do 'ee think they be saying now, Charlotte?"

Charlotte sighed. It were good of her to keep coming round, especially in this hot weather, so burdensome for so stout a body as Lizzie. But her roundabout way of telling her tale was enough to make a soul feel weary.

"This be the latest, according to that there Olwen Pugh, The Chip Shop, (her mother had that stroke eight year back, and not able to stir nor hand nor foot ever since, you mind her, Charlotte?), she be telling I the best way to save food if theest have a big family..."

She paused, but getting no encouragement from Charlotte, went on: "Come bedtime – this be Olwen Pugh talking, this be, mind, Charlotte - thee say to the little uns 'what do 'ee want, threepence or thee supper?' .They says 'threepence'. Threepence be a deal of money for a young un. A deal of money for anybody, young or old. See now, threepence buys thee a pint and a half o' milk or a pound o' neck of mutton, or a pound and a half of sugar..."

"O aye, Lizzie." *When* would she come to the point of her story? As if anybody was interested in that there Olwen Pugh, or her bedridden mother, in the first place, and about the prices of food, Charlotte needed no reminders.

"So, theest give them their threepenny bit. And the food gets put by for next day. But, and see the cunning of it, Charlotte, in the night theest feel under the pillows and theest put the threepenny bits in thee pocket. Next day then, theest say 'oh, they be lost somewhere.' What do 'ee make on it?"

"Well, I tell thee this, Lizzie. Only once thee cuss play that trick on Our Arthur. Er 'ud be wise to that in no time. Er be getting that sharp. Hass thee heard en arguing the toss wi' our Jack? Like a boy twice his age in sense. He puts I in mind o' my brother Richard every time I looks at en."

Lizzie nodded sympathetically. Charlotte had gone downhill ever since her brother had died, thought Lizzie. She had hardly gone outside the door for weeks, and seemed to have lost interest in everything except her family.

"Aye," she said with mechanical kindness. "All your boys be fine-looking lads." Then, trying to divert Charlotte's attention, "That there Vanw-next-door's husband be a funny feller, baint he?"

"Fairy Feet?" said Charlotte. "He be alright."

"Summat funny about en" said Lizzie. "Vanw were out on the door as I were coming along, so o' course I stops and chats. He comes from the back o' the house and says to Vanw 'Same as usual for dinner, gel?' Of course I says 'What might that be, Mr. Jones?' 'Fried Valentines', he says and disappears quick as anything into the house again, shutting the door. But I'll swear I heard them all laughing inside, he and all them kiddies, fit to bust...Vanw seems nice enough though."

Charlotte had barely heard, and she answered listlessly "Well, it be hard enough to find summat to feed a family these days. Jack and Our Arthur, they be finicky fellers but Thomas and Bert be hearty eaters. An hearty eater do take some satisfying, theest know."

Lizzie was preparing to go. At the door she turned and said "How be married life suiting your Ethel then?" Charlotte felt irritated. Lizzie knew that Ethel had not 'had to get married' and she was fishing to find out whether there was a baby on the way yet, Ethel being that plump she wouldn't be showing. Before she could answer, Our Arthur came rushing up the back. "Mother! The strike! The strike's over!" He was followed by Jack, and with him Dick Jenkins.

Dick was saying: "So what has it all been for? Mabon got the owners to budge from one and tenpence last October. He got two shillings and a third of a penny per ton for the Bute boys way back last October. *By negotiating with the owners.* And now it's August. And that's the sum they're going to accept. That's the sum we are giving up the strike for. All that bloodshed. Those miners imprisoned on account of that blackleg. Near-starvation for whole families. Debts it'll take years to pay off. What gain has there been?"

The strike had convinced Dick that it was a two-edged weapon and that the strikers had lost more than they had gained. Jack led the way into the middle kitchen, where Lizzie Totterdale had settled herself again, all thought of Ethel and her married life temporarily banished. The miners were going back to work on September first on the terms offered ten months earlier, but Jack could not agree that they had gained nothing by the strike, terrible though the effects of that strike had been on all Rhondda miners and their families.

"We'd have won more and sooner" he said, "if Mabon and the Exec. had been whole-heartedly behind us rank and file from the beginning. Remember, it took them till midsummer to back us properly in our demand for a minimum wage. But they are behind us now, and that's a gain. If only the Miners' Federation of Great Britain could have adopted the Fed's resolution about the minimum wage..."

"They still think the Cambrian dispute is a local affair," said Dick.

"But the question of abnormal places must be an issue for all miners now," said Jack, "after this strike, it must be. And more than that, the whole of the South Wales coalfield is behind us in our pressing for a minimum wage. Every miner in the land will soon be behind us on that one."

It was strange, thought Jack, how he and Dick had changed their positions during the strike. Dick's sense of outrage during the months of suffering caused by what he considered a needless strike was preventing him from seeing that good might come of it. The strike with its violence and misery had shattered Dick's long-held dream that a united mining force where the Miners' Federation of Great Britain, led by the South Wales 'Fed', would agree with the owners a fair guaranteed minimum wage taking into account abnormal places.

But to Jack, that dream was on the point of fulfilment. The endurance and courage of the Cambrian strikers had shone the searchlight not only on the issue of abnormal places, but also on the minimum wage question, and that light was not going to be put out in a hurry. Before the strike, Jack's commitment to the Fed had been lukewarm and critical compared with his conviction after it that the miners by their solidarity in suffering could bring about far reaching changes for the better. The strike had strengthened his certainty that the men could wrest nothing from the coal owners without a fight. To get the mines out of the hands of the owners and under State control was a distant ideal, not to be realised in Jack's lifetime, but it was a goal towards which he more and more bent his energies.

The Cambrian miners were beaten in their claim for the two and sixpenny ton. But just over a month after their pits re-started, the 'Fed's' fight for a minimum wage became the official demand of the Miners' Federation of Great Britain. The struggle was not yet over, for all the negotiations ended in failure. Dick was one of the few who felt that something would be gained if talks could be re-opened. Most shared Jack's conviction that only a strike by the nation's miners would bring any result, a belief justified when on the first of March 1912 the first-ever national strike of miners began.

"St. David's Day." said Dick ruefully. "The Lion and Dragon are united. The opposition could crumble."

The opposition did crumble. The National Strike was short-lived and effective, for on the nineteenth of March the Prime Minister, Herbert Asquith, introduced the Minimum Wage Bill in Parliament. The Cambrian strikers had written a paragraph in Trade Union history.

Chapter Ten

But for Charlotte, the year of the strike was the year when Ethel left home and the year when Richard died. It marked the beginning of her decline. From then on, she began to be an invalid.

CHAPTER ELEVEN

PENMAEN

1912

"We are placed in this world, as in a great theatre, where the true springs and causes of every event are entirely concealed from us."

David Hume, The Natural History of Religion

Chapter Eleven

For the life of her, Lily couldn't see what Ethel had gained by getting married to Will Shepherd, and it seemed as if the neighbours agreed with her, for Lily had overheard Bopa Jones saying something to Vanw-next-door about Ethel's being married for nearly eighteen months and having nothing to show for it.

Babies usually appeared soon enough after a wedding, though they were not often as prompt as Millie Rogers' little boy who had set everybody talking by being born on her wedding day, just six hours after the ceremony in, of all places, Bethlehem Chapel. "Cutting it fine, mind you. But a lovely boy all the same."

It could be, thought Lily, that Ethel was like one of those women in the Bible, barren. In that case, she might go back to Evans, the shoe shop on Ystrad Road where she had worked for two years, seeing and handling the very latest in footwear, and being able to buy anything she fancied at a discount. She had enjoyed that, with her size three feet, so much more dainty than Lily's great big five and a half.

Lily had decided never to get married, or not for years and years, and never to any man she had met so far. So many of the girls she had known in school were 'courting' and were putting aside linen and china for their bottom drawers. Lily, at fifteen, thought they were mad to tie themselves down so young and to lose the excitement of the chase.

Charlotte was giving warnings about being thought 'forward', but that was an admonition which Lily took lightly, as lightly as she was taking the attentions which Charlotte was fearing. There was no harm in being admired. It meant nothing as far as she was concerned. So she was rather pleased to overhear Olive from Gelli Crossing advising her cousin Fanny "Don't introduce your boy to Lily Callow. She'll take him away from you." But Olive had to admit that Lily was not out deliberately to steal anybody's boy. And as Fanny pointed out, it was up to every girl to hold on to her chap if she wanted him. Lily didn't want any of them, but it was pleasing to know that except with Ethel, she was popular with everybody.

People were drawn to her partly because she was so happy. She had been contented at Ma Morgan's, but she was glad to move. Lily enjoyed life at Penmaen. She was young, she was pretty, she was not overworked. When she looked back, and in her middle age Lily often looked back, she used to say "Those three years in Penmaen with the Rayners were the happiest years of my life." And if she felt more than usually melancholy, she would add, as if to reassure herself that there had been such a time, "I *was* happy. The only time in my life when I had no worries or regrets." Happiness made Lily boisterous, and at home she was so lively and full of laughter that Thomas urged Charlotte to "say summat as might stop 'er gallop."

Charlotte's "word in season" was a warning: "I can see it coming Lily, see it wi' half an eye. Theest be losing thee place there if thee dussn't calm down. All that laughing and giggling all the time, it baint seemly. Folks don't like all that tomfoolery, Lily, especially not in their own homes they don't. I don't care for it meself, no more do

Jack. Jack do hate it. Thee'st know 'er do...skylarking about..."

Lily tossed her head. She had no intention of calming down. Her place at Penmaen was safe. She was a housemaid as she had been at Ma Morgan's, but at the Sub-Post Office, Lily had done all the work. At Penmaen the Rayners and their grown-up children Maud and Harry were outnumbered by the servants they kept. There was not only the other housemaid Ellen to share the cleaning and the polishing with Lily, and to be at Cook's beck and call, but also Sarah, Cook's assistant, Nan and Polly the two kitchen maids, Nellie the laundry-maid, Alice the parlour maid, Edith the lady's maid, and the distant Mr. Ellis the Butler, whose duties Lily never discovered. Outside there was old Jim the odd job man, Bob Willis the gardener and his three garden boys, who did all the work and who were at hand to help John Jones and the stable boys with the two horses and the old-fashioned victoria which Mrs. Rayner had not yet persuaded her husband to exchange for a horseless carriage.

Jane Elizabeth Morgan and her daughter Edith were well known as part of the community and lived in a terraced house like their customers, but the Rayners were generally known only by name and reputation as the people who lived in the Big House, the Tŷ Mawr, one of the very few detached houses in the Rhondda. Amongst the comfortably-off middle class, they would have been unremarkable. In Lily's world, their accents, their clothes, their money, their grand house, their aspirations, all were alien. Frank Rayner was an ironmonger, one of those self-made men who qualified for inclusion in the class designated by Charlotte "jumped-up mommocks".

"I started from the humblest of beginnings" was a favourite sentence of his, designed to draw attention to his present exalted position as property owner. There were streets of houses in Ystrad and Trealaw which paid rent to Frank Rayner, while his three hardware shops were the biggest in mid-Rhondda. If he were self-made, he had built big, and he had every right to be pleased with his edifice. Like Ewart Denmer he had not married for money, but he had married where money was, for Beatrice Rayner was related, though only distantly, to the Bute family, and must have brought with her a tidy sum. She was haughty enough to have brought with her a fortune. She had let it be known that she would have preferred to live in the Vale of Glamorgan, somewhere more salubrious than the Rhondda, but since it was best for her husband's business that he live on the spot, then she was bravely "putting up with it all".

Most people would have thought she had little to put up with. Penmaen had been home for the Rayners from the early days of their marriage. Here Harry and Maud had been born, and from here Harry had left to take up his commission in the Regular Army. Set on the hillside and screened from the road by conifers and overgrown rhododendrons, Penmaen was a solid stone-built house about thirty years old, with a long sloping front lawn and stabling for three horses at the back. The façade was built on a massive scale. The pillared porch with its stained glass panels, the bay windows reaching the floor on either side of the studded door, the sash windows of the first floor, each with its twelve square panes, even the dormers of the attics, all were imposing enough to impress Beatrice's family, even if they were not grand enough to suit her own taste.

More than half a century was to pass before Penmaen became too baronial to house any single family and was transformed by the Council into a Welfare Clinic to serve a community whose lives had changed as drastically as had the landscape around them.

Lily had known the outside of the house almost as long as they had been in Gelli, for she had noticed it in the early days when she and Jack used to go to the Workman's Library on Ystrad Road. It was the last house before you got to the mountain, the other side of the valley from Railway Terrace, and separated from the streets near the colliery by both the river and the railway. Though Lily had less than half a mile to walk to Penmaen, when she got there she was entering a different world, a world of wealth.

There were ten bedrooms, not counting the servants' attics, and five main rooms downstairs. The drawing-room and the dining room were both handsomely panelled, with moulded ceilings and parquet floors. The dining room in particular was vast, big enough, according to Alice the parlour maid, for a carriage and pair to be driven round the table. Here the family always dined, and even when Mrs. Rayner had taken Miss Maud on extended visits to friends in Cardiff or in Brecon, Frank Rayner still presided at the head of the mahogany table, his bald dome gleaming under the chandelier whose twenty five candles were lit and replaced only under the supervision of Mr. Ellis the butler.

The Rayners were always "having a few friends in", even though one of Beatrice Rayner's complaints was that she Never Saw Anybody or lived near Anybody Who Was Anybody, and when they held a dinner party, Lily was thought to be personable enough to help Alice with the table and even to catch a glimpse of the guests at a distance.

Lily never forgot the weekend of the Coronation. Beatrice Rayner invited a dozen friends to:

"A Loyal Celebration Supper on the Occasion of the Coronation of His

Majesty King George the Fifth and Queen Mary.

Thursday 22nd of June 1911

R.S.V.P."

Lily saw the gold-lettered invitation cards ready to be put into their envelopes laid out on the table in what they called the library. She saw Miss Maud's cream chiffon evening dress with its lace inserts, and the tapering cream satin shoes with diamante buckles. She saw Mrs. Rayner's pink watered silk tunic dress with its back skirt falling into a square train, and she had memorised all the details so as to describe them to Ethel.

Four of the guests had stayed on for the weekend, and Lily was pleased when Mrs. Rayner, through Mr. Ellis, asked her to work extra hours - "to be recompensed, please make it clear" - to help Alice by waiting on table.

Chapter Eleven

Days of preparation had gone into that weekend, days of polishing the silver and the glasses, of laundering the double damask table cloths and napkins, of cleaning the hall, dining room and bedrooms, and most important, of cooking the food. When there were weekend guests, even ordinary weekend guests, Cook would be bad-tempered for a week before-hand, and Edith the lady's maid would be reduced to tears by her inability to dress Mrs. Rayner's hair to her satisfaction. The garden boys would slave to make the grounds immaculate and Bob Willis would raid the greenhouse for the carnations and roses which Miss Maud herself would arrange for the table.

The guests would be impressed, as Beatrice Rayner intended they should be, by this evidence of civilisation in a place which "as you can see for yourself, my dear, is exactly like the Yukon in the days of the goldrush." She would laugh delicately, "a pretty laugh" someone had once called it. "It's quite a frontier town."

Lily was astonished at the amount of food that was sent up from the kitchen, and no less surprised at the bird-like appetites which allowed so much of it to be sent back untouched. There were always left-overs for below stairs, and Lily had sometimes taken home "something from the feast" as he called it, for Our Arthur.

Charlotte, her appetite always small, would have nothing to do with "stuff from other folk's tables", while if Jack was at home, Lily dared not even describe the number and composition of the courses for fear of provoking an outburst.

Chapter Eleven

Jack was scornful of the capitalist economic theory of Adam Smith which held it as a maxim that as the rich get richer so the poor also become better-off. He could see the coal-owners and the industrialists amassing fortunes whilst paying their workers at bare subsistence levels. The successors of the first coal owner, Walter Coffin, were getting richer, but Vanw-next-door was finding it harder to keep the bellies of her four children filled. The oppression of the working classes and the need for social revolution to bring about more equal distribution of wealth was uppermost in Jack's mind, and Lily herself was learning at first hand of the gulf which separated rich from poor.

Her first few months at Penmaen had coincided with the beginning of the Cambrian Strike, and all through that year she saw how the men and women in the streets she passed on her way to and from work became more shabby and shrunken as the weeks wore on. In every family the children were the last to suffer, but they too grew thin and hollow-eyed, wearing clothes which were either much too big or which they had long outgrown. Boys of Our Arthur's age she noticed particularly, ten year olds and younger, wearing shoes with soles which flipped loose as they walked, and whose jackets had sleeves ending half-way up their forearms. But even these were better off than the boys and girls she saw who went barefoot and had no coats at all.

The ministers and the better-off amongst the congregations of three or four of the chapels, Bethel, Bethesda, Nazareth and Jerusalem, had organised soup kitchens, and as she passed the vestry of Bethesda on her way home, Lily would see the aproned helpers filling the steaming jugfuls and hear them cautioning the children "Don't you run now, bach. It's hot and you'll spill it." It was usually the children who came to collect the soup, bringing their jugs and fully accepting Going Down the Soup Kitchen as part of their life. The parents were glad of the food, but most of them were ashamed to be seen to be in want.

Lily had heard the Rayners, among whose friends were colliery managers, denouncing the strike and declaring early on that "the men should come to their senses and eat humble pie." But Alice, who knew everything, told her that Frank Rayner had more than once given his rent-collectors enough money to buy bread for all his tenants who were mining families, and as Mr. Ellis said "that's ninety per cent of his tenants. A generous gesture."

Some shopkeepers too, were generous. They found themselves somehow or other with remarkably large stocks of unsold bread, buns, fruit, and vegetables which would have been wasted had they not begged their customers as a favour to take them off their hands for next to nothing. And nearly all the shopkeepers allowed 'tick', even though as the weeks lengthened into months, the unpaid bills mounted alarmingly high.

There were families who received parcels of food bought with money donated by readers of newspapers, *The Times*, and *The Daily Telegraph and Morning Post*, and when Christmas came, all the children in the Infant and Junior Schools were given toys and books collected by

the Salvation Army from all over the country. Our Arthur
was a slow reader, and he would have picked out one of
the card games in a coloured box, but he was willing to be
pleased when his teacher handed him a copy of Kinglake's
Eothen. It was bound in red leather and looked brand new,
but when he looked inside he saw on the flyleaf,
imperfectly erased, the inscription "To dear Julian, on the
occasion of his fifteenth birthday, from his ever-loving
godmother. 12th September 1899".

Charlotte was close to tears at Arthur's indignant
"This aint my book, mother!" She tried to explain that not a
single one of the books was new, that none of the toys
either was straight from the shop, but his disappointment
was all the deeper.

"It aint my book, and I don't want it. I shan't read it.
Boring old book."

Thomas might have given Our Arthur a lecture on
Gratitude, enlarging on the theme of Beggars Not Being
Able To Be Choosers, but he bit back the words when he
saw Charlotte's sympathy with the "poor little feller".
Besides which, any minute Jack might walk in and hear
him, and Jack had strong and vociferous opinions about
the easy charity of the comfortably-off and their patronising
complacency towards the poor.

Jack had friends amongst those same poor who,
despite their superior intellectual and moral qualities, were
condemned to live in poverty, never fulfilling any ambition,
never moving out of that state of life into which it had
pleased God to call them.

Chapter Eleven

And if a man found it hard to fight his way up in the world, it was doubly difficult for a woman to better herself. She was more dependent on others for her advancement. Jack could see that Lily's talents were being wasted. She had an enchanting singing voice, and she had a gift for writing. She might well be a second Mrs. Humphrey Ward, he thought, or a Charlotte M. Yonge. But because she was a housemaid, her gifts were not even recognised, let alone encouraged or appreciated. If only she had stayed on at school there might have been some hope; but she had not been given the chance.

Jack had tried: "Why can't our Lily stay on to Secondary School mother? Even go on to be a pupil teacher down in Porth..."

"Whatever for, Jack? Our Lily can't wait to leave the Elementary. And she got a good place of service in Morgan's."

Jack had not given up straightaway. "She'd have a better life than service if she had some education. You were all for *me* being educated – at the Blue Coat School. It was Father who stopped that."

"Different for a boy, Jack, different altogether. Our Lily'll get married. No call for her to get schooling. Taint for the likes of us, Jack."

"Well, Mother, it's for the likes of Mary Williams, off to College in the autumn, and Gwyn Rees training for the ministry, and their fathers are working alongside our Bert in the Bryn."

"They be Welsh, both on 'em. They believes in it. We don't. We don't want our childer to leave home and go to England when they becomes teachers and preachers. Ourn stays here wi' us. We baint like the Welsh, all for the school and the chapel. Mind you, Jack, I'd a gone to a place o' worship many a time but for the pain in me insides. I be Christian when all's said and done, Church of England I be, and proud on it.""

When they first settled in Railway Terrace Charlotte went once to Hope Baptist Church, where Lily and Our Arthur had joined the Sunday School, to hear them sing in the Anniversary Service. And once and once only, she accompanied Vanw-next-door and Fairy Feet to the Welsh Congregational Church to hear, though not to understand, the children's service.

Angharad the eldest had recited all six verses of the Twenty-third Psalm, keeping in more or less perfect time with four other ten-year-olds, from the first "Yr Arglwydd yw fy mugail", "The Lord is my shepherd", to the last "a phreswyliaf yn nhy yr Arglwydd yn dragywydd", "and I shall dwell in the house of the Lord for ever". It had been Charlotte's first and last experience of hearing "cydadrodd", the art of reciting together, and it had baffled her.

More understandable had been the fate of the youngest, Rhodri Bach, who had to be led weeping from the platform. Overcome with nerves, he had been unable to get off the mark with his solo despite Miss Pomeroy's insistent repetition of the opening bars on the piano, and the desperate prompting of his Sunday School teacher.

Chapter Eleven

None of the Callows had been church-goers in Bristol and when they came to the Rhondda, only Lily and Our Arthur were young enough to adopt the Welsh habit of attending services and Sunday School. It was a pattern which gained them acceptance and which in its turn helped them to accept the Rhondda, with no allegiance to Bristol, their birthplace, as their 'real' home.

None of the Callows ever left Gelli nor moved more than a few yards from the original house in Railway Terrace and none, except for Jack, ever "bettered" himself. Charlotte had once hoped that Jack would "make his mark" in the world, and to Our Arthur she offered an apprenticeship to a cabinet maker. For Bert she knew that there was only work underground in the colliery, and for Lily there was domestic service.

When she was older, Lily regretted that she had not developed her gifts. She would read every now and then in the *Rhondda Leader* that a contemporary had "got a good job", and she would read out the paragraph: "Head of the French Department. H'm. That's the girl I used to sit next to in school and help her with her sums."

But when she was young, she wanted to go into service, especially after Miss Richards helped to get her the 'proper job' of housemaid at Penmaen, with uniform provided, a wage of four shillings a week and possibility of promotion to parlour maid. Lily was proud to work at Penmaen and be part of an organised household, and her accounts of what They did and what They were like up at the Big House were detailed enough to satisfy even Ethel's curiosity.

Chapter Eleven

"Cook's a tartar!" said Lily with relish. "She makes me and Ellen scrub the big kitchen table and the pastry boards, because she says Nan and Polly don't do it right."

"How can you scrub a table wrong?" Ethel wanted to know.

Lily was smug. "I only know how to do it right" she said. She knew that Ethel was interested only in hearing about people, and not at all in the details of the table and pastry boards, but she was determined to tell her all the same. "And the right way, if you want to know, well, you get all the solid bits off first with the back of a knife. Cook caught Polly using the sharp edge, and scoring the board. "'I'll give you sharp edge, my girl" she said, "the sharp edge of my tongue.'" Then Ellen and me, we get plain warm water and wash them, no soap or soda, so that takes a time, I can tell you. And even then we haven't finished."

Ethel rolled her eyes to heaven. "What a fuss about old pastry boards."

Lily was going on: "No, we haven't finished. We got to get dry sand to sprinkle on, and then we scrub. We do scrub then till our arms do ache. You don't know you're born here, our Eth. Cook told Ellen off the other day for scrubbing against the grain. Oh, and then more water to get all the sand off, and dry them with a clean cloth. And then the same with the table. A huge big table it is, right in the middle of the kitchen. Takes us best part of a morning to do that job, me and Ellen one each side, and meeting in the middle."

"Ooh, what a palaver," said Our Arthur.

Lily had not quite finished with the pastry boards. "If it's fine, we do open the windows a bit at the bottom, and let the boards dry in the air."

"But what do they Rayners do, then?" Ethel wanted to know.

Lily was not often enough in the company of any of them to give a truthful answer, but she could say "Mrs. Rayner's out a lot, and Miss Maud's ill a lot."

Our Arthur winked at Ethel before appealing to Charlotte with a straight face: "Sounds like she be one of them sufferin' jets, don't she, mother?"

Charlotte had not looked up from her mending. She shook her head. "No, my son, I reckon she be too much a lady to be caught up wi' they fooligans. Er wouldn't stoop to be wanting any vote nonsense for 'erself or any decent womenfolk."

Ethel laughed appreciatively, and Lily went on with a sigh, "*If* you still want to know, they got Edith to wait on them, do their hair and put their clothes out ready for them and that. They got whole rooms full of clothes, all good clothes they are. And they always got clean hands and long nails. Mrs. Rayner got nothing to do but try on dresses all day long, dresses and shoes and gloves. She got hundreds of hats I should think. And their stockings are real silk."

"That's the life ud suit you, Eth," said Charlotte. "The daughter baint idle all day, be she?"

"Miss Maud, well, she do play the piano a bit. You can hear her thumping out all over the house. She do never play anything I know though, so I can't sing to it."

Chapter Eleven

"And a good thing too, Lily." said Charlotte. "I knows only too well about thee singing, cracking a glass with them high notes thee bist so fond on. Them Rayners wouldn't be wanting thee to crack all their glasses. Cut-glass glasses they'd be for sure, summat like your Aunt Denmer had."

Lily sighed. If only Charlotte would take her part sometimes... She went on: "Miss Maud do spend a lot of time at her easel. Wishy-washy things, trees and that. Not half as good as our Jack's dogs."

"Better than you can do though, Our Lily." Ethel could always be relied upon to taunt. She was infuriating, especially when Charlotte supported her:

"Yes Lily, don't be unkind. That's the worst you can be, unkind." Our Arthur looked up : "Worse than killing somebody, mother?"

Charlotte was never irritated with Our Arthur, and he was the only one who could ever joke and be cheeky with her. "No, no, that be worse my son. But we be all God's critturs and that Frank Rayner baint all bad by what they say."

"What about Captain Harry?" Ethel wanted to know.

Lily started to smile. "Like a horse, exactly like a horse. He comes in stinking of them and he looks like one." She was remembering how she had seen Captain Harry Rayner admiring his reflection in the long glass-fronted china cabinet in the drawing-room. He had thought Lily absorbed in cleaning the grate and laying the fire ready for lighting, and he had stayed some minutes, stroking his jaw complacently and turning his head to scrutinise his profile, which was indeed remarkably equine. Sandy-haired, tall, well-built, Captain Rayner was confident that all who knew him considered him a "fine figure of a man". "His mother all over," said Alice. "Cocky." His expression was arrogant, his glance aloof but long-held in a knowing stare. Lily disliked it, but, by her own confession, it sent shivers right down Ellen's back. He was handsome enough, in a florid sort of way, especially in his uniform. But he was not as dashing nor as irresistible to women as he imagined himself to be. Lily found him completely resistible. Ellen might long for Captain Harry to notice her, but Lily had plenty of admirers. As Ellen recognised with some envy, "Boys just fall for you, Lily. You got IT."

"Well, if they do," said Lily, "I don't fall for any of *them*."

If Boys played only a small part in Lily's life, then Captain Harry was a most minor figure, which made it ironic that it was on his account that Charlotte's prophecy came true, and Lily lost her place at Penmaen.

When it was Lily's turn to polish the quarry tiles in the hall, the mosaic diamonds of blue, green, rust and fawn shone like pieces of stained glass. The whole floor gleamed, even that part of it hidden beneath the Persian rug just inside the front door, for no-one could ever accuse Lily of scamping her work. Alice had been the first, and then Miss Maud herself had passed judgement: "Mr. Ellis, this floor is like a skating rink. Please tell whichever maid is responsible not to polish beneath the rug. It is dangerous. Someone might slip on it." The warning came too late. The unhappy victim, Captain Rayner. Lily had just started brushing the staircase when she heard him coming in through the front door humming a tune which she recognised. "When we are married..."

He stepped firmly into the hall, riding whip in hand, to take the stairs at his two-at-a-time gallop. But his "how happy we'll be..." gave way to a string of oaths as, without warning, he found himself sliding on his back the full length of the hall. The riding whip clattered on the tiles as he struggled to regain his balance, to be joined moments later by the dustpan and brush which Lily, helpless with laughter, had let drop through the bannisters. It was all over in seconds. Captain Harry heaved himself to his feet, still swearing, while Lily tried in vain to turn her laugh into a cough, hiding her face in her apron.

Mrs. Rayner was attracted by the noise and came hurrying from the drawing-room, interpreting the situation in one single solicitous glance. She was a woman who prided herself on her knowledge of the world and of human nature. Born and bred in affluence, used to a society more sophisticated than these valley people could imagine, she knew every trick by which a girl could get herself noticed. Especially by such an eligible young man as Harry. Lily had been only thirteen when she had started at Penmaen, but that was three years ago. The girl was well-developed and not too bad-looking, despite all that unruly mass of hair...rather well-spoken for a housemaid...but boisterous, too lively for her own good. The girl had been getting ideas above her station, no doubt setting her cap at Harry, a catch for any girl. Just as well to be alerted to the danger... Poor Harry, so sheltered and so inexperienced, he would suspect nothing. Indeed, until the unseemly episode of the rug, she herself had suspected nothing. But it was up to every mother to protect her son... The girl was a good worker... Mr. Ellis had spoken well of her... Even Cook had no fault to find... But really, that laughter! It was callous. That boy might have been seriously injured. He might have broken his back, never to ride again. It would not bear thinking about. The girl would have to go...but not without a character, that would be unChristian. And besides, although her behaviour had been outrageous, it was only natural that a boy like Harry should attract attention, even from persons of that class. She would try and help the girl to better herself, but somewhere away from Penmaen.

PART THREE

CHAPTER TWELVE

ENTER WALTER

1913

"Let's all go down the Strand
 (have a banana!)
 Oh what a merry band..."

Charles Whittle, popular song

Chapter Twelve

As soon as Lily reported that Mrs. Rayner was going to give her "an excellent *written* character testimonial", and had found for her a most satisfactory place, subject to personal inspection of course, down in Tonypandy with a Mrs. Baumann of The Dairy, Charlotte knew that her suspicions were well-founded. "Tell the truth now, Lily. Tell the truth and shame the Devil. Why do 'er want to get rid on 'ee?"

Lily told, but ended with a defiant "I don't care, mother. All I did was laugh. He was like a big fat beetle on its back, couldn't get up, waving his arms and legs..." Even now, Lily had to smile at the thought. She went on: "And it's alright. She's got me a much better place, more money and everything. Seven shillings a week mother! I'm glad to be going from there."

"Well," said Charlotte, "I can't say as I likes any on it. Tonypandy, with all them riots and such, and only coming home of a Sunday. Lily, theest be set on worriting I into the grave."

Lily might have reminded Charlotte that the rioting, maiming and looting during the winter of the Cambrian strike were not everyday occurrences in Tonypandy, and that it was a place very much like Gelli. True, it was bigger, with more houses, people and shops, and if you were looking for differences, you noticed that its streets harboured none of the dirty-grey sheep from the hills which scavenged the ashbuckets, despoiled the back gardens and huddled for shelter against the house walls in Gelli and Ton Pentre. But in all essentials, Tonypandy *was* a place very much like Gelli. It was a place very much like all the places from Pontypridd right up to Treherbert. In going to Tonypandy, Lily was not going far from home. But she kept silence, unable or unwilling to offer any reassurance, and when Charlotte spoke again, her voice was harder.

"I says no more, Lily. Theest been wanting to fly thee kite off for many a long day. Theest be getting into a regular fly-be-night."

Charlotte could think of no worse epithet... A rebel, a fly-by-night, an undutiful child leaving home... Charlotte was not the most loving of mothers, but she was possessive, as much with her daughters as with her sons, so that it was a source of pleasure to her that neither Bert, nor Jack, nor Our Arthur ever "took up wi' anybody".

As for the girls, Lily was getting a bit of a handful, and her going away from home was a new worry. Ethel seemed happy enough with Will Shepherd, and only just a stone's throw away in Byrom Street, near enough for her to come home every day.

Thomas would have been more pleased to see the boys leaving home instead of Lily, for he shared Jack's concern about Charlotte's frail health, and he knew that Lily would have been a help in looking after the men.

He could see Charlotte beginning to sink into the inertia and self-absorption of the invalid. She had been conscious of stomach pain for more than ten years, pain constant enough not to be dismissed as "just summat the matter wi' my insides, a woman's complaint most likely". But although the pain could not be ignored, she was resisting Jack's plea that she see a doctor about it.

Chapter Twelve

When she did finally give way, the diagnosis proved to be 'benign stomach tumour', but for many years Charlotte felt that to submit to medical scrutiny was to allow her pain to assume a permanent position. Until the pain was officially recognised, it could be thought of as temporary, and she could go on hoping that it would yield to the spoonfuls of chalky medicine, "Our Gran's medicine", which was all that the youngest of her grandchildren ever remembered about her.

Lily felt sympathy, but she recognised that physical suffering was only part of Charlotte's pain. Her grief at her brother Richard's death was still fresh, and here Lily was untouched. Only when she herself mourned the loss of a beloved brother did Lily recall and echo Charlotte's desolation. Only then did she realise that for Charlotte too, husband and children had offered no compensation for the breaking of her strongest link with the past. But the demands of husband and children had still to be met, and now there was no daughter at home to help Charlotte clean and cook for the men in the family, Thomas, Jack, Bert and Our Arthur, who at twelve was "more trouble" according to Thomas, "with his fads and fancies, than the whole lot on us put together, and that includes the lodger." The lodger had come only a few weeks before Lily left Penmaen for The Dairy in Tonypandy.

"I'll never forget the day, never," said Charlotte to Lizzie Totterdale who had "just popped in to see how thee bist this morning."

Chapter Twelve

"It were raining," said Charlotte. "Had been, all the live-long day, not the good downpour rain, but that greasy black drizzly rain."

"Aye," agreed Lizzie, settling her bulk on the hard leatherette of the couch in the back kitchen. "Aye, Rhondda rain."

"There were this knock on the door, and when our Jack went to open it there were this boy, like a little boy 'er looked, streaming wet, standing on the door step and asking for our Bert. Just like a drownded rat, hair plastered all over his face, and shivering with the cold."

"Good Lor', what a sight 'er must have looked!" said Lizzie comfortably.

"'Er were a boy our Bert knowed when they was all working out at Long Ashton. Thee'st mind Cottle's farm, Lizzie?"

"O aye," said Lizzie. "Our boys knew it well."

"Jack didn't seem too sure about the boy, and o' course I never heard tell on en, but our Bert knowed en in a minute. 'Come on in Wally 'er shouted. Thee'st managed to find us then!'"

Lizzie was glad to see Charlotte animated for once, and murmured encouragingly "who were he exactly then?".

Charlotte was willing to talk to Lizzie, though as a rule she was still reluctant to "let any of our business go outside of this house." She went on "Well, none on us knowed much about en at first. It all came out bit be bit. They be four in family, three boys and a girl. The mother died when the girl was born so far as I can make out. The father's a seaman, that much I knows. The four on em's been brought up by an aunt up Lawrence Hill way. Walter be the eldest, twenty one, same age as our Bert exactly."

Lizzie showed her surprise. "Same age as your Bert, Charlotte? Your Bert 'ud make two on 'en."

Charlotte nodded, not displeased at the interruption: "Same month, November, and just twenty one."

"Well, well. I never seed such a scrawny feller in all me life" said Lizzie, adding "But a nice-looking boy, though."

"Aye, well, Lizzie, handsome is as handsome does. A pathetic morsel if theest ask I anything, like as if he be all alone in the world. Walter do never hear a peep out of any on 'em, not his brother in the navy, not the aunt, not the two youngest back in Lawrence Hill. Never talks about his father, never says much about hisself at all. Theest got to drag it all out on him, bit be bit."

"Well, him and your Bert look like they be good pals," said Lizzie. "I sees them going everywhere together."

Back in Bristol, Bert had got on well enough with Walter in a casual sort of way, but he had almost forgotten him. So he had been surprised, and pleased, that Walter had sought him out. They were alike in temperament, uncomplicated and easily pleased. They were both quick-tempered and unthinking, but they soon forgot, and never held grudges. Whereas Jack would brood over other men's conduct, and morbidly analyse his own, Bert and

Chapter Twelve

Walter rarely sat in judgement on others and never wasted the present in regretting the past.

Unlike Bert, though, who lived entirely for the present, Walter took a keen interest in what might be to come. He was avid to read horoscopes, superstitious about omens, eager to buy charms and amulets, meticulous about keeping to lucky numbers and colours. He carried about in an inner pocket a tiny metal Cornish Pisky, although he would have had to admit that it had brought him no noticeably good fortune to date. He would back a horse solely on the strength of an association with its name or the name of its jockey, even if Form would have told him he was placing a bad bet, arguing that Luck after all was a matter of the unexpected. Bert thought it all pointless, but he would not have told Walter so, for he was glad of Walter's company now that he saw so little of his father and brothers.

Thomas had taken to staying at home more with Charlotte, while Jack had always been loath to spend much time out drinking, and had made it plain that he preferred the company of Dick Jenkins and his red hot socialists, as Thomas called them. So for Bert, Walter had come at the right time to fill a gap.

Charlotte had not minded taking in Walter as a lodger, even though it meant that the house was full and that the sleeping arrangements had to be altered. Jack had moved in, rather unwillingly, to share a bed with Thomas in the big front bed room; Bert, Our Arthur and Walter slept in the back bedroom and Charlotte and, until she left for Tonypandy, Lily, slept in the smaller front bedroom.

There were not always three at once sleeping in the same bed because of the different shifts they worked, so that they were no more cramped than many of their neighbours. They were less overcrowded than some, where the number of young single colliers sharing with a family meant that, in Charlotte's opinion, "them beds be never cold, let alone changed."

Walter had made himself at home from the beginning, encouraged by the warmth of Bert's welcome and untroubled by the coolness which he might have sensed coming from every other member of the family except perhaps Lily and Our Arthur.

He looked as Charlotte had said, very young for his age, for he was small, less than five foot four inches in height, and as thin as a lath. He had an attractive cheeky face, dark wavy hair flopping over his forehead, bushy eyebrows above lively blue eyes, and a wide innocent-looking grin. He was fond of practical jokes, "too damned fond for my liking" said Thomas, and to those who appreciated his sense of humour he was "a good sort", "a card", "a character".

He had a pleasing tenor voice which would have made him an asset to any chapel or workmen's choir, if only he had mastered the pronunciation of Welsh words, and if only he could have been bothered to learn to read music by the new Tonic Solfa method which had swept the valleys and which Lily tried to tell him, "made reading music easy, all easy". But Tonic Solfa or Old Notation, the pieces set for the singing festivals and the local eistedfodau were not to Walter's taste. Not for him Parts I or II of Handel's *Messiah*, or Haydn's *Creation* or Beethoven's *Mount of Olives*, let alone *Y Tylwyth Teg* or *Gweddi Habacuc*. During the whole of his long life, and Walter lived to be ninety-six, he set foot inside a church but twice, and that was on his wedding day in 1915, and thirty-six years later, when his daughter got married.

Church music held no appeal for Walter, but music of another kind was important in his life. He had been just ten years old when his father, on shore-leave in Bristol, had taken him to the Peoples Palace in Baldwin Street. There he had seen Lily Langtry, whose charms he had not fully appreciated, Harry Nation, "the character and laughing comedian", most of whose jokes passed over his head, the singer L.B. Athel, discovered at the London Drivers and Conductors Annual Concert, whose songs Walter was to hum all his life, and best of all, Professor Duncan and his troupe of performing collie dogs. Walter had been enthralled. Right up to his leaving Bristol he had gone every week, sometimes more than once, to one of the music halls, especially to the Empire in Old Market. The Empire, disinfected throughout with Jeyes Fluid, boasted an impressive variety of comedians, dancers and singers, as well as being host to occasional more esoteric entertainments like the World's Greatest Hoop Rollers, and Walter enjoyed them all.

Charlotte knew the Empire well by repute. No decent woman would have gone there herself nor wished any of her family to be seen there. She was not impressed with Walter's repertoire of the songs of Vesta Tilley, Marie Lloyd and Lottie Collins, nor interested in his praises of Eugene Stratton: "What a man! Blacked up and singing like an American Negro!" And she had no comment when she heard Walter bragging about his visits to the newly-opened, very grand and very expensive Hippodrome in St. Augustine's Parade. From his sixpenny seat in the Balcony, Walter had watched the spectacular *Sands o' Dee* "with," he told a fascinated Lily, "hundreds and hundreds of gallons of water making waves across the stage."

"Real water?" said Lily incredulously.

"Real water." said Walter impressively. "Gallons and gallons of real water, making real waves. And a horse diving into them."

"Not a real horse?" said Lily doubtfully.

"A real horse!" said Walter in triumph. "A real horse diving in to rescue the heroine tied to a stake on the seashore. Mary her name was."

"A real heroine, no doubt."

Jack had come in, and his voice reflected the scornful amusement he felt with folk who could take pleasure in such nonsense. He had held aloof from Walter from the very beginning, and it irritated him now to see how quickly first Bert and then Lily had accepted him into the family. "Capering about and jabbering like a monkey on a barrel organ" he thought, wincing as he endured yet another "Put me among the girls! Those with the curly curls! They'll enjoy themselves and so will I, If you put me among the girls!"

Chapter Twelve

It seemed to be one of Walter's favourite songs, although Jack had to admit that Walter never craved the company of girls and would have to be sure his attentions were welcomed before he gave any girl the glad eye. He never even mentioned any girls, probably never knew any to speak to except Ethel and Lily.

Lily. It amazed Jack to see how eagerly Lily listened to Walter's stories, laughed at his jokes and joined in his songs. He himself found it hard to tolerate a fellow whose only conversation was either about horses or about music hall turns, whose usual reading matter was the racing results and *Comic Cuts*, and whose idea of a good book was a thriller by Edgar Wallace. He was loud, cheerful and boisterous and he got on Jack's nerves.

But it was just that liveliness which attracted Lily. Even when he came back from work he was full of life, not like Thomas and the boys, who came home at the end of their shift with dragging footsteps. There was always a hot dinner waiting to be put out on their plates, and kettles of water that Charlotte had boiled ready for their baths, but Lily had seen them sometimes too exhausted to do more than wash the blackness from their faces and hands and sit down to rest before they could touch their food. There was very little talk on these days. But of course the boys and her father were all coal-face men, their job much harder and more dirty than any other jobs in the pit, and more dangerous. Lily used to think that it was like living in the shadow of a volcano, a hidden volcano smouldering underground, a volcano which could erupt at any time. It would be without warning, and it could overwhelm hundreds of men at a time, as it had done in October in the Universal pit in Senghenydd.

"In the other valley, the other side of Pontypridd, on the way to Caerphilly," Jack had tried to reassure Charlotte, "another valley altogether."

But he could not hide from her that over four hundred men had been killed in the explosion and fire, and that it was the worst disaster in the history of British coal-mining, "to date" he added to himself.

The disaster fund was already mounting, but "what good be money to they widows?" said Charlotte. "Fitter they had made the place safer for they men to work in. Any amount o' money won't bring they men back again."

She said nothing about the anxiety she felt every time she saw them off to work. Women did not speak about such fears any more than men spoke about the dangers they faced every day. But she couldn't help wishing that their jobs were easier, more like Walter's, and safer. Walter working in the stables brought home less money than the boys, but then, he had an easier job.

Walter had been taken on as horse keeper, an ostler in the Gelli, and the job suited him, for he understood and liked horses, and had been used to working them on the farm at Long Ashton. His pit 'ponies' were not much smaller than the Long Ashton shire horses, and he was responsible for their feeding and general care while they were in the stables. Walter was competent and humane, and he had quickly won the respect of the hauliers who collected and returned their animals at the beginning and end of each shift. They recognised that Walter had a keen eye for any mistreatment or mishandling of a horse, and had a rough tongue with any driver who brought back a horse marked in any way. Even with good treatment, the pit ponies had a hard life. "They aint got long enough to rest up, mun, out for another shift before they'm ready. And theest should see the state on some of they horses when they comes back. Damn shame to see em sometimes."

Bert would nod. He had seen cruelty in his own pit, where a horse had dropped from exhaustion, and the haulier had taken off the heavy shafts to whip the animal until it staggered up to have the harness replaced again. But such instances were rare. In Bert's experience hauliers did not mistreat their horses out of brutality but out of ignorance, or maybe, as Jack argued, out of necessity.

Jack had no hesitation in blaming it on the greed of the owners: "It's nothing but the system. Put it to yourself. What are we down the pit for? Only to get out as much coal as we can and in as quick a time as we can. The more drams that come out in a day, the more they can sell, right? The more money for the owners. More profit. So the horses have to haul the drams, non-stop, like as if they were machines. Never mind if the haulier's got a tired horse to take out, he's still got to get his full drams back as fast as the one who's working a fresh horse."

Walter would try to hold his own with Jack, especially when he felt he was on sure ground. "Maybe, Jack. But that don't excuse a bloody haulier who'll leave his horse without water hour after hour. You aint seen the state of them animals when I has to do wi' em back in the stables."

Bert could see both sides, and before Jack could finish his indignant "We've seen them alright", he put in: "There's some bad hauliers, Wally, sure enough, and we all know who they be. But most of 'em don't want to ill-treat their animals, mun, not most of 'em don't. But they got to keep up with the loads that we gives em. Like Jack says, they got to."

Walter was not going to give up that easily. "I still says that them hauliers could take a leaf out they waggoners' books. When I were out at Long Ashton, *there* was horsemen for thee. Them horsemen there could respect their animals, mun."

"Farm waggoners? Think of their different conditions," Jack would insist. "How can a haulier refuse to work a horse? What under-manager you ever met would listen to a haulier saying that the horse was unfit to work? He'd laugh in his face, and give him the sack for Insolence to the Boss, for daring to say something. No, it would be more than they could risk, that."

Walter's voice would rise: "I'd tell 'im, whoever he were. I wouldn't kowtow to no man. When I seed a hoss not fit, I'd..."

Jack would never lose his temper, but his irritation would show: "You've never been anywhere underground except in the stables. You'd damn well soon change your tune if you had to work at the coal-face and if you had a wife and kids to keep. You'd have to mind your p's and q's like any other poor devil. If it's a choice of your job or your horse, what can you do?"

Walter would see red at what he took to be Jack's callous attitude. "I wouldn't let that stop I. No bloody fear. No man dictates to I about hosses..."

Bert would act as peace-maker when he saw that a conversation which had begun about horses was descending to an argument based on personal qualities, and Jack would leave. He could never stand much of Walter's bragging about what he would say to the bosses, and about his superiority to other "mealy-mouthed buggers". Walter would glare after him, his face angry-red and his blue eyes opened very wide, and splutter about bloody Union men and their high-falutin' ideas.

Bert would lead his thoughts back to the animals, and listen while Walter described again the gashes he had seen on the back of one of the horses which had been forced to drag the tram back and fore under too low a roof. Bert knew the situation only too well, for the roadways and headings in any pit were always cut with very little headroom to spare, so that if a sudden 'squeeze' pressed in the roof or forced the bottom up, there would be too little height for the horse to get through.

"Of course, Wally, there'd be a few inches to spare at the beginning of the shift, 'snow. No man 'ud force a horse to his knees a-purpose, mun, to get through. Things change in a shift, 'snow."

But he himself had seen how when a horse had not bent his knees quickly enough, the stones in the surface of the roof had torn the skin off his back. The coal had had to be brought out, no matter what. Walter would be hard to stop once he had begun on one of his favourite topics, and when Jack had left, in Bert and Lily he had an appreciative audience.

"Some of they hosses is only vicious when they be underground, mind. I seed one on 'em brought in, kicking like the devil. Two men couldn't hold 'en. Had to be sold in the end, sold to a coal-merchant and put to draw a coal cart." Walter paused, smiled and shook his head. "Quiet as a lamb, then, mun! Going round the streets above ground. Damn clever, that hoss. Didn't want to be a pit pony, 'snow. It don't suit all on em. They Welsh cobs now, they be bred for speed, and they wants to be dashing. It don't do for what we wants of 'em underground. We gets a lot of trouble with they Welsh cobs. Some of t'others too, mind. Depends on an horse's temperament. Like human beings, they be just like an human being, all different. They be cleverer than a man..."

Lily raised her eyebrows and looked doubtful, but Walter was going on: "Cleverer than a man. They'll tell thee if there be danger. Quicker'n any man they can sense danger, and lead thee out on it too."

"Lead a man through darkness" said Bert, "and give the warning of water in the seam."

"Aye," said Walter. "If they do rub theirselves agen thee, theest can venture it be safe, water'll go down. And another thing. Theest know this, Bert, an horse'll always know a man he can trust."

Bert laughed. "More than a man can say sometimes Wally! Thee bist right. We got one that thinks he's human, mun! Drinks out of a bottle, and chews tobacco! And then they looks for their treats like fresh-cut grass and carrots and apples as well as a bit o' snap."

"Aye, that's one thing," said Walter. "We gives them as much as they can eat. It's their bellies that tells them how much they get. Good mix we gives them mind, ready mixed hay and clover chop, with their bran and oats in with it. They never goes short."

There was a look on Walter's face and a tone in his voice when he spoke about his pit ponies that touched Lily. Bert got on so well with Walter; if only Jack could see that he wasn't all drinking and sport, maybe he would be more patient with him.

But Jack would never change his mind about Walter. It was the mindless singing he hated most, that and what Thomas called "acting the giddy goat all the time." Walter seemed to know not only the tune but also all the words of the latest hits from the music halls and from the current musical comedies. "Burlesques, all burlesques" thought Jack, "and Walter not even knowing the meaning of the word."

Lily had learnt them all, and could put the words to the tunes the errand boys were whistling and, against his will, Jack was getting to know them too. He had become sick of "I've gotter motter, always merry and bright", but he disliked its successors even more, for to his annoyance he had caught himself humming the tunes and thinking the words of "I'm such a silly when the moon comes out" and "At Trinity Church I met my Doom". Jack would never have sung the words aloud, but Walter had no inhibitions.

Chapter Twelve

No words were ever too embarrassingly sentimental, no chorus too inane for Walter, and the more meaningless the sounds, the greater gusto he gave to them. Jack had heard Lily giggling at his "Yip-i-addy-i-ay" and "Itchy-Koo", and even drowning Walter with her own "Tararaboomdeay". Jack had not thought anything could be more jarring, but the latest favourite, hot from America, had been the worst. Rag Time! "Alexander's Rag Time Band!" And Walter's loud though tuneful "It's the best band in the land..."

Lily had been bad enough before with her singing, but now with Walter to egg her on, she fairly made the house ring. "It's syncopated Jack, that's what makes it so catchy." Not for Jack it didn't. Lily's explanation left Jack cold. No wonder that he had been spending more time than ever with Dick Jenkins since Walter came to live in Railway Terrace.

If it wasn't singing, he was boasting about what he had won on the horses or about the animal acts he had seen: "Captain Fred Woodward and his performing sea-lions! A marvellous act, Lily. Seeth's twenty one lions, forest-bred lions, mind, Jack!" and to beat them all, "Merion's Canine Company. The greatest dog act in the world, Jack, thee'st know!" Jack did not know, nor did he wish to know. He disliked Walter, not only because of the triviality of his stock of knowledge, but because he suspected him of being a low influence in the house.

Only the other day Our Arthur had been given a hiding which for once had been sanctioned, albeit unwillingly, by Charlotte herself. Our Arthur, with Lily present in the room, had been chanting "Lottie Collins lost her drawers. Won't you kindly lend her yours?" Such vulgarity could not be allowed to pass unchecked and unpunished. Our Arthur said that he had heard it somewhere, but there was no doubt in anybody's mind that the "somewhere" was number eleven Railway Terrace, and that it was from Walter it had come.

When Lily had challenged Walter, he denied teaching Our Arthur anything of the sort, reminding her that since Lottie Collins had been dead for three years, she would hardly be in need of drawers at all, hers or anybody else's. Walter was pleased with what he considered to be a very witty reply, but Lily thought it even more vulgar than the original offence. But the more she frowned, the louder Walter laughed, for he was impervious to disapproval.

Charlotte too was sometimes offended by Walter's rough manners, but she was charitable enough to blame his shortcomings on his having had to "drag hisself up". She had found out that he had left his aunt's house in Lawrence Hill when he was twelve and had had to fend for himself ever since. What, thought Charlotte, would Our Arthur be like, without a mother to care for him.

Considering his background, she reflected, Walter had a lot of good points. He was always cheerful for one thing. Even Jack couldn't help laughing at some of his tales, he was that droll in the telling of them. He was without malice, and so completely without subtlety that as Charlotte said, "theest could read Walter like a book". All his faults lay on the surface, but so did his virtues. He was always willing to lend a hand, even to do women's work, like bringing in a lineful of washing out of the rain, as well as the jobs reserved for the men in the family, like shovelling into the coal-house the regular loads of cheap "miners' coal" dumped in the gwli outside the back door.

Above all, he was generous with his money, foolish the way he spent everything he earned, but generous and unselfish in the way he spent it. He had brought back from Sharpes in Treorchy the Parlour Palm in the front room, he had bought Our Arthur the iron hoop he had been craving, and he was for ever bringing sweets into the house to share with anybody and everybody. No wonder he was always stony broke before the end of the week and had to spend his Friday nights at home.

Charlotte was forever warning: "This smoking, drinking and swearing though, 'll have to stop, or else you'll have to find another place. I can't abide such habits, especially when our own boys aint like it."

About the gambling she wasn't supposed to know anything. Our Arthur knew only too well, for sometimes Walter would say "I comed up lucky on the hosses, Art, fetch I a packet of Woodbines, wuss? And here be sixpence for theeself." Even when, as happened more often than not, it was "Down the course again today, mun", Walter would tip generously in return for errands to the corner shop, for he believed implicitly in the maxim formulated, all unbeknownst to Walter, by Francis Bacon, as "money is like muck, not good except it be spread".

Walter never earned, or won, much money in all his life, and he never saved a penny of it. When he married, he left all the worry of making ends meet to his wife, one of whose bitter causes for complaint was that "money burns a hole in his pocket".

But neither Walter nor Bert had any intention of saddling themselves with a wife and family. Nor were they, unlike many of the young miners they knew, on the look out for girls "to get off with". There were too many other interesting things to be doing. Nothing much went on in Gelli, they agreed, unless you were mad on choral singing or, like Jack, up to your neck in union politics.

But in Tonypandy at the Theatre Royal, Will Stone's bioscope was showing moving pictures of the adventures of Pearl White, with lively piano accompaniment, and at the Empire they could see jugglers, hear Robb Wilton "the confiding comedian", enjoy sketches and dramas, and catcall to their heart's content the soloists whose songs they hollered through the streets and all the way home in the train, the last train up from Pontypridd, the so-called "Rodney Train". Walter had even, once, been bold enough to venture on to the new roller skating rink up in Pentre, though he had not enjoyed it enough to want to repeat the experience.

Life was mostly work. But there was enjoyment too, drinking, smoking, gambling, theatre-going, which left no time for the complications of spooning. That time was to come for Walter. For Bert it never came.

CHAPTER THIRTEEN

DANCING AT THE DAIRY

1913-1914

"Our characters are the result of our conduct"

Aristotle, Nicomachean Ethics III

Chapter Thirteen

When Lily started In Service as housemaid cum parlour-maid to the Baumanns in the autumn of 1913, Charlotte was relieved to think that Bert and Walter, who seemed to be for ever gallivanting off down to Tonypandy, could keep an eye on her during her evenings off. She would have been disturbed had she known how often Lily went with them to the shows at the Empire, but as Lily said, "what the eye don't see, the heart can't grieve over", and she herself could see nothing in her life to grieve over.

Lily was sixteen and a half. She had reached her full height of five foot three and a quarter inches, and had lost all of her early plumpness. Her long light brown curls were brushed back from her forehead and tamed into a soft plaited coil at the nape of her neck, which made her look older and more dignified, so that Ethel had begun to think that our Lily had some style about her after all, if only she could grow out of her tomboy ways and childish giggling.

Lily was taller and slimmer than Ethel so that the clothes which came in parcels from Bristol happened to be exactly her size. Cousin Julie's cast-offs were not only of good quality but were still pretty much in fashion. Ethel had particularly coveted one white embroidered muslin afternoon dress which had a high neck and three-quarter sleeves, but she was too short and fat for it. In order to fit Ethel, the bodice would have had to be unpicked and two inserts made, the gathers in the waist would have had to be let out, and the flounce of bobbin-lace bordering the hem of the skirt would have had to be removed altogether.

Chapter Thirteen

Ethel was the first to see that such alterations would have completely spoilt the line, and she could not bring herself to undertake such destruction, even though it meant sacrificing the dress to Lily. So Lily wore it, and to go with it she was spendthrift enough to buy herself a green and white chip hat trimmed with silk ribbon and white cotton daisies, an extravagance handsomely repaid by overhearing that she looked "a stunner".

The clothes from Cousin Julie were all of them wearable, either by Lily or, after hours of unpicking. letting out and shortening, by Ethel, but the things that Aunt Elsie Denmer put in for Charlotte might have been included solely to show up the differences in their lives, for nothing she sent was useful. The evening dresses had to be made over very carefully before they were suitable for Railway Terrace, for Byrom Street or even Tonypandy. They were beautifully made dresses, pink and blue shot silk and watered silk, with transparent tunics of cream and blue gauze to wear over them, embroidered with net and Honiton appliqued lace. Nothing in the Denmer parcels was made of artificial silk, so that to transform the long skirts into blouses, the only practical use for them, was both tedious and difficult.

The motoring costume was never made over. It had an ankle-length pleated skirt and a cutaway jacket, and was made of fine plum-coloured barathea. The cut was unmistakeably sporty, impossible to adapt, and Ethel mourned over the waste of such good material and of such a sweet colour.

Chapter Thirteen

But Charlotte suspected that the outfit had been sent merely as an excuse for the letter which accompanied it. Elsie had written about Ewart's new motor car in which they had all gone "for a spin down to Weston Super Mare". The Daimler (she had written the name in capital letters so that it could not be mis-read) was a most comfortable motor car, but its turn of speed quite alarming. They had completed the whole journey in an hour and a quarter, travelling at eighteen miles per hour for most of the time but more than once touching the speed limit of twenty.

Charlotte could hear Ewart's voice in the details of time and speed, could picture the self-satisfied look on his face. Thomas was scornful of such blatant showing off, Jack unimpressed and Bert indifferent. Walter, though, could see himself at the wheel, bowling along and singing "The Man Who Broke the Bank at Monte Carlo". And Our Arthur boasted at school that his Uncle Ewart in Bristol had a different motor car for every day of the week, and maintained that he was willing to fight any boy who called him a liar.

Aunt Denmer's letters were a welcome indication to Charlotte that she still had Family back in Bristol, but more heart-warming were the letters which came from her brother Richard's widow, Iris, and those which her daughter Mary exchanged with Lily. Aunt Iris Milsom never sent clothes or food or money, but she sent something far more valuable, a pledge of continuing affection. Charlotte was grateful, and showed it by writing, or sometimes dictating to Jack, such speedy replies that Iris or Elsie always seemed to be in her debt, and her question "Any letters?" was heard so often it became almost automatic for the answer to be "None from Bristol, mother".

Charlotte had grown in sympathy with her neighbours, but as she became less able to leave her home, her life became centred in her family. She could see them scattering these days. Ethel came three or four times a week, but she never stayed for long. She was always wearing something different, but her face was setting into lines of discontent and she was always moaning.

Our Eth was getting too pride-y about her appearance, thought Charlotte. Pity she didn't have summat else by now to occupy her mind. Now that Lily had gone for good, Charlotte was surprised how much she missed her, and how much she looked forward to seeing her every Sunday afternoon. She missed Lily's housework too, and had begun paying out to Vanw-next-door's eldest, Angharad, who was glad to earn sixpence by coming in to "fetch the errands and do the front for Mrs. Callow".

Lily had stepped outside the circle of the family and although she was not as happy at first as she had expected to be, it was still exhilarating to be free from the restraints of home, where Jack and Charlotte were both ready with anxious criticism, Thomas with hostility and Ethel with conscious or unconscious malice. She was sure that once she got used to standing on her own feet, it would feel like dancing.

The Baumanns were just the kind of employers to suit Lily, but her reply to Charlotte's "What sort of people be they?" gave no indication of the reasons for her liking her job. It was hard for her to describe the atmosphere in The Dairy, to explain how the Baumanns could have such high standards of work and yet be so tolerant of the mistakes they knew people were bound to make. It was even harder to say how relaxed she felt to be living amongst men and women to whom she owed no emotional dues. As always, Lily found it more easy to gain the approval of strangers than to win the affection of her family. No wonder that she preferred the company of strangers, even though her love was for Jack and her mother.

"Well, for a start, they're not English nor Welsh" she said, knowing that that was often the first thing Charlotte would want to find out.

"German I should think, with a name like that" said Jack.

"Yes," said Lily vaguely. "But been here for years and years. They still talk funny though. They're old, well Mr. Baumann, Mr. Frederick they call him, he's really old. He's thin, and as tall as you, Jack. Mrs. Baumann's younger; she's small, always on the go. They're nice, really nice people. They've got a dairy..."

"I thought there was a shop that was called The Dairy," said Jack.

"Yes. There is," said Lily. "There's a proper dairy as well though, behind the shop, and they make all the butter and cheese and cream and that. There's three or four of them working there. Then they sell it in The Dairy, that's the shop. It's big, and all the milk comes from the farms above Clydach."

Chapter Thirteen

"You baint in the shop though, Lily?" Charlotte felt uneasy. A respectable place of service was one thing. With our Lily so fly-be-night, a shop held that much more temptation to be giddy. Lily's next words were reassuring.

"No mother, me and Vi, that's the other maid with me, clean the rooms above the shop and the house next door where they live."

"It sounds as if they work you harder even than those Rayners, and *they* were slave-drivers" said Jack.

But Jack was wrong. Frederick and Marta Baumann were not hard task-masters. Frederick was sixty-five, a humorous man with a deceptively ascetic face, very proud of his pretty wife Marta. She was seventeen years younger than Frederick, and almost the same age as Charlotte. But Charlotte had begun to look frail and grandmotherly, while Marta moved with the briskness of youth, and could well have been mistaken for the daughter she had never had.

People knew that, as Lily insisted when she described it at home, The Dairy was "a really nice shop, a high-class shop", not at all like those Provision Merchants where you could buy starch and matches, carbolic soap and candles as well as foodstuffs, and where the mingled smell of paraffin and sawdust was condemned by Charlotte as "a stench fit to kill".

The Dairy Shop had a spicy smell from the raisins, sultanas and currants displayed on the Dry Goods counter, ready for the shop girls to weigh out on the brass scales and pack into dark blue paper sugar bags. Drums of rice, flour, sugar and pulses were stacked on the shelves, together with the tins of cocoa, tea in fancy caddies as well as in packets, the jars of jam, marmalade and treacle which made almost as much profit for the Baumanns as did their dairy produce.

The shop was inviting, with its cream painted walls, meticulously arranged shelves and spotless counters, for nothing escaped the manager Mr. Owen's scrutiny, not even the two identical posters in the windows. They showed an elegant lady by the fireside, the book on her lap laid aside, her gaze directed to the clock pointing to four o'clock. Above the comfortable scene, in huge letters was written TIME FOR CEYLON TEA. The posters were renewed long before they became grimy let alone fly-blown, quite unlike the advertisements in the Dispensing Chemist's opposite The Dairy. There, Lily had noticed, the poster vaunting "Kurakold, Richards' Unrivalled Remedy 1/- and 2/9 Per Bottle" was stuck in the side window when she first went to Baumanns, and it was still there, faded and almost illegible, two years later when she left to get married.

The dairy itself and the warehouse were cheerful places, noisy with the clanking of the milk churns from Troedyrhiw and Pentwyn farms in the mornings, and with the arrival and departure of delivery vans at all hours of the day. Dry goods stored in the warehouse, and the cheese and butter from the dairy, were delivered to those shops up and down the valley whose proprietors boasted of their stocks being "supplied by The Dairy", and the loading and unloading of goods and the voices of delivery boys and

Chapter Thirteen

shopmen made Lily feel she had begun to live in an exciting world.

Behind the curtained glass door at the back of the shop lay a different world, where the most important person to Lily, after Marta herself, was Vi. Vi, the other live-in maid, with whom she shared a bedroom and with whom she shared the cleaning, was three years older than Lily, and had been with the Baumanns for almost eighteen months. She had many interests, nearly all of them centred on herself, so that she never lacked topics of conversation. Her favoured subjects were her face, her figure, her hair, her clothes, her boyfriends and, some way behind, her friends' boyfriends. She secretly painted her face and openly boasted that she smoked cigarettes, though Lily had never seen any evidence of that apart from the long ivory-handled cigarette-holder conspicuous amongst the bottles and jars on the chest of drawers but looking brand-new.

Vi had auburn hair and deep blue eyes, and with her pink cheeks she looked like a china doll. Lily thought she was a very pretty girl, but she knew that Charlotte would consider her to be "common" and "forward", and even positively "fast". So when she went home on Sundays, Vi's character was clearly spelled out as "such a hard worker, mother, and never leaves me to do the dirty jobs though she's been there a lot longer than me. And there's no nasty temper about her", this with a glance at Ethel, "not a bit spiteful. She'd do anything for anybody."

Every story about Vi showed her in a favourable light. Not a word about her vanity, her unpredictability, her craving for attention, especially from the opposite sex. ("Boy-mad". Charlotte would have had the label ready before the description was hardly out of Lily's mouth). And particularly not a word about what endeared her most of all to Lily - that she was fun to be with.

Charlotte would have condemned Vi's lightheartedness as "giddiness", and would have feared that Lily was being encouraged to be flighty. But she would have been forgetting that Lily's character had been formed, and that it owed much to her family's influence, and most of all to Charlotte and Jack. She would not have known, either, that Marta Baumann was a good judge of character and that Vi herself hid a responsible nature beneath her frivolity. Vi had as respected a place as any at The Dairy, where it was Marta's policy to discourage those undercurrents of jealousy surging beneath the surface of most natural families she had ever known.

It was a policy which made for harmony, and once she had stopped being homesick, Lily realised that Mrs. Rayner had spoken nothing but the truth when she had promised Lily a better place than Penmaen. Not that Beatrice Rayner had believed that. In her eyes, the Baumanns could never overcome the disadvantage of their having been born in Germany, even though they had tried to make amends by becoming naturalised British subjects. Also, by living above and next door to The Dairy, they could never hide the stigma of being In Trade. Of course the Baumanns had retail shops in Treorchy and in Pontypridd, and they were Suppliers to a list of smaller grocers, so that in the little matter of bank balances, they were not inferior to the Rayners.

But the Rayners' family home, Penmaen, was at a safe distance from any of the ironmongery shops, and that alone enabled Beatrice Rayner to regard Marta as nothing more than an acquaintance who had proved useful in getting the girl Lily off her hands. A pity that Lily's replacement should be so slapdash, and so clumsy that Cook was constantly reporting breakages from the kitchen. Fortunately the replacements came out of the girl's wages.

Lily, it seemed, was turning out to be yet another of Marta's "treasures". But then, unlike Beatrice Rayner, Marta had no son to protect, and could afford to judge her maids solely on their work performance.

Marta was not a harsh judge, for she realised that the heavy furniture and fragile ornaments crammed into sitting rooms, dining room and bedrooms alike, made cleaning difficult. And when she looked at her brass trays and candlesticks, fire-irons and coal scuttle, her copper bowls and kettles, her pewter plates and her silver cutlery, she knew that their gleaming surfaces owed as much to elbow-grease as to Brasso.

Only one room was left untouched, and that was Frederick's "den". On the rare occasions when he had to be away for the whole day, Marta would, like a conspirator, let Vi and Lily in to sprinkle the carpet with dry tea-leaves and sweep it clean, to polish the parts of the desk and bookcases not covered with papers, and to flick away the ceiling cobwebs with the long-handled 'magic wand' of a feather duster.

Chapter Thirteen

The kitchen and the scullery alone were uncluttered, and these were work-rooms, more efficient by far, thought Lily, than the cavernous kitchen at Penmaen where Beatrice Rayner had spared no expense in setting Cook to impress her guests.

The Baumanns lived in far less pretentious a manner and in far less grand an establishment than the Rayners. But they were more happily employed, more comfortably housed, more generous with money, and far more well-fed than the Rayners could ever be. Lily had never tasted such food, never dreamed there could be such cakes.

In Penmaen, Cook had a repertoire of main courses, fowls, roasts, stews, soups, steak and kidney pies. But her desserts seldom included anything more exotic than a sorbet or a sweet soufflé, and usually stopped at a fruit tart or a suet pudding. As for cakes, "plain and good, nothing fancy" was her motto, and at tea-time Mrs. Rayner would have to choose between bara brith or Victoria sponge or rock cakes to go with the wafer-thin bread and butter sent up on the trolley.

At home, Lily had been used to plain cooking. Charlotte was a competent cook, and true to her boast, she never stinted on wholesome food. But she was seldom well enough to stand for any length of time mixing cakes or rolling out pastry, so that "sweet stuff" was something the Callow children associated with the tables of other families. Ethel would make a caraway seed cake now and then, or a slab sultana cake, which Our Arthur had christened "Railway Cake" because he vowed that in every slice the sultanas were spread out at regular intervals, like stations along a railway line. And just occasionally "shop cake" made its way into the house. Only at Christmas was there nothing shop-bought, and the cake and puddings at number 11 were amongst the earliest to be made in the whole street, for Charlotte always mixed them the day after "Stir-up Sunday".

Charlotte's education, such as it was, had been gained at a Church of England school attached to St. Luke's in Wells, and for her, the framework of the year was still the seasons of the Church, from Advent and Christmas through Lent, Easter and Whitsun to Trinity and the long haul of Sundays after Trinity. Every Sunday throughout the year she had had to learn the collect for the Day and even after nearly forty years she still knew many of them off by heart. The first words of the collect for the Sunday before Advent, a month before Christmas, were "stir up we beseech thee O Lord", and right from her childhood Charlotte had known that "stir up Sunday" signalled the making of the Christmas pudding and the Christmas cake. It was a timetable she had been used to in the Denmer household, and it was something she passed on to all her daughters.

Lily would take Charlotte's two two-pound cakes on the Tuesday to be baked in the communal bakehouse, Mr. Rowlands' bakehouse on Gelli Road, where everybody took their cakes. The "loaf tins", discoloured and shiny from years of use, were marked with an indented 'C' for Callow, made by Thomas' hammering a nail just so far into the side as to make the mark, and the cakes themselves were identified by paper labels bearing name and address. Each label was impaled on a half matchstick and inserted into the top of the uncooked cake, a ceremony reserved for Ethel or Lily since Our Arthur proved unsuitable for the task. Only once had he been allowed to take charge of the labelling. He had skewered so enthusiastically that the matchstick, the paper and half his fist had been sucked down into the mixture. There was no question of scolding the "poor little feller", but it was intolerable to risk the waste of mixture a second time - "such a wicked waste with raisins at five pence a pound".

The paper label would turn brown and brittle in the baking, but the name would still be legible, to be recognised excitedly by Our Arthur when he went with Lily to collect the cakes after school on the Wednesday. Not so many oblong tins had 'C' on them, so the initial and the label was enough identification. But the numerous Joneses and Evanses, Williamses and Davieses all had to have further marks to indicate their ownership. Next to the 'J' or the 'E' they would hammer stars, crosses, circles or triangles, so that the women, or the children, in front of them would be claiming their cakes with a "Jones the cross please, Mr. Rowlands" or an "Evans Triangle, by there, see" or a "Williams y seren os gwelwch yn dda".

When it came to her turn, Lily would try to be conversational, but her polite "I've come for Mrs. Callow's cakes please" would be spoilt by Our Arthur rudely pointing and claiming "Ourn! Ourn!" at the top of his voice. By the time that Our Arthur had stopped using the genitive 'ourn' and learned to say *ours* like all the others in Gelli Infants, he considered himself too grownup to go to the bakehouse. Only the youngest of boys went anywhere with their sisters, especially to a place where, apart from Mr. Rowlands himself, no man was likely ever to show his face.

The cakes were rich, dark, and solid with fruit, but when Christmas Day came they were never cut into, for they had to compete with the chestnuts, crystallised fruits, fondant sugar mice and trellis-work bird cages made of spun sugar which, like the cake, appeared once a year. Lily had a sweet tooth, but Charlotte's Christmas cake was not her favourite. She was unprepared for the variety of cakes and tea breads at the Baumanns. Ethel and Our Arthur would listen incredulously as she described the nut breads and cinnamon breads - "not like bread at all", the crescents dredged with icing sugar and the puff pastries which Mrs. Ford could produce at will.

Better than all these though, in Lily's opinion, was the nusskuchen, baked by Marta herself for special occasions. It was, Lily had observed, made with ground hazelnuts, filled with a soft apple mixture and topped with melted chocolate. There was always some left over after the guests had gone, and Lily thought it tasted "heavenly".

But when, one day, she took a slice home, Charlotte had no praise for it. "I don't care much for it, Lily, if the truth be known." Why was it, Lily wondered, that the truth that had to be known was always so unwelcome? "They muffins as we bought from the muffin man in Bedminster was a heap more tasty, toasted and spread wi' butter." Charlotte turned to Jack: "You mind they muffins,

Jack? In a tray they was, and the muffin man carried en in a big tray on his head. Come round the streets 'er did, and ring a bell. Our Arthur, poor little feller, 'er used to look out for the muffin man. Er knew his bell, from being ever such a little 'un."

Lily was silent. She had come a long way from the days when she would have flounced out of the room, in one of her famous tempers to see her offering being rejected so ungraciously. She was seeing some things more clearly now that she had left the shelter of home, and she understood what lay behind Charlotte's words. Her preference for muffins over nusskuchen had nothing to do with Charlotte's taste-buds. What she meant, and Lily recognised it, was that nothing in the Rhondda could ever match up to anything in Bristol, and that she still hankered after going back to Bedminster.

And more immediately, she was showing how uneasy she felt at Lily's being so far away from home. Tonypandy was less than three miles away from Railway Terrace, but to Charlotte it felt distant, and dangerous. She would never forget the reports of the strike riots, and for the rest of her days she considered that if they were sensible, folk would stay away from Tonypandy. Even to venture into it was unwise, but to stay and work and live there was downright foolish.

And another worry was the way that Lily was becoming so independent. "Coming home all dolled up and not caring a fig about any on us," said Charlotte, confiding her fears to Thomas. "I'll be bound it be that Vi working on our Lily. Our Lily be cracking her up that much.

Er sounds too good to be true. Our Lily be hiding summat." Charlotte's suspicions would have been confirmed had she seen Vi sitting in front of the tiny black-spotted looking-glass in their top-floor bedroom and observed how intently she stared at her reflection.

The ritual was always the same. First she would shape her mouth into an astonished 'O', raise her eyebrows and shake her head slowly from side to side in mock disapproval, her wide eyes never leaving the mirror. Next she would pause to nod sagely, forgivingly, before leaning forward interestedly until her forehead nearly touched the glass. Then she would draw back, pout, and smile roguishly, putting her forefinger lightly on her lips and holding her head on one side. Last of all she would begin an animated soundless conversation, an enthralled and enthralling tête-à-tête, as if with one of her captivated beaux. From the shelter of the bedclothes, Lily would watch the performance with a fascination tinged with envy. Charlotte had always been so vehement about the snares of vanity that Lily felt uneasy about spending time before a mirror, even when she was alone. But it would have been nice, she thought, to be more like Vi and not be shy of indulging blatant self-love, and that in front of someone else.

Not that Vi ignored Lily. Far from it. She was always eager to give Lily the benefit of her superior years and experience of life, even if Lily was not always keen to hear it. Her advice was kindly meant. "Try some of my rouge, Lily," she offered. "I'll show you how to put it on. You want to put some colour in your face, just to show up your eyes, like. Boys go wild about a girl with a bit of colour. I should know, after all." She smiled and added "But then, you got a sweetheart." Her eyes met Lily's in the mirror.

"A sweetheart?" said Lily, sitting up straight in bed. "Vi, who do you mean? What sweetheart? You don't mean Mr. Owen, do you? When he was talking to me outside the shop the other day he was only saying it was a nice day."

Vi pulled the hair pins out of the bun at the back of her neck and shook her hair free. "Oh no" she said, "not him. I'm not thinking of *him*." She began to sing softly: "Who were you with last night? Tra la tra la la ...out in the pale moonlight...tarala..."

Lily had to laugh. She leaned back on her pillow. "Oh Vi! That was only my brother Bert. You know my brother Bert..."

Vi ran her fingers through her hair, lifting it high above her head and letting it fall back on to her shoulders. She paused to admire how it shone red in the candle light before she went on, more loudly this time: "It wasn't your brother, it wasn't your pa, a-a-a-a-a-a-ha-ha."

Lily slid down the bed again. "Oh, the other one," she said. "That was Walter, Walter our lodger at home, that's all." Vi shook her head knowingly. "No," she said. "That's not all. He's the one. He's sweet on you, Lily. You mark my words."

Vi was notorious for her ability to spot a romance, even in the exchange of a single glance, and she was very often proved right. But this time, thought Lily, Vi was completely off course. Suddenly, for the first time, she felt some sympathy for the girls in the shop she had overheard complaining that it was "downright mad" the way Vi saw a secret admirer in every passer-by in trousers who happened to look into the shop.

"Look Vi," she said, "there's *nothing* in it. I never see Walter unless Bert's there as well. And Walter wouldn't try to get fresh with me, if that's what you're after. He's not that type."

Vi turned away from the mirror to look at Lily. For once, her face was serious. "Lily," she said, "Lily, they're *all* that type. Believe me."

Lily hardly knew whether to be pleased or irritated. She turned over on her side towards the wall and tried to put sleep into her voice: "And here endeth today's lesson, I suppose. For goodness sake Vi, blow the candle out. I want to go to sleep."

The candle was blown out, but Lily lay awake for a long time. Into her head had come Charlotte's words: "Have a care Lily, and don't go encouraging Walter, whatever you do." She had dismissed them as being just the kind of warning Charlotte felt it her duty to give, but she was disagreeably aware that had Charlotte witnessed her behaviour of the past few months, she would have condemned it as 'encouraging'. Lily had not meant it to be 'encouraging', but she fancied she could hear Charlotte saying "Such goings-on Lily! All that giggling and laughing...taint proper for a young girl...you be giving the wrong impression, Lily." She plumped up her pillow and lay on her back.

Chapter Thirteen

But surely Walter wasn't getting the wrong impression. She didn't want to give Walter the wrong impression - a good laugh never did anybody any harm... Just because some people were so serious all the time. Jack didn't like Walter, but he didn't really know him, not like she did... Walter was alright. He was a good sport. Jack was different, just different...clever, with a good head on him, but thinking that people ought to be talking about deep things all the time. Walter wasn't clever, anybody could see that. He was more like Bert, except that Bert never made her laugh like Walter did... Even Bert was quicker than Walter though. You had to feel sorry for Walter; he could never fight back with words. You felt like warning him "Don't get into an argument with Jack about anything." Except perhaps horses. Walter knew about horses... But he always ended up looking small... Jack didn't mean to make him look small. It was Walter who showed himself up, like the last Sunday they had all been home... Jack going on *again* about war, war with Germany. You could see Walter was out on a limb...everybody saying they could see it coming, she couldn't see it coming, Walter couldn't see it coming...arguing with Jack, "We be a sea-faring nation thee'st know, we got the biggest navy in the world...nobody to touch us at sea"...the look on Jack's face when Walter began to sing "It's the Navy, the British Navy, that keeps our foes at bay"...Jack shutting him up by talking about Germany's army, quoting figures, massive figures...Jack read a lot...Walter wasn't very clever, but if there was a

Chapter Thirteen

war, we would win, Walter was right about that...if there was a war...

Lily fell asleep at last, but only to dream that she and Walter were in a boat drifting out to sea, and that Jack was standing on the shore cupping his hands and shouting something at them in German. But Walter was singing so loudly that she could scarcely hear a word Jack was saying: "You are my Lily of Laguna, You are my Lily and my Rose."

CHAPTER FOURTEEN

WAR WITH GERMANY

1914-1915

"Not even the astutest and most far-seeing statesman foresaw in the early summer of 1914 that the autumn would find the nations of the world interlocked in the most terrible conflict that had ever been witnessed in the history of mankind; and if you came to the ordinary men and women who were engaged in their daily avocations in all countries there was not one of them who suspected the imminence of such a catastrophe."

War Memoirs of David Lloyd George, Chapter II

Chapter Fourteen

"There's allus summat to worrit about," said Charlotte. "Our Eth seemed so happy at first, but not now. Looking miserable as sin and talking about babies all the time. It's all 'Emmy's expecting again', or 'saw that Tulip woman out with her latest in the shawl. It's a downright disgrace...' There's our Lily, out of sight down in Tonypandy at that there Dairy, but never out of me mind, getting up to Lord knows what mischief, but sure as eggs is eggs, not up to any good."

Thomas was impatient. "I never knowd a woman carry on like thee, Charlotte, and that's a fact. If it aint one thing worrying thee, it be another," adding more gently: "She be alright, old lady. Our Bert and Walter be down there wi' her a lot o' the time."

Charlotte looked up from her mending. It was summat to do wi' being a mother, maybe, but she had an uneasy feeling about our Lily, had done for a bit now. Thomas of course couldn't see further than his nose. "*Walter* be down there wi' her, aye, but our Bert be hanging about here like a lost soul. They never goes out together much lately."

Thomas had noticed that Bert seemed to be at a loose end, but before he could finish his "Our Lily be able to take care on 'erself. She baint a child..." Charlotte had gone on to "I can't stop meself thinking about Our Arthur, poor little feller. He be heading for a decline, right enough."

This was too much. Thomas made no attempt to hide his irritation: "That gurt lad! A decline! Theest be trying to wrap that lad in cotton wool. It ud do er good to rough it a bit more. A decline! My Lord! *Theeself* theest ought to be worriting about. What theest get down thee gullet in a week udn't keep a bird alive, no, not for a day it udn't."

He had to admit that Our Arthur's cough, which had plagued him all winter "and kept us all awake night after night", had not eased off despite the coming of the hot summer days, and that the boy was always lolling about like a wet week. But there was nothing wrong with him that a good strong dose of senna tea wouldn't put right.

"Out-growing his strength" indeed! Too much molly-coddling, that was his trouble.

Charlotte found Lizzie Totterdale hardly more sympathetic than Thomas to her worry about Our Arthur: "He be that finicky and faddy about his food, Lizzie. I be at me wits' end to know what to tempt 'er wi'. Er be like our Jack, in looks and in his ways."

"Well, Charlotte, I tell thee this. Wi' bread going up a halfpenny a loaf, thee doesn't want to tempt 'un to eat more bread, that's a fact. There's my two lads well-nigh eating Joe and me out of house and home."

To Charlotte, everything of any importance happened either in Railway Terrace or in Byrom Street. So the newspaper headlines of June the 28th proclaiming the assassination of the Archduke Franz Ferdinand and his wife held nothing to claim from her a second glance. The heir to the throne of Austria had been shot by a young Slav student, and they believed that the Serbian government was behind it, that seemed to be the upshot of it by what she heard the boys saying.

But Charlotte had never heard of the Archduke Franz Ferdinand, and had no idea of where Austria, much less Serbia, could be in the world. No wonder that in the weeks following the assassination, she felt impatient with the talk, talk, talk, in the back kitchen, in the middle kitchen, Jack and that Dick Jenkins, with Thomas and Bert putting in their oars now and then. She was used to getting lost early on in their argy-bargy, especially when Dick started on that there Welsh speaking, but the same names cropped up over and over again, and it was always clear whose side Jack was on. Before this latest carry-on, it had been "The Fed" and that there "Mabon", right out of "the Exec", and a good riddance, to judge by Jack's tone at any rate. But now that Austria had declared war on that Serbia, it was Germany, Germany all the time.

"It's a matter of treaties," said Jack. "Russia of course, protecting the Slav people, Russia's on the side of Serbia."

Dick nodded, as Jack went on "France is bound by treaty to Russia, so she'll mobilise and send her troops in to support her. Russia and France joining Serbia to fight against Austria and against her ally Germany."

So that was it. They was all in it together, dragging one another in. Nothing to do with us after all, thought Charlotte. Trust Jack to be bothering his head about foreign parts, and not seeing under his very nose the state Our Arthur was getting into, poor little feller. If she had been in London, and seen the "John Bull" posters on the buses proclaiming "To Hell With Serbia", Charlotte would have agreed. If Germany wanted to fight Russia and France because of this row between those other two, then let em get on wi' it.

"The Germans've been spoiling for a fight," said Jack.

Familiar ground. The Germans and their preparation for war. It was all old hat. Nothing to lose any sleep about. Just their talk, been talking that way for years, you'd a thought they'd get fed up wi' talking about it.

"Spoiling for a fight for years. And now they've got their chance. Been building up their army for years and they want to prove that it works."

"Well," said Dick. "The Germans have been doing no more than anybody else in Europe. They've all been building up their armies, even Belgium, and they are all of them armies of conscripts. Except for ours."

"Aye," agreed Jack. "Our Regular Army isn't like any other in Europe. The Germans are ready now - they want to crush the French. So they'll make straight for Paris. And how? They'll march through Luxembourg. Then they'll march through Belgium..."

"No, no," Dick interrupted. "They won't do that. You said it yourself; it's a matter of treaties. The Germans have signed a treaty to respect the neutrality of Belgium. Well, more than that, to *protect* the neutrality of Belgium. And we're a party to that treaty. Mark my words Jack, the Germans will keep to that treaty. National honour. France is supporting Russia isn't she? Bound by treaty? Well, depend on it, Germany will abide by *her* treaty. She can't march through Belgium."

Jack snorted. If politicians were like Dick Jenkins, treaties would be binding and there would be no march through Belgium. *But...* "Don't be too sure about Germany and national honour, Dick. And if they do invade Belgium, we are bound to send our troops against them. We are pledged to do that. *Our* national honour demands that."

Easy to talk about national honour and justice, thought Jack, but not easy to keep faith in those ideals when you worked in a Rhondda mine and could see every day how men's lives were put at risk from the greed of the coal-owners and the incompetence of the managers. There were enough battles against oppression to be fought on the doorstep, without rushing to defend a distant country and a faceless people.

But when Germany declared war on Russia and then on France and, on the day following Bank Holiday Monday, August the 4th, marched into Belgium, there were none who cried "To Hell With Belgium". The Germans could not be allowed to attack neutral Belgium in defiance of treaty. France would be the next to be over-run, and then the Hun would be at the Channel. It was unthinkable. Germany, the aggressor, would have to be stopped.

"Easy matter to send the Germans back where they came from and teach ';em a lesson," said Thomas. "Our boys'll finish the war in double quick time. Be all over by Christmas, I reckon."

"It's like a fever," said Dick. "People delirious with hatred of the Germans and calling it patriotism. All those stories of atrocities in Belgium. I can't believe it... A civilised people, a nation which gave birth to Kant and to Goethe wouldn't..."

Thomas had never liked Dick Jenkins, and his voice was rough as he burst in with "Thee cassn't believe it? I knows nothing about any Gertie. She might be all right. But t'others are all on em bloody butchers. It be all here in black and white for thee to see. Hassn't thee been reading the papers? Cutting off they babbies hands, crucifying they nuns? They Belgian refugees be coming over here in droves, 'snow. Or dost thee think it be all made up and there baint a war on at all?" He turned without waiting for Dick's reply, and went out muttering an audible "Bloody coward...er wants a white feather sent 'en."

It was harder to stand against the tide than to flow with it, thought Jack. He felt unable to join Dick in his pacifist stand, but equally unable to share Bert's eagerness "to get in on the show before it was all over."

Dick was uncompromising. To him, the Commandment "Thou shalt not kill" was an Absolute, carrying no corollary such as "except thou be in uniform". But he was no coward. "Cowards die many times before their deaths; The valiant never taste of death but once", and in the pit Jack had seen enough unrecorded acts of incidental bravery to be sure that Dick was to be counted amongst the valiant.

His thoughts ran on... "If all men were like Dick there'd be no war, of course. But the point is that they are *not* all like Dick. Far from it. Maybe the tales of German atrocity in Belgium are exaggerated, but it's a fact that Belgium's been invaded and innocent people killed. People are fleeing for their lives with no more than the clothes they stand up in. Wounded Belgian soldiers are already being nursed in hospitals in England. Our troops in France are pushing back the Germans, thank God, at a place called Mons, and at a tremendous rate according to the papers..."

But there was no fight in Dick. So many evenings he had spent in discussion with Jack and the others, demolishing the proposition that Might is Right.

"Turn the other cheek and forgive your enemies, even until seventy times seven, isn't it? All very well Dick, but surely self-preservation tells us to stand up for ourselves? For our own self-respect. "Turning the other cheek" could mean that a man be destroyed by the villains of this world."

Dick would listen attentively. Then he would smile. "Listen, Jack. Saint Matthew again, 'Pwy bynnag a ewyllysio gadw ei fywyd, a'i cyll: a phwy bynnag a gollo ei fywyd o'm plegid i, a'i caiff'. That's it, isn't it, 'whosoever will save his life shall lose it: and whosoever will lose his life for my sake shall find it.' Why do people think that death is the worst that can happen to a man? Remember what you tell me your favourite, your Donne, says about death? That death is 'but a groom that brings a taper to the outer room'. That's it. Not the worst thing, only something we can't escape. What matters is that we follow the gospel of love while we are alive on this earth. 'This is my commandment. That ye love one another, as I have loved you.' And that love is stronger than death."

Jack would have felt embarrassed to hear such words from anyone else, but in Dick's mouth they were spoken with such conviction that they almost seemed to make sense. Almost. But not quite. "It's against human nature to let the aggressor trample all over you, Dick, and give in without a fight. We're at war in a just cause. The Belgians are fighting for their lives, and in a war not of their making. It's up to us to take their part, the side of the weak. It's defence, Dick. Surely you would defend your family against an invader? And aren't our soldiers doing just that? Fighting the Germans so that England stays safe?"

Dick spoke slowly: "I know what you are thinking of, Jack. 'Greater love hath no man than this, that a man lay down his life for his friends.' St. John's words, St. John the beloved disciple. Wonderful words. And even more wonderful, to my ears whatever, in the Welsh." Jack braced himself for another flow, for when Dick began on the Bible in his mother tongue, his voice took on a special quality, a sonorous and musical *hwyl* often sustained for verse upon verse, or so it seemed to the unappreciative Jack:

"'Cariad mwy na hwn nid oes gan neb; sef, bod i un roi ei einioes dros ei gyfeillion...' To lay down one's life, to sacrifice oneself, to lose one's life for others, that doesn't entail killing, Jack. It simply implies dying. Rather different, bachgen."

"That's martyrdom Dick. That's what you're advocating. And you won't find many takers these days for that philosophy. And anyway, say we don't care about our own lives, what about our duty to defend the weak against the bully? By using force." Jack played his trump card. "What about righteous anger? What about Christ in the temple throwing out those who bought and sold? Overturning the tables of the money-changers I seem to remember?"

Dick peered over his glasses affectionately. "Good, Jack. Always good to bring in illustrations, examples. But you see, bach, there's a world of difference between throwing somebody out and killing them."

Jack said no more. He recognised that Dick's refusal to fight was based on thought and conviction. Of those who had already rushed to volunteer, many were no idealistic crusaders but men who saw the war as a chance to escape the hard and dangerous monotony of daily life in the pit. You couldn't blame them. Simply to wear the uniform and go to France was to be regarded as a hero. Dick had another kind of courage, the kind of courage it took to face men who reviled you and turned from you in disgust because you refused to give up your convictions and follow them.

Our Arthur was wishing he had been born in Lily's place. He would have been seventeen and a man then, instead of a useless boy of thirteen. But he was careful not to say as much in front of Charlotte, for she felt as strongly as Dick against the war, though not for his reasons. Thomas was too old at fifty-eight to take the King's shilling, but there was still Jack and Bert. Our Eth's Will had too much sense to go haring off to the recruiting office, while Walter was acting as if he were bent on denying there was any war on at all. He was still as irritating as ever, singing his "I love a lassie" and "Roamin' in the gloaming" in his best Harry Lauder imitation until Charlotte could have screamed.

But Walter was true to his own description of himself as "a dark horse", and surprised everybody by being among the first in Gelli to volunteer to join Kitchener's New Army. He and Lily had "come to an understanding" and it was only with reluctance that he had agreed not to tell a soul about it. When he left at the end of June to join the Gloucesters, it was with the promise of marrying her when the war was over.

"Been going on ten months already. Can't go on much longer, especially when they gets I out there to show em how. I'll come back safe, Lily, thee'll see. I got me Touchwood Imp to bring I luck. We'll have the rest of our lives you and me." He smiled, remembering how Bert had ragged him for his faith in his "wonderful Eastern Charm", the tiny crossed-legged imp with sparkling eyes and khaki cap. What with that and his years-old Cornish Pisky he could come to no harm.

He saw that Lily's eyes had filled with tears, and he thought how lucky he was. Lily returned the pressure of his hand. She felt miserable. Vi had been right. Walter did love her. But she had realised with certainty that he was not the man she wanted for her husband. She could not marry Walter when the war was over. It would not be fair to him. She didn't think enough of him, not nearly enough, and she was only sorry now that she had allowed herself to be so carried away. He would feel dreadfully hurt when he came back from the war. *If* he came back from the war. The sense of relief was only fleeting, but Lily felt wretched that she had entertained it at all. He was dashing, and really handsome, and fun to be with. And he was soon to go away. But if there hadn't been a war, nothing would have happened between them. She was sure of that. The war had altered everything, everybody. If only there hadn't been a war and life could have gone on as before, at a pace you could keep up with.

Thomas was encouraging Jack and Bert to follow Walter's example and enlist. "They don't need no encouragement," said Charlotte. "It be water off a duck's back to try and reason wi' em. Like as if they be deaf for all the notice they takes of I. 'Thee'st got no need to join up', I told 'em. 'Theest be doing thee bit working down the pit. They needs coal. Let em send for ee when they wants thee, not rush into it of thee own accord. That Walter got nobody much to care about en. Thee boys has got thee father and me to think on, 'snow.'"

But there were few who echoed Charlotte's words. Parents declared themselves proud to think that their boys had gone to be soldiers, and all over Gelli and Ton notices were appearing in front room windows drawing attention to the fact that 'this house has sent all its sons to fight for their country'. "Aye," said Charlotte. "The house has sent em, but the mothers ud have kept em at home."

Chapter Fourteen

In the pit there were some who thought and said openly that religious bloody maniacs like Dick ought to be shot as traitors, but those who knew him wondered whether somehow he wasn't right, especially since nobody seemed to be sure exactly what the war was all about, except of course that the Germans were our enemies.

And as the months went by and the end of the war still nowhere in sight, there was angry talk among some miners about their low wages. The owners were reaping the profits of the high coal prices "like the flaming armaments manufacturers, making a damn good thing out of the war and not wanting it to come to an end in a hurry".

"Profiteers and spies," said Lizzie Totterdale "and the price of butter. That be all people be talking about."

"People must be going mad," said Lily. "Raving mad." She had come home upset because the Baumanns had had all the windows of their shop in Pontypridd smashed, and the goods inside looted, even though they had changed their name to Bowman, and had put notices in all their shops stating that they had been officially British since 1900. "And," said Lily, "everybody knows how good they were to people in the Strikes and that. I remember only about a month after I started, that they gave an awful lot of money when there was that explosion in `Senghenydd. In October it was. Worst ever they said."

Jack cut in. He spoke drily: "Over four hundred men killed in the Universal. Yes I'm sure the Baumanns gave generously to the Disaster Fund. But not as generously as the men who gave their all."

Chapter Fourteen

Lily was abashed; she felt she had earned Jack's reproof though she had not been prepared for it. It was usually Our Arthur who complained that "our Jack comes down on me like a ton of bricks". She said quickly: "Well, they got ever such a good name. There's nobody in Tonypandy who'd attack The Dairy. They must be mad in Pontypridd."

Charlotte looked uneasy. If people in Pontypridd thought them Baumanns was spies, never mind how much money they gave away, she saw no reason to believe that folk in Tonypandy would think different. She would have felt still more disturbed had she known that a woman had called after Vi in the street asking her, and not very politely at that, what she thought she was doing, working for an enemy. But Lily was not going to worry Charlotte with telling her that. She had long ago decided that some things were best kept back and not mentioned unless events made secrecy pointless.

"Well, what can you expect?" said Jack. "It's all because of the sinking of the *Lusitania*. The Germans have made a bloomer there, attacking and sinking a defenceless passenger ship flying the American flag. It's turned people more than ever against the Germans, even the Germans who've been living and working here for years. Of course it's just an excuse for looting, some of it. And people want a scapegoat near at hand, an enemy at home, somebody to hate. It makes them feel better. Now you've got to seem to be 'British-and-proud-of-it' or else you'll be branded an enemy, especially if you've got a German-sounding name. Talk about the Baumanns

Chapter Fourteen

changing their name! The King will have to change his before long."

"What's wrong with George?" Our Arthur wanted to know.

"Nothing wrong with George." said Jack. "It's Saxe-Gotha that'll have to go. Like the Bechstein Hall."

"Is that gone?" asked Our Arthur. "Where's that gone to?"

"Gone nowhere. It's the name. It's been re-christened. The Wigmore Hall it is now. All part of the same thing. Look at the way companies are advertising themselves. Lyons say they are an all-British company, with all-British directors, so many thousand British shareholders - they don't count the foreign shareholders, mind - and so many thousand all-British shopkeepers selling Lyons tea."

"We sell Lyons tea in The Dairy," said Lily, "pounds and pounds of Lyons tea. Mr. Owen and the two men in the shop have joined up already, and they think that Mr. Frederick will have to go away somewhere to be interned. I don't know how we are going to manage without them."

She had been on the point of blurting out that Vi too was going to leave The Dairy to go and work in the new munitions factory in Swansea, but she had stopped herself just in time. Charlotte would have jumped to the conclusion that Lily was about to follow her, leaving a respectable place of service to go even further away from home, to go among strangers and to pick up even more forward ways. Had she seen her, Charlotte would have thought that Vi was acting more like a trollop than ever these days, for she had gone out and had her long hair cut to just below her ears and, worse still, she was showing a good five or six inches of leg above her ankle. Even Lily was shocked at how common she looked, though she had to admire the patriotism which had made Vi sacrifice her lovely hair, something Lily could never do, and all to make shells for our soldiers to fire at the enemy.

"All the boys are leaving," said Vi. "There's not much fun in hanging round here any more. It's getting to be a dreary hole. Better come and help me win the war Lily, and make a bit of money as well. Munitions girls are well paid you know, a lot more than we get here. See life before it passes you by!"

It was quiet in The Dairy after July, when Vi decided to See Life, with or without Lily, in Swansea. But it was even more quiet in Railway Terrace when Lily went home on a Sunday, for before the following month was over, there was only Our Arthur at home with Charlotte and Thomas.

Jack and Bert had enlisted in the Welch Regiment. And it was from then onwards that Lily began noticing how many women were dressed in mourning, and how many of the old men were wearing crepe armbands on the sleeves of their jackets.

CHAPTER FIFTEEN

TILL DEATH DO US PART

1915

"Happiness in marriage is entirely a matter of chance...it is better to know as little as possible of the defects of the person with whom you are to pass your life"

Jane Austen, Pride and Prejudice, Chapter 6

Chapter Fifteen

"Well mother, she's not the first, and I dare say she won't be the last."

Ethel was doing her best, but Charlotte was bitter.

"No better than she should be. The same as if she'd been dragged up in the gutter. What's to become of her?"

"He'll marry her, mother. He's still in this country. He can get compassionate leave, and they can be married. The baby aint due till beginning of May..."

"If only Jack was here..."

Charlotte was getting more and more agitated, and Ethel more and more brisk.

"Oh, do talk sense mother, do. What could Jack do, even if he was here? No, it'll be alright. Walter'll be man enough to marry her. He's proved himself enough of a man already."

Charlotte was off on a new tack. "And there's your father to contend wi'. He won't hear of her staying here. He be dead agin her, and married or no, it'll be the same. Not under this roof 'er says."

"I'll talk to him, mother. He might listen to me. But in any case, she can go into 'partments next door to Dick Jenkins. There's two rooms to let with Milly and Fred Wilkins, in Hillside. They got nobody there but theirselves now, their boy were in the Reserves, he been in France ages. Tidy people they be. Not a bad-looking woman, always smart. Something the same stamp as Queen Mary. Same toque hat as Queen Mary."

"Share it, do they, our Eth?" Our Arthur had listened to it all, wondering why everybody was making such a fuss and why Lily couldn't come back home if she was going to leave Bowmans. She didn't want to marry Walter he knew, and as far as he could see, the one and only reason for the wedding was to give Ethel the chance to show off her new costume.

It was a three-quarter coat of brown and fawn tweed, with a matching skirt of the latest length. Ethel had paid dear for it, and even more dear for the hat with the dyed ostrich feathers, but she had felt satisfied that the outlay had been worthwhile when she saw her reflection in the shop windows on the way down to Railway Terrace. Like one of the wax models in Lewis', exactly. She was deaf to Our Arthur's aside as she made her dignified entrance into the middle kitchen, but his "Look! The big fat Hen!" was loud enough for Thomas to overhear and threaten to catch him a clout 'longside the ear'ole if ever he dared show disrespect to his sister again. It was no good for Our Arthur to protest that he felt nothing but respect for our Ethel and our Lily, and indeed, but under his breath, for big fat hens. He had to be heard to make amends.

Ethel cared nothing for the "cheeky little monkey's" opinion, and his "very nice. A very nice costume. Very *very* nice. A very *very* nice costume." she dismissed with a "get out of my sight before I turn nasty with you." She was not going to make an issue of it this time, so that Thomas had to be satisfied, although he went off muttering about spoilt mommocks with too much old buck about them.

It was going to be a very quiet sort of wedding, on Christmas Day, without Charlotte, Jack or Bert. At the last minute Ethel had coaxed Thomas into giving Lily away, and Will Shepherd had agreed to be Walter's Best Man.

All Lily's good clothes had become just that bit too tight for comfort or concealment, and it was too much of an extravagance to buy new, considering that they would fit for only a short time. So Ethel had been kind enough to lend her second-best costume, an ecru tussore silk two-piece with front embroidered panels and high collar, and now that skirts were beginning to be worn shorter, the length on Lily looked just right. Quite up to the minute really. Funny how our Lily always managed to carry her clothes so well, even when it was a borrowed outfit. With that loose-fitting jacket, nobody would have guessed that she was nearly five months gone. Except of course that everybody in that small congregation knew.

Walter was sullen. Lily had not given him the welcome he felt he deserved. He had come back to do his duty by her, not unwillingly, although he had been bargaining on a bit more freedom before he settled down, and he had begun gently enough: "Theest could look a bit more pleased to see I."

But Lily had rounded on him.

"Pleased to see you? What have I got to be pleased about? Carrying *your* baby. I don't want your baby. I don't want anybody's baby."

"Well I baint overjoyed about the babby neither. Cassn't thee do summat to get rid on it?"

Lily's anger "So that's what you think of me" had turned to tears, desperate crying such as she had never known before.

232

Chapter Fifteen

Walter had comforted her. "No need to take on so, Lily. We be going to get married, not buried. When I comes back, our luck'll turn, bound to. I got me Touchwood Imp..."

But it had been enough to make a bloke feel like going out and bloody well putting an end to it all. Well, where he was going, Jerry could do that for him soon enough. He could cop it in double-quick time, Touchwood Imp or no.

And yet now that the day had come and Lily was going to be his wife, he said to himself that if, and it was big if, he did come out of this lot alive, he would try and make a go of it. It might turn out, after all. She was a good-looker, no doubt about that, a girl to be proud of. They had had good times together. And a bloke ought to buck up on his wedding day.

But Walter was not finding it easy to buck up. To the best of his knowledge, he had never been in a church in his life before, much less to a wedding service, and he was finding the unfamiliar surroundings both oppressive and intimidating, as if he were a player forced on to the stage in front of a critical audience without knowing any of his lines.

"There was I, waiting at the church... Oh, how it *did* upset me!" The rollicking tune would keep running through his head, bringing with it familiar echoes of its music hall context, and reminding him that both it and he were out of place in this silent church, before this quiet congregation, standing next to the taciturn Will Shepherd, and waiting for Lily.

Chapter Fifteen

Lily was trembling slightly as she walked down the aisle on Thomas' stiffly-held arm. St. John's was unfamiliar to her too. St. John's was not "her" church. Her church was St. David's, where one Easter she sang the solo soprano anthem, 'I know that my Redeemer liveth'. But St David's was not licensed for weddings. St John's was the Parish Church of Ystradyfodwg where marriages were solemnized. It was a Victorian church built on a seventeenth century site, in a style which justified Our Arthur's dismissive "a dark and gloomy old church". It felt dark and unwelcoming to Lily.

The late December sunlight filtered only feebly through the stained glass of the chancel windows, and it was very cold. The tussore silk was not nearly warm enough. She could have done with the fur stole she could see draped round Ethel's broad tweed shoulders. The stole was fastened with the miniature head and front paws of a fox, to the delight of Our Arthur to whom the combination of Big Fat Hen and Fox had proved irresistible.

It was very cold. She should have insisted on borrowing something warmer, a winter-weight, something woollen, anything but the tussore silk. She had not thought to insist on anything. There was nothing she could have insisted on. If she could have had any say at all, she would not have agreed to be married, and she would not be making the vows which were to bind her to Walter until the day she died. But Lily had not been able to stand out. She had given in to what everybody said was best for her. So Mr. Phillips the vicar had published the banns, Ethel had chosen the tussore silk, and she was standing beside Walter, her right arm almost touching the sleeve of his uniform.

"Dearly beloved, we are gathered together here in the sight of God, and in the face of this congregation, to join together this Man and this Woman in Holy Matrimony..." His voice rang out. Mr. Phillips was pleased with its sound. "...First, it was ordained for the procreation of children..." It seemed to Lily that his eyes rested on her as he paused, and she knew her cheeks were burning. She had felt the baby move, a full seven weeks past. "Aye, the quickening." Charlotte had been unsmiling, and Lily wondered what it must be like to be expecting a baby and to want it enough to sing Magnificat.

Mr. Phillips was leaning forward slightly, his voice lower, as if there was nobody but Walter and Lily to hear. "I require you and charge you both, as ye will answer at the dreadful day of judgement when the secrets of all hearts shall be disclosed..."

There was no secret about her not wanting the baby. She didn't want the baby, and she told Walter that. She didn't want to marry Walter. She hadn't told him that in so many words. She had told only Charlotte and Thomas that, but they had brushed her words aside, insisting that Walter "be made to give the child a name". So it was like keeping a secret in her heart. Except it was the kind of secret that it would become impossible to hide, least of all from Walter.

She felt his gaze. He had so willingly agreed to give the child a name. So he should, it was his child after all. But one of Vi's friends had found that her chap had kept her on tenterhooks wondering if he was going to marry her. Walter had done nothing like that. If only she could feel love for Walter, or even fondness. But she had never loved Walter, not even when... That had been reckless pity for a man who loved her and who was going away to a war from which he might never return.

"Wilt thou have this woman to thy wedded wife..." Mr. Phillips had lost count of the number of times he had put that question in his fifteen years at St. John's. And since the beginning of the war, there had been more weddings than ever, with the young men in uniform. The war had made young men and young women so precipitate in their relationships, and some of the young women so forward. "So long as ye both shall live?"

Always he was struck by the solemnity of the words. Shot-gun weddings, some with a bold face... But not the girl in front of him. One of the handsomest couples he had seen for a long time, and the most subdued. There was nothing joyous about this ceremony, even though Walter's "I will" was loud enough to make Lily's voice sound all the more tremulous. Her hand as she took Walter's was cold as ice, and he felt a surge of protective love towards her as she repeated:

"I Lily Maud take thee Walter George to my wedded husband, to have and to hold from this day forward, for better for worse, for richer for poorer, in sickness and in health, to love, cherish and to obey until death do us part, according to God's holy ordinance: and thereto I give thee my troth."

Chapter Fifteen

The ring was on her finger. They were kneeling down, the last words of the unfamiliar prayer ..."may they ever remain in perfect love and peace together..." almost drowned in Dick Jenkins' fervent "Amen". The pronouncement "Man and Wife together" almost theatrically loud in Mr. Phillips' baritone, the Blessing, the Psalm, "God be merciful unto us", more prayers, would it never end? Then the Lord's Prayer, and Dick Jenkins' voice again, pronouncing the unfamiliar English version reverently and slowly, out of step with Mr. Phillips' professional pace, and those in the pews following Dick Jenkins, so that their "deliver us from evil" was being heard seconds after the vicar had begun on the versicle "O Lord save thy servant and thy handmaid..." Then into the vestry to sign the register. Lily Maud Besant. There was no turning back. She had done what they had all expected her to do, Charlotte, Thomas, Walter himself. If she had not married Walter, Charlotte and Thomas would never have forgiven her for bringing disgrace on a respectable family.

And what else could she have done? She had no money of her own, and if her family had turned against her, she would have been homeless and destitute. Charlotte's words kept ringing in her head... "Otherwise, it's the workhouse for thee Lily, thee and the babby." That, she couldn't have borne.

Lily knew of more than one family where the daughter who had got into trouble had been sheltered at home and not forced into any marriage. Their babies had been unofficially adopted by the grandparents and brought up to look upon their real mother as one of their sisters. That was not uncommon. But those must have been more forgiving parents, younger and stronger than Charlotte and Thomas, maybe with less offended pride, certainly with more charity. If Lily had not married Walter, she would have been disowned. She couldn't help feeling like an outcast as it was, the black sheep outside the circle of virtue so tightly enclosing Charlotte and Ethel.

Ethel would never have thought of lowering herself, never have found herself in her state. Of course she had done wrong but she wondered, if Thomas and Charlotte had been wealthy, would they have been so ready to force her into this marriage? If they could have supported her and the baby, would they have condemned so heartily? Or was it more because of the disgrace than lack of money that they were so bitter against her? Charlotte by keeping away from the wedding was showing the world, or that part of it that mattered, that Lily was an unfavoured daughter. To Lily she had said simply "I couldn't stand it. And us couldn't afford to keep thee and a babby."

Lily hoped the baby would be a boy. Boys didn't get themselves into trouble, didn't have to marry anybody they didn't want to. Lily had always wanted to be a boy, and never more so than on her wedding day. Boys were free to please themselves.

Charlotte had said it was best to marry. But how could it be the best to do something you knew to be a mistake? Charlotte had had the last word. "Should have thought of that before, Lily. It's too late now, my girl." Lily had felt the force of that. It had been her own fault. Now she must abide by the consequences.

The bitterness she felt against her parents vanished when she thought of her own folly. Her affection for Charlotte, if not for Thomas, survived unchanged. Charlotte had been ready to reject Lily, but the cause of that rejection was Walter. Lily could forgive her parents. Walter she could not forgive. Walter had not begun to realise how desperately unwilling Lily had been to marry him. Of course he could see she was unhappy because of the baby, and because of what he knew Charlotte and Thomas had been saying.

He had told Lily: "If anybody treated I the same as they buggers was treating thee, I'd drop em like a shot and never darken their doorstep again. They be all the same, all except your Bert. He be the best o' the bunch. Your Arthur be getting too much like that bloody know-all, Jack."

If only, thought Lily, if only Jack had been at home to advise her and even perhaps to take her part. He had never thought much of Walter. He might not have been so eager to see her married to him, in spite of the baby. The baby, the baby she didn't want to think about, the baby she didn't want to have. For the sake of that unwanted baby, Lily knew she had forfeited any chance of happiness she might have had in her life, and not only in hers, but in Walter's too. She knew that by that ceremony before witnesses, in that parish church of St. John, she had entered into a contract which could bring nothing but misery. And she knew it with an intensity which frightened her.

Chapter Fifteen

"'Er looked as white as a sheet, as if 'er might have fainted away afore it were all over," said Lizzie Totterdale. "Vicar were a bit anxious as well, I fancy. And as for Walter, there was none of that cheeky grin. I never seed en afore without that cheeky grin. When they comed out o' the vestry, I tell thee Charlotte, I couldn't help meself shedding a tear or two. Your Lily, shaking like a leaf, both on 'em looking like children, that pitiful, and like two innocent..."

Charlotte cut her short. "Eighteen baint a child, and she baint innocent, Lizzie."

Charlotte's thoughts were bitter: "Lizzie got no girls. She wouldn't talk so silly if she'd a had girls. Well, Lily been and made her bed and er'll have to lie on it. Thank God Richard baint alive to see this day. Ewart and his wife 'ud be self-righteous when they heard on it, with Cousin Julie engaged to be married but not in the family way, not likely. Our Ethel still with no babby. Our Lily. Foolish maid. Foolish, foolish maid. But she be a respectable married woman now. Nobody got no right to point the finger of scorn at her. If only she'd stayed with them Rayners. That Tonypandy. A wicked place. And that Vi, whoever she be. She were nothing but a bad influence. Thomas be hard. A hard man. Denied Jack his place at the Blue Coat School, turned his face from Lily now. Childer, when they'm young, they breaks your arm, and when they'm growed, they breaks your heart. They brings down your grey hairs with sorrow to the grave. Lily were married but to the wrong feller. Er would live to repent it. And the babby...unwanted. Funny old life. No freedom in any on it. And with pain added to it, worse at times than any pain of childbed...the pains of hell...

"O' course," said Lizzie Totterdale, "Charlotte be in pain a lot o' the time. And *he* be a funny feller to live wi'. Er has a lot to put up wi'. A mortmain to put up wi'. But they always been hard on Lily, right from er being a little 'un. They baint like it wi' Ethel, that there band-box. Lily be worth ten o' that sort, like it or no." She glanced at Joe's impassive face. "I tell thee this, Joe Totterdale, that if it was my little maid that had got into trouble, I couldn't be like they Callows. I couldn't live wi' meself, let alone wi' thee, if I was to talk and act that harsh towards her."

CHAPTER SIXTEEN

HILLSIDE

1916

"War is nothing more than the continuation of politics by other means"

Karl von Clausewitz

"By nature's law we all are born to die,
But where or when, the best uncertain be;
No time prefixed, no goods our life shall buy,
Of dreadful death no friends shall set us free"

Thomas Proctor, <u>Respice Finem</u> 1578

Chapter Sixteen

Lily's apartments with Milly and Fred Wilkins in number five Hillside were two rooms at the front of the house, a bedroom and a living room. Here she was to spend the first ten years of her married life, and here both her daughters were born. The rent was two shillings and threepence a week, there was a penny-in-the-slot gas meter hidden in the lower cupboard in the alcove beside the chimney breast, and "you'll find your own coal, of course".

"The rent's a bit steep," said Ethel, "and most people would see that you got enough coal for that one little grate and not charge you for it. They gets it by the load, when all's said and done. Not like us, having to buy it all at full price. I tell you, Lily, it ain't all honey having a chap on the railway. Not by a long chalk it ain't."

Lily said nothing, but she knew that Ethel was comparatively well-off. Her own allowance from Walter's pay as a soldier was small. It would be increased when the baby came, and the thirty-shilling maternity benefit would be a Godsend, but it was to be many years before Lily felt herself to be free from worry about money. By the end of her life she was "comfortable", but she began in Hillside by owning nothing and having no prospect of acquiring anything.

Milly Wilkins' two rooms to let were furnished with other people's cast-offs, but they were clean and free from bugs. Lily could see that when our Eth got round to giving her the curtains she had been promising, and the chairs she was throwing out, it would all look homely enough.

Chapter Sixteen

"Tidy people," Ethel went on. "You'll never see Milly Wilkins without she's got summat new on, even if it's only a different jabot on her blouse or a fancy tippet over her shoulders. And Mr. Wilkins do keep his age well. He must be near enough our Dad's age."

Lily had little interest in Milly Wilkins' wardrobe, and none in Fred Wilkins' age. The coal she could foresee being an expense, not knowing that Dick Jenkins had already filled her part of the coal shed with big lumps and some slack for banking up the fire, and that he had arranged that either he or Fred would put in a few shovelsful from Dick's load every time it was delivered in the back gwli.

"The least we can do, isn't it," said Dick, "for any neighbour, but for Jack's sister most of all. 'Yn gymmaint a'i wneuthur ohonoch i un o'r rhai hyn fy mrodyr lleiaf, i mi y gwnaethoch.' St. Matthew, of course. 'Inasmuch as we do anything for the least of our brethren, we do it for the Lord Himself.' Mind you," with a sly glance, "I'm not saying that Lily fach is one of the least, neither. To tell the truth, I wouldn't be surprised if it was twins she was carrying."

Dick was a good neighbour. Lily never found a better, not in all her seventy years in the Rhondda, although in Milly Wilkins she could have found a better landlady. Number 5 Hillside was exactly like 11 Railway Terrace with the same number and size of rooms. Downstairs, two rooms and a back kitchen, upstairs, two front bedrooms, one small and the other smaller, with a tiny bedroom at the back. No front garden, but a paved yard behind the house leading to a narrow strip of black earth beside a brick path. At the end of the pathway, next to the coal shed, the unheated and sometimes rather smelly W.C.

The house was identical, but it was in a very different street from Railway Terrace. Hillside was less than five minutes' walk away from Railway Terrace, but it had none of the "shut-in" feel which weighed so much on Charlotte's spirits, especially when she became housebound. There were only six houses in Hillside. Built at right angles to the valley floor, they clung to the steep Eastern slope of Gelli Mountain, and with no other houses opposite to cast their shadow, Lily's front windows caught the sun from early morning to late afternoon. The houses at the lower end of the street, nearest the main road and the shops, faced Harry Clements' stabling, the biggest stables in Gelli, but immediately opposite the houses further up towards the mountain, at Lily's end, there were no buildings of any kind.

Number five was the last but one house at the top of the hill, and when she looked out of her bedroom window, Lily was high enough up to be almost on a level with the head of the monstrous waste-tip from the Bryn, which had greened over and become camouflaged with grass to look like part of the mountain side.

Right opposite lay the expanse of field belonging to Coedcae farm, and beyond that she could see the thick woodland stretching unbroken all the way down to Tonypandy. Even in winter the view was pleasant. In early spring, when the hedges were budding and the rough pasture was dotted with lambs, it reminded Lily of the

Walter Crane illustration to "Little Bo-Peep" in the book of Nursery Rhymes she had so often read to Our Arthur. It was a countrified prospect rare in Gelli, and a more open outlook, thought Lily, even than the view from the windows of Penmaen, where she had been in service with the Rayners, for Penmaen was enclosed by the barrier of trees and tall shrubs which protected their privacy.

There was little privacy in Hillside even had Lily craved it, for the neighbours had entered into an unspoken agreement to "see to" Lily, as they would have done to any newcomer, let alone a slip of a girl in that condition, and only married forty eight hours before Walter had to go back to join his regiment again.

Lily's next-door neighbours were Dick Jenkins and his wife Annie May in number six, the very last house before the mountain. Every day Lily would see Annie May's father, Wil Ifan, pass her window on his way to Bwllfa Bridge and back. He was gone the whole morning because he walked so slowly, and had to stop so often. Wil Ifan's face was grey, the skin stretched taut across his cheek-bones, his eyes deep-sunken, his limbs wasted and trembling, all clear signs of "The Dust", coal-dust which had accumulated and cemented together to tear the delicate lining of his lungs so that every breath he took was painful. It would soon become impossible and yet he counted himself "lucky to be here at all," he would say. "Men don't usually last long in our job!"

In number four, going down the hill towards the main road, lived Miss Evans Dressmaker, and her invalid sister Amy. Lily was quick to notice that the windows of number four shone as gleaming, the brass as bright as any in the street, the door-step and stretch of pavement to the kerb scoured as white as any, "and that" said Lily to herself "is saying something, because fair play, there are some good cleaners in Hillside." And yet Miss Evans Dressmaker was past fifty, was frail and bent, and not only had Amy to look after but was at the beck and call of women and children for fittings.

"Tired of making up black, she is," confided Amy. "All mourning clothes now, most of it, deep mourning."

Lily would call in to number four of an afternoon to sit a while with Amy while Miss Evans sewed in the middle kitchen workroom or, her mouth full of pins, knelt and measured a customer for a dress, a blouse, a skirt, and sometimes for a long coat or a jacket, for "A tailoress she is by rights" said Amy proudly.

But it was in number one that Lily made her closest friend, Louisa. Everybody knew that Louisa Pearce had given up a good place of service in Cardiff with a family in Cathedral Road to come and look after her widowed brother Alf and his babies, twin sons barely a year old. People had not forgotten the rail disaster in Hopkinstown at the end of January 1911, when Ivy Pearce had been killed, for three members of the Federation Executive had also lost their lives. One of them had been a Treherbert man, and Lily remembered how Jack had gone with Dick Jenkins to walk with the mourners behind the hearse to Treorchy cemetery. It had been one more sadness in the terrible year of the Cambrian strike.

Chapter Sixteen

Alf Pearce was the blacksmith at The Smithy on the main road at the corner of Hillside and River Street. He was nearly thirty two years old and had not a single grey hair on his head, while his massive frame, strong arms and bright complexion all bore witness to his youth and health. He was known to everybody as "Old Pearce the Forge".

Lily knew Old Pearce the Forge not only because his personal history was common knowledge, but also because he was, if not exactly a friend, then at least an acquaintance of Walter's, for they shared a love of horses and a knowledge of animals which gave them respect for each other.

Walter reckoned to know better than any hostler, better than any farrier, better than any horse-doctor what ought to be done in treating horses, but in Old Pearce he acknowledged he had an equal. It was as to an equal that he would give accounts of his pit ponies: "A star fracture Alf! Kicked on the back leg by t'other black 'un theest heard I tell on!" or "Lame through nail-bind! That bloody farrier, don't know what the 'ell he thinks he's doing. I could a told en as how them nails was drove in too damn close..." Old Pearce the Forge would never be so unskilled. There were few if any who could hold a candle to Old Pearce the Forge in Walter's eyes.

Lily had heard him reporting to Bert, with embellishments, that he had told Old Pearce the Forge to chuck The Smithy and come and do a proper job where it was needed, in the pit. But she knew him well enough to know that no such advice had ever been given. Walter would not have spoken to Old Pearce the Forge in those terms though, while he was giving the details of the conversation, he was convinced it had actually taken place. Many a conversation in which Walter had taken the wise, the masterful, the brilliant part was relayed as a faithful recollection, and in the beginning, Lily had found it more endearing than embarrassing to recognise his need to 'crack himself up'.

"Damn liar!" Thomas would say. "Thee cassn't trust that feller an inch." But others, recognising that the story was meant to entertain, would laugh and egg him on, would stand him another drink and chalk up another yarn to good old Wally's account. "I be the life and soul of the party, mun." This was Walter's assessment of his own character, and away from the company of kill-joys such as Jack, he very often was. Even Thomas had to recognise that as drinking companion Walter was hard to fault, for he was open-handed with his money, full of good humour and jokes and never aggressive in drink. Thomas could well understand why Bert had liked to hang round with him. But for Lily to have taken up with a feller like that! She could have had any feller. Always did have a wild streak in her. Not like our Ethel. Our Eth was twice the girl of she. Trust Lily to go and make a damn fool of herself, throwing herself away, and near bringing shame on them all.

Lily was surprised how quickly and pleasantly the days passed at first. Cleaning the nine-foot square living room and the tiny bedroom took no time at all, even though she was becoming enormous, and clumsy, and very conscious of how swollen her feet and ankles had become by the end of the day.

The grate in the living room was a tiny parlour grate, meant only for occasional "company" use, and although she could balance a kettle or a saucepan on the bars, it was impossible to cook on it anything much more ambitious than a piece of toasted bread. The only oven was in Milly Wilkins' back kitchen range, and although Milly had kept saying that she was welcome to use the oven "any time my gel, any time. Fred and me don't care much for cooked stuff", it seemed to happen that on the rare occasions when Lily had a piece of meat or a rice pudding, Milly had let the fire die down so that the oven was uselessly cool. Lily knew she was unwelcome. She tried not to go into Milly's part of the house any more than she could help, but since the only way out to the outside lavatory and the coal shed lay through Milly's back kitchen, she was forced to make some journeys every day. Tap water too, cold water only, had to be fetched from Milly's kitchen, and however careful she tried to be, Lily found that a kettle-full seemed to last no time at all. So she would wait until she heard Milly leave the house, look through her window to see what Milly was wearing, and judge by her clothes whether she was going Up the Road or just popping across to her sister Jinnie. Either way, she would be gone some time. Lily would fill not only the kettle but her two iron saucepans and the enamel washing-up bowl as well and push them out of sight under the table until they were needed.

Chapter Sixteen

All her clothes she washed in a bowl placed on the table, hanging them to dry on the line strung right across the room, and emptying the dirty water in the gutter outside her window. She could see that the room would be damp with wet clothes when the baby came, but that would be better than waiting for Milly to clear the one and only clothes line in the garden. It had been agreed that Lily would only use the line when it was empty, but on fine days Milly usually had something drying, even if it were only a tea towel or a pair of socks, showing that the line was in use and might be filled up at any time before the day was out.

Lily had never had a landlady before, and she sometimes wondered whether all those who shared their house made it so hard for their tenants. She knew that Milly disliked her, but it took Louisa to tell her why.

"Lily, try not to let Milly Wilkins see you talking to Fred. I was in with her the other day and I saw her face when he came in from the back carrying your bucket of coal for you and you laughing at something he was saying."

Lily looked at her in amazement as she went on: "She's a jealous woman, and Fred's a bit of a lady-killer."

Lily began to laugh. Fred Wilkins a lady-killer! Sixty if he was a day, fat, bald and bandy-legged, and his face scarred and pocked. And Lily, her figure gone, her legs and feet twice the size they were so that she often put on a pair of Walter's shoes for comfort! It was ludicrous. "Milly Wilkins jealous of me? Why should Milly Wilkins be jealous of *me*? I don't want her silly old husband and I don't want her either..."

Unexpectedly, she felt the laughter turning to tears. Her voice trembled: "Oh Louisa, what a mess everything is. Isn't there anybody happy in this world? There's Milly Wilkins tormenting herself. She must think *everybody's* after her husband if she thinks *I* am. There's my mother, sick with pain and worry about our boys being sent out to France. There's our Ethel, really nasty about anybody having a baby, because she hasn't got one herself, and there's so many of the boys we knew who are getting killed..."

Lily was thinking of Captain Harry Rayner who had been dead for nearly a year, killed in Flanders in October 1914 at a place which Lily was to hear called Wipers, and which the *Rhondda Gazette* identified as Ypres. Captain Harry was one of the first soldiers in Gelli to be killed in action, one of the "Old Contemptibles" of the British Expeditionary Force. Such an odd name thought Lily. The *Rhondda Gazette* had published the news on its front page and then devoted some inside columns to Harry Rayner and all the family in its account of the "Engagement at Ypres in which a Gallant Officer lost his life".

Lily had been shocked at the news. The Rayners' son. With all their money the Rayners, the "Prominent Local Family", had not been able to ensure their son's safety. Nobody's son could be made safe. And now they were all in it, Jack and Bert, oh, and of course Walter. They were all in it, and would they all come back, and if they did, would they be like Olive from Gelli Crossing's brother who they said was off his head, with shell-shock, or like Vanw-next-door's cousin, who would never walk again. What she found hard to understand was how the war could be going so well for us and yet there be so many dead and wounded. Every week there'd be somebody she or one of the neighbours knew, reported killed or else wounded and in hospital somewhere, and yet in the newspapers there'd be the good news of successes and break-throughs and accounts of how pleased our brave troops were to be in the thick of it all.

Dick Jenkins would go to the Workmen's Library in Ystrad and see the casualty lists in *The Times* and *The Daily Telegraph*. "Thousands of names every day, Annie. Never less than one thousand, just lists of names under headings. Roll of Honour. Fallen Officers, then Losses in the Ranks, names of men, Regiment by Regiment."

Through the years Annie May Jenkins had grieved that they were childless, but seeing how Dick was mourning over the death of other men's sons, she couldn't help saying a silent prayer of gratitude that God had spared them the anguish of finding their boy's name in a list they would weep to see.

Dick could not hide his emotion: "So many young men who will never return, so many who will come back so badly wounded in mind or body... Oh, cariad, pity, pity. Those poor parents, who will never again look up in pride, never again find pleasure in their boys' good looks or their bright intelligence. The flower of the nation, merchi, the flower of the nation, cut down and wasted."

Chapter Sixteen

The figures preyed on Dick's mind, and haunted his imagination. "From thirty five in the first casualty list, on the third of September 1914, from just thirty five killed, wounded or posted as missing to *this*. Lists, just lists of names, nothing more. And in France and Germany lists like this, longer than this by all accounts."

On the first of July, the first day of the Battle of the Somme, there were over 57,000 casualties, and of these more than 19,000 would be listed as "killed" or "died of wounds". By the last day, November the thirteenth, there were 420,000 casualties, and of these 60,000 were dead men.

"No need to look at the paper to see the losses, merchi. So many wounded wearing their blue uniform, so many mourners wearing black, everywhere you go. Men killing each other, blinding, maiming...how long is it going to go on? Till all the young men are wasted?" Dick paused. His voice hardened. "And then the fruits of victory will be dust and ashes indeed."

Dick was not alone in mourning the futility of the fighting, but the inexorable and impersonal war machine had not yet been set by the politicians and generals at STOP. In camps all over England, men like Jack, Bert and Walter were being trained in the use of those modern weapons of warfare, the Mills bomb and the Lewis gun. Most of all they were being drilled in the use of that older weapon, the bayonet, against the time when they would meet the enemy face to face, at Ypres, at Passchendaele, on the Somme and at Arras where "the monstrous anger of the guns" would be their constant companion.

Chapter Sixteen

In the barracks at Kingston-on-Thames Jack was seeing how the Poor Bloody Infantry were trained by the book. The official notes about bayonet fighting included the need "to encourage the lust for blood", so that when they charged the stuffed sacks marked with discs for 'eyes' and 'heart', they would yell and shout as they twisted the bayonet to disembowel, as they lunged to thrust with an upward jab into the throat, and as they swung the butt into the private parts.

Jack wrote to Lily nothing about the obscenity of bayonet drill, very little about rifle instruction or the punishing physical training. Instead, "we are near a huge park," he wrote. "Richmond Park. I wish I had the chance to paint. It's a beautiful place with herds of fallow deer and masses of rhododendrons all in flower. You would love it. I shall be sorry to leave it."

He wrote cheerfully to Charlotte and Thomas, that he and Bert were together, were enjoying the beautiful weather, had met with a good bunch of fellows. He might have been on holiday, but his tone could not lessen Charlotte's anxiety. She had taken a stride forward into old age, for continual pain had made her frail. She had given up going upstairs to bed, and was spending all her days too on the single bed Thomas had brought down from the girls' room and put downstairs in the middle kitchen.

As she got nearer her time, Lily became obsessed with images of death and with foreboding of what might happen to Jack. It was not that she thought Bert or Walter or Ethel's Will bore a charmed life; she hardly thought of them at all. It was always Jack's name she imagined on the telegram "Deeply regret to inform you...killed in action", always Jack's name on the letter of condolence sent by the commanding officer "It is my sad duty to have to tell you...hope it will be of some comfort to know he died bravely...assure you he did not suffer...buried where he fell...deepest sympathy...", always Jack's name on the black-edged card put in the front room window "William John Callow..." It was always for Jack she felt fearful with a dread she recognised as the look on some women's faces.

And yet in Hillside she could see the Phillips children in number three still going sliding down the tip, and the little Richards boy in number two still trying to whip his top up and down the hill pavement without a break, just as she and Our Arthur used to do in Railway Terrace. There were still little children playing games, still children laughing. And there were plenty of girls like Vi, who were earning good money for the first time in their lives, and who were enjoying their freedom. Girls like Vi were not "tied down". Lily was envious. She had always thought that those girls were mad who couldn't wait to get married, and all her life she thought that the unmarried state was best. To be single was good. To be single and well-off! That must be bliss.

Ethel had not been favourably impressed when she met Vi. "Whatever be the matter with her face, Lily? She looks like she got the yellow janders."

"It's something in the factory," Lily explained. "It's not the jaundice. It's something they put in them shells or something. Vi said that some of the girls go that yellow that people call them canaries. And she said that there were a couple of girls she knew in Bridgend who died of it."

Ethel was still not inclined to sympathy. "Well, whatever it is, it don't go with them red cheeks, I can tell you. All that muck on her face. Like a clown."

It was only jealousy, thought Lily, pure jealousy, for she had seen Ethel's attempts to bleach her own sallow skin with great dollops of Pond's Vanishing Cream and thick pastes of Fuller's Earth. Ethel would not have dared use rouge to paint her face, and the natural means of bringing colour, by pinching the cheeks and biting the lips, were short-lived and not very effective. Vi's artificial colour was more blatant, more long-lasting, and more successful. No wonder Ethel was irritated. Even worse, Vi was wearing expensive clothes, expensive and elegant. Ethel had to admit it, Vi might be "common", but she did know how to dress.

"Did you notice the collar of that voile blouse she was wearing, Lily? Muslin, and trimmed with lace. Very dainty. Must have cost a pretty penny. Nine and elevenpence I should think, if not more. And that costume! Gabardine twill don't come cheap, not with jackets lined with silk, real silk, it don't. A good few guineas-worth there. How ever can she afford it?"

"Well, she's earning good money, Eth. Nearly two pounds every week. A bit better than the seven and six we were getting at Bowmans. And she's got nobody to spend it on but herself."

Lily was glad that Charlotte had not met Vi. She would have been even more shocked than Ethel at Vi's smoking and at her bold talk. It was still all boys, boys, and how ready they were to be saucy, especially when they were on embarkation leave. Some of the girls on Vi's bench had taken up with "temporary gentlemen". Lily saw Ethel look away in embarrassment. Some, according to Vi, were saying "Better to be married a minute than die an old maid", and others, even respectable girls, weren't bothering with any ceremony at all. Lily couldn't help wondering where Vi herself stood, but with Ethel casting a damper on any personal revelations, Lily could only guess, and say truthfully in answer to Ethel's questions after she'd gone that she had no idea about Vi's private life. But it all seemed to chime in with what Dick Jenkins had been saying only the other day.

"You see, merchi, it's not only that the war is maiming and killing soldiers, and now civilians as well, and that it's bringing want and misery and disease after it. No, you can add another to that list of evils, and that's the breakdown of morality. When this war is over, our world will have lost any innocence it ever had, and any idealism with it."

Lily was not sorry that Vi came up to see her so few times before the beginning of May when the baby was born, for she feared that Vi would have antagonised Ethel. Our Ethel had become a daily visitor and had also become an unexpected go-between. When Lily went down to Railway Terrace, as she did two or three times every week, ostensibly to see whether there had been any letters from Jack or Bert, it was clear to her that Ethel had been "putting in a word" to soften Charlotte and Thomas, for their attitude was becoming, if not exactly welcoming, yet noticeably less hostile as the weeks went by.

But Lily was pining for her lost freedom and grieving for the life of personal fulfilment she knew she would never be able to have. She was nearly nineteen and it seemed to her that her life was over. It would be worse when the baby came, physical relief though that would be. It would be worse still when Walter came back. *If* Walter came back. But she would not let herself think of that. There was nobody to whom Lily could show her true feelings, for nobody but Jack, she thought, would have listened with understanding. Dick Jenkins wore a look as if he pitied his fellow creatures, a look which invited confidences, but it was unthinkable for her to confide in any man outside the family.

It was in writing that Lily found her release. In the weeks before her daughter Ruth was born, compulsive writing about her life absorbed Lily to the neglect of everything else, so that Ethel would take away the half-sewn nightgowns, telling Charlotte that if it were left to our Lily, that poor little creature would have to stay as naked as it would come into the world.

"She don't seem to care a bit, mother. 'Taint Christian. Poor little mite."

Lily was glad enough to see the growing pile of flannel binders, woollen matinee jackets and cotton petticoats, but nothing mattered more to her than putting down on paper those feelings which threatened to overwhelm her. All that she wrote she crammed into' penny books bought from Danny-the-paper-shop on Gelli

Chapter Sixteen

Road, books made up of twenty-four lined grey pages stapled together in dark blue paper covers the colour of sugar bags. The words "Exercise Book" in black capitals took up the middle of the front cover, and beneath them, in smaller letters, "Ruled, Feint". The back cover was completely filled with Multiplication Tables and Tables of Measurement. Such a busy cover, thought Lily, all those yards, feet, and inches, and then there were the gills, pints, gallons, the stones, pounds and ounces. She could still hear Miss Richards' voice leading the class in their daily intonation:

"12 inches, *one* foot

3 feet, *one* yard

22 yards, *one* chain

10 chains, *one* furlong

8 furlongs, *one* mile"

and the final shout of triumph:

"one thousand, seven hundred and sixty yards, *one* mile".

The cover boasted title "Lion Brand" but the paper belied its promise. It was thin and porous and showed the writing through to the other side, so that after the first few pages, Lily abandoned her steel nib and her bottle of watery Stephens' Blue Black ink and began to use a pencil instead. She could then fill every page since the writing was legible on both sides of every leaf, but she still needed to go back for another and yet another Exercise Book.

"Four of them books, merchi!" said Danny-the-paper-shop's wife. "Writing your life story, gul, sure to be."

Chapter Sixteen

Lily smiled and handed over the coppers. Danny-the-paper-shop's wife could not suspect how nearly she had hit the mark. Lily *was* writing her life story. She wrote rapidly, without revising, without stopping to correct the spelling even of those words that looked wrong on the page, without reading over what she had put down so hastily. She wrote about all that had happened to her, and she wrote until she felt there was no more she had to write. It was all there in her neat rather curly script, with hardly any punctuation and no separate paragraphs. She wrote about her relationship with Thomas and Charlotte, about her feelings for Ethel, for Bert, Our Arthur, and for Jack. She wrote about Ma Morgan and her daughter Edith. She wrote about Penmaen and about the Rayners, Captain Harry, and Miss Beatrice, about Ellen, about Cook. She wrote what she felt about Vi, the Bowmans, about Mr. Owen. She wrote about Alf Pearce and Louisa, about Dick and Annie May Jenkins, about Milly and Fred Wilkins. Most of all she wrote about Walter. There was a lot to write about Walter.

When at last she had finished writing, she wrapped all the exercise books in a piece of *The Rhondda Gazette* and put them away in the cardboard suitcase under the bed. And there they stayed, unseen and all but forgotten through the years. Not until she was old and nearing the end of a life which had grown burdensome was Lily ever again driven by such a need to record her thoughts, her experiences and her feelings, and by that time she had become too feeble to hold a pen. Instead she talked, the details of her life saddening her listener. And then at last the compulsive talking itself had to stop when her voice, once so powerful, lost its strength and sank into a whisper.

But when she was young, Lily wrote only for herself and for her own release, not for communication. Trapped between the covers of the Lion Brand Exercise Books lay experiences too raw to be shared with anyone, except perhaps Jack. But Jack was far away. By the time the baby was born, on May the tenth, Jack and Bert had crossed from Southampton to Le Havre, on the first stage of a journey which was to take them North to Flanders and end for one of them in a devastated wood in Passchendaele.

"Wednesday's child," said Charlotte. "Wednesday's child is full of woe."

"Oh mother," sighed Ethel. "Don't 'ee make it worse. There's our Lily acting like as if she can't bear the child. I only wish it was my little un."

It was Ethel who named the baby Ruth, patronisingly informed by Our Arthur that "that means Pity, our Eth, in case you don't know", and it was on Ethel that all the blame would be laid for "ruining the child, spoiling her completely, too much giving in all the time..."

Years later, Lily realised bitterly that had she obeyed her instinct and offered Ethel the baby she herself could never love, she might have been able to use her life "to make something of myself". Ethel was still childless. She would have cherished the little girl and Lily would not have had to live with the constant reminder of the man she had married and whom she grew to despise.

Chapter Sixteen

She would still have had to live with Walter. Lily was not rebel and not financially independent enough to flout the convention that a married woman stays with her husband. If only Ethel had showed any sign earlier that she would have taken the child...if only Lily had not been forced into marrying Walter...if only Lily had known what Charlotte accidentally let slip later, that almost a year before Ethel got married she had a miscarriage...

"Very early on, might have lost it of its own accord..."

Lily would have felt less of an outcast. It explained Ethel's obsession with babies, and why she had been so good to her...it was her *guilt* thought Lily. But she couldn't help feeling that it was all part of a family conspiracy to make of her a scapegoat, but for what reason, she couldn't fathom. *If only* - so much of Lily's misery hinged on those two words; so much of the world's misery too, as the war entered its third year of stalemate, making more wives widows, and more children fatherless.

CHAPTER SEVENTEEN

"GWELL ANGAU NA CHYWILYDD"

1917-1918

"THE BRITISH REPORTS   THURSDAY
10 20 MORNING
Welsh troops carried out a successful raid last night south-east of Armentieres. Fourteen prisoners were captured by us, in addition to other losses inflicted on the enemy. Our own casualties were light."

The Manchester Guardian, Friday November 9

1917

" I have a rendez-vous with Death
  At some disputed barricade
  When spring comes back with rustling shade...
  And I to my pledged word am true
  I shall not fail that rendez-vous"

Alan Seeger, 1917

Chapter Seventeen

Dick Jenkins sat in the Newspaper and Periodical Room of the Workmans' Library on Ystrad Road reading *The Manchester Guardian*. Monday November 12th, 1917, Annie May's fortieth birthday, a day which would be remembered by so many as the day on which their son or their husband died. He turned over the pages of the newspaper secured on its long wooden rod to find the war reports. They were on the same page as the paragraph, headed "Civil Conflict in Russia" describing Kerensky's march on Petrograd. His glance fell on the last half of the page:

"The British Reports. Saturday morning. At dawn this morning our troops attacked the German positions north and north-west of Passchendaele. First reports indicate that good progress has been made. The weather has become stormy, with high wind and heavy rain."

Good progress thought Dick. Good progress despite bad weather. As if the weather were the greatest obstacle to be overcome before ground could be gained from the Enemy. According to the newspapers we were always Making Good Progress, just as our casualties were always Light and our raids Successful. In all the news since August of the attacks on Passchendaele, it was the Germans it seemed who were suffering the Heavy Losses, the German counter-attacks which were Failing. The English Reports proclaiming "German Misery in Flanders" described the failure of the enemy to recapture positions gained by our troops and dwelt on the agony of German soldiers enduring the sweep of shell-fire our men were flinging over the enemy lines and mud-holes. We had advanced through the swamps of Passchendaele, and those same swamps were making it impossible now for the Germans to develop a strong counter-attack. Yes, if you read only the English Reports, you were bound to feel hopeful about the way the war was going, even if you did wonder why it was taking so long for the defeated Germans to admit their defeat. Three and a quarter years, and we had still not won, although of course we were still officially winning.

But in the adjoining column the German Reports were telling a different story. They too were claiming victories over the enemy.

"Saturday afternoon.

Violent drum-fire preceded English attacks which commenced at day-break north-east of Poelcappelle. They were repulsed in hand-to-hand fighting.

Night.

Strong English attacks between Poelcappelle and Passchendaele broke down with sanguinary losses in our defensive zone.

Sunday Afternoon.

The crater-land between Poelcappelle and Passchendaele yesterday was again the scene of a desperate struggle. The English brought up into the battle fresh divisions in order to win the high land north of Passchendaele. They penetrated into our defence zone in the middle of the front of attack and stormed the heights striven for. There they encountered the counter-thrust of Pomeranian and West Prussian battalions and were repulsed. The enemy repeated his attacks five times. As a consequence of our effective artillery work the attackers were shattered, mostly before our lines. Where the enemy for a time gained ground, he was struck down by our infantry by means of bayonets. Brandenburg troops pursued the enemy and wrested from him portions of the positions from which he had started. An English local attack launched in the evening east of Zonnebeke failed. The day's fighting in Flanders yesterday cost the enemy heavy losses; 100 prisoners fell into our hands.

Evening.

North-west of Passchendaele an English local attack sanguinarily collapsed. - Admiralty, per Wireless Press."

Dick raised his eyes from the page, the words imprinted on his mind. "Effective artillery work...struck down by means of bayonets...heavy losses...sanguinary losses..." In other words, mutilation and bloody death for men at the Front, heartbreak for those at home. Men dying for a few square miles of land, crater-land fought over yard by yard.

"Heavy losses," each loss, each man's death bringing the telegram from the War Office every family dreaded to receive. Like the two telegrams which had been delivered to Railway Terrace, both in the same week, the one for Lizzie and Joe Totterdale, with the words every family dreaded to read, "Regret to inform you...missing, presumed killed." That was their eldest son Frank. And the other fulfilling all Charlotte's foreboding, the following day, "Private Albert James Callow...Killed in Action."

Chapter Seventeen

Our Bert. Of his three sons, Bert was the one Thomas would miss the most. Bert was the one with whom he had felt completely at ease, the one who never bore a grudge, never gave the Smart-Alec answer, never picked a quarrel. Bert was the one who always fell in with everybody else, the peace-maker, the go-between. Thomas was not the man to hide his feelings, but for Charlotte's sake he was trying to stifle his pain. Only with Ethel he could drop his guard:

"Both on us to give way, it 'ouldn't do...theest know she be eating her heart out on the quiet..."

Ethel nodded as he went on:

"Eating 'er heart out, fretting night and day, that she be, I tell thee this, our Eth, 'er won't live to see none o' the rest come back if it don't stop soon. 'Er don't listen a word to I. Waiting and watching for another telegram..."

Ethel poured him out another cup of tea. She could always go without herself, would have to, with tea being that scarce, but Thomas was not often at her table. He spoke again:

"Totterdales be in a bad way be all accounts now that Frank be taken."

"Aye," said Ethel. "Lost their all now. Their George killed over a year ago."

George Totterdale was just one of the expendable infantrymen in the Ninth Welch Battalion, killed in the battle of Mametz Wood early in July 1916.

"But no good calling that to mind, Dad. Our Lily was in here yesterday, saying that Fred and Milly Wilkins heard about their boy. They had a letter from him, wounded and in hospital. In France. So he's alive at any rate."

She spoke listlessly. If her Will Shepherd was to be killed, he'd have left no child behind him...and with her being nearly twenty nine years old, there was fat chance of getting another husband...so many boys gone, so many widows, too many spinsters...she would never have a child of her own...

Thomas had taken up her last words. "Aye. Just to be alive mun. They gets better of their wounds, a lot on 'em. And there be some Miraculous Escapes."

Thomas was thinking of Jack's story about the captain saved by the New Testament in his breast pocket, the bullet going right through all the pages and stopping at the very last page, or the company who came through, every man jack of them, with hardly a scratch, and all because they recited the ninety-first psalm every day of their lives -

"Whoso dwelleth under the defence of the most High shall abide under the shadow of the Almighty...a thousand shall fall beside thee, and ten thousand at thy right hand, but it shall not come nigh thee... For he shall give his angels charge over thee to keep thee in all thy ways..."

Jack had come home on leave only twice from the time they enlisted in 1915 to being demoblised in 1919. "Home leave?" said Jack. "No fear, Dick. Strictly for officers, not for Other Ranks. No, not for the likes of us. When it comes to billets and food and leave, it's Them and Us. See here, Dick. One chap, Idwal Morgan from

Chapter Seventeen

Bedwellty, got a letter to say his youngest little girl had been run over and killed. Eight years old she was. Think he could get leave? No, not on your life. He was told that since the child was dead, there was nothing he could usefully do. That was the official attitude. Well, he wasn't thinking that he could work any miracle of raising the dead - don't look at me like that Dick. He wanted to comfort his wife. And if it had been Captain Phillips' little girl, there'd have been no question. Of course *he* would have been granted fourteen days compassionate leave. No they're a different breed, Dick. They look different and they talk different."

Dick's voice was calm: "But bachgen, they don't die different."

Jack bowed his head. No, they didn't die different. Commissioned and non-commissioned, officers and privates alike, they all died in the same way. Officers too were blown apart by exploding shells, officers too were impaled on the barbed wire, decapitated and shot through by machine gun fire, officers too were trampled into the stinking ooze and listed as buried in an unknown grave. But he wished Dick's words had been left unspoken. They brought it home to him that he had not yet succeeded in forcing out of his waking mind those images of death which disturbed his sleep and made his night thoughts hideous.

"A successful raid..."

"Our own casualties were light..."

Jack had known men who had lost their memory, whose response to what they had seen and heard had been to blot it all out. His own memories were sickeningly clear. He would never forget the lice, the mud, the stench of decay, the bloated rats in the dugouts, the deafening rattle of the machine guns, the crack of rifle fire, the scream of the shells as they left the howitzer and the shower of earth thrown up where they fell.

He would never forget the sight of the wounded on their stretchers, nor the sound of those left lying in No Mans Land moaning in pain or calling out in delirium. Worst of all were the images of the dead who had lain unburied between the trenches and who were brought in by night for burial. Or when they had lain too long for removal, were covered with chloride of lime. He thought of the salvage men following the army forward, then the Graves Registration Unit digging, prospecting for the dead and never failing in their search, re-burying the decomposing fragments under wooden crosses, making graveyards where there had been fields and woods. Piles of salvaged identity discs proving there had been men who had worn them, food parcels arriving where it seemed callous to be sharing the cakes intended for the dead... "GWELL ANGAU NA CHYWILYDD." Jack had needed Dick to translate the Welch Regimental motto. "Better death than dishonour."

The words would not leave Jack's mind. Death, dishonour, Death, disgrace. Death or dishonour. Bert had died. But if he had lived, it would not have been dishonour. Bert was honourable in life. It was the manner of his death that was disgrace. Nothing in his life deserved such obscenity. A warrior's death on the field of battle, dying for his country. "Dulce et decorum est pro patria mori". So sweet a sacrifice, devoutly to be wished, a fitting end to a life. It sounded heroic. But it was a lie, part of the conspiracy of concealment of the truth. Not all lies exactly, just platitudes written home on the squarish plain postcards officially stamped at the Army Base Post Office, "feeling fine, weather good", but half-truths in the letters to Lily, and now lies about Bert. "Killed instantaneously," when he had seen otherwise.

Yet the truth could not be told, except perhaps, sometime, to Dick. Dick could bear more reality than most, and he had known fear and danger every day of his working life underground. He would recognise the love and comradeship which bound men together to make bearable even the hell of Flanders. He was no stranger to the relief at having survived under fire, the exhilaration of being alive in the midst of death, and he knew too the guilt of being a survivor. But all Dick knew about life in the trenches was from newspaper accounts and from the film which everybody but Charlotte had seen, the official film which even toured the battle fields, the film of the Battle of the Somme.

"And that film," said Jack, "has no soundtrack. You can't imagine the noise Dick, the ear-shattering noise. It's like an Inferno, the guns, the explosions, the scream of shells. It's like as if the Devil was tearing calico sheets...hour after hour. In a bombardment Dick, the earth shakes. It's like the end of the world, and yet there's something beautiful about it, the Very lights, the sky is lit up, everything is torn apart. It's like lightning, like a firework display, and all on a scale that's gigantic. They say that film is Like Being There. It's not Like Being There Dick. Nothing is."

Dick got up and laid his hand on Jack's shoulder. The boy had got to talk and he was prepared to listen.

"It's a funny thing, Dick, but out there we don't hate The Enemy. He's there facing us behind a stretch of ruined land and some barbed wire, and we know that they are in the same boat as us, poor devils sick to death of the cold and the wet and the killing. No, we don't hate them. We kill, or try to, so as not to be killed ourselves. But it's senseless slaughter." He paused before he went on. "I never met a German before I went to France, and the only ones I ever see now are prisoners or else dead, lying side by side with our own. I don't want to fight, I don't want to kill. I don't want to die. So what does that make me? A bloody coward I suppose. I know that if I refused to fight now, I'd be shot for a coward. And serve me right some would say."

Dick went back to his chair. "Let's hope this will be a war to end war, my boy, so that all the sacrifice and the slaughter of the innocents will not be in vain."

He could see that Jack's nerves were at breaking point, but that he would go back to the front with a sense of relief. To Jack it had seemed a kind of betrayal of Bert and all those others to be sleeping in a bed with sheets, to be safe when every minute men he had known were dying. Life at home seemed unreal and trivial. It was all food or else hatred of the Hun. That was all anybody seemed to think about.

Chapter Seventeen

"Us don't never see a bit of bacon hardly, and as for jam or marmalade..." Charlotte had not been outside the front door for months, let alone gone up the road to the shops, but she knew better than anybody the exact price of all the food Ethel managed to bring home. "Oh aint everything dear" was her refrain. "Poor folk can't hardly afford to eat a bit of bread even. Elevenpence halfpenny a loaf! It's wicked. I mind when it were fourpence halfpenny, and that aint so very long ago, only just afore this wicked wicked war." She would look to Jack for sympathy, but he would sit silent. Better her grumbles about long queues at the Maypole and food shortages than Thomas' repeated stories about Bloody Hun Atrocities, but he was finding their company hard to bear.

"Our Jack aint the same boy that he were," Charlotte mourned. "Like as if 'er hated to be wi' us. 'Er can't wait to get back there. Our Bert gone and Our Jack like as if er don't belong to us...wi' Dick Jenkins all the time...never mind about his poor old mother fretting..."

Jack was not indifferent to his mother's anxiety, and he shared her grief about Bert. But although he was saddened to see how frail she had become, he could not overcome his feeling of being alien to them all at home. It was no better when he spoke to Lily, for she seemed to have changed more than any of them. Lily, who had been so full of life and so carefree, had begun to withdraw into unhappiness and resentment. There was nothing to be light-hearted about as far as she could see, trapped in Hillside with a baby off walking and into everything, all that awful washing and drying of the clothes and the napkins all the time and Milly Wilkins watching her like a hawk, seeing every move and making it pretty plain she disapproved... It mightn't have been so bad if the baby hadn't been so ridiculously like Walter, not only in looks, but in her ways. Like Walter, she was full of fun.

"Such a happy, good little soul," Charlotte would say, and even Our Arthur who had an utter contempt for girls and a supreme indifference towards babies, had been heard to admit that she wasn't so bad, for a baby.

Everybody liked Ruth, everybody except her mother. Ethel would play with her and encourage her to sing as soon as ever she could talk. She would lift her on to the kitchen table, and standing by in case she fell, would summon Charlotte and Thomas and a reluctant Our Arthur to "just come and listen to this child singing", as she was to do when later on she had children of her own. But then, Ethel would always expect everybody to share her love of children and drop everything to attend to them.

Ruth had inherited Lily's musical talent, and with it, Walter's sense of showmanship. She would take the stage, demanding "Now, all of you, you must clap and clap and then I'll sing it again for you", running from the back kitchen to the middle kitchen to take her bow and sing her favourite "How d'you like to be a baby girl?" confident in the knowledge that "Down Gran's" she was petted.

At home she was unloved, and even before she could talk and walk properly she knew she wanted to be somewhere away from her mother. "Down Gran's" was the best, but there were other places of refuge too. There was Louisa only a few doors away, "Bopa Loulou" who could be relied upon for comfort, and nearer at hand still, there was Milly Wilkins. Ruth's "Opey door, bopa, opey door, bopa" would bring Milly in from the yard. "Come in cariad, come to your old bopa then. Tell bopa all about it then..."

It irritated Lily, but she knew that if she tried to keep Ruth to their own room, Ruth would scream and sob so piteously that Milly and the rest of the neighbours would be sure to think she was ill-treating the child. Even as it was, Milly lost no chance of gossiping about Lily's "goings-on", for Milly was "one of they dangerous women" with a tongue, according to Charlotte, "like a viper's".

"She do neglect that little child something shameful." Milly's sister Jinnie was her best and almost her only audience. "Hour after hour, gallivanting up the road, so-say queueing for food like the rest of us, it's not good enough... Leave the poor little dab down her mother's she do, all day and every day, little angel of light. Neglect it is, nothing but neglect. Her sister do knock spots off her, for all she do think herself *it*. That Ethel Shepherd, couldn't be better with that little Ruth. And that little un do love *her* too, mind. Ethel Shepherd, Byrom Street, you do know her Jinnie, always smart, never nothing out of place, mornings even. And the poor old lady down there so bad with pain they do say. No, she can thank her lucky stars for her family. A damn sight more than she do deserve if you ask me. Fine hole she'd be in without that family behind her. "Choir practice. Milly" indeed! I ask you Jinnie, tell me what choir practice you know of that do go on till ten o'clock at night? Eleven o'clock and gone sometimes. She must think people are blind and soft in the head, mun. Pity for the little girl though. Pity for him as well, so far away, serving his King and Country. Like our Idwal. I do know her type... Somebody ought to say something to him when he do come back. If he do come back..."

Milly had never taken to Lily, but even she might have felt a little sorry for her had she known what misery Lily was hiding. In years to come Lily confessed to her daughter that she was frightened at the way she was beginning to feel.

"I tried not to hope he wouldn't come back from the war. So many of them didn't... I didn't want him to get killed but I didn't want him back. I used to think if only it had been Walter instead of our Bert. Nobody would have been sorry then. And I'd have had a widow's pension. I might as well have been a widow for all he sent me..."

Walter had never come home on leave, not even once, and he had written not a single letter. He knew how to both read and write, but to compose a letter would have been beyond him. Before he got married, there had been no need for any writing; afterwards, if there was any business to be done, he would leave it to Lily - "theest can put words on paper, mun". When he was in France he sent her field service postcards with their formal pre-arranged printed sentences like "I am quite well", "I have/have not received your letter", chosen out of the list, with the inappropriate ones like "I am in hospital" crossed out. The signature alone was Walter's, and of course the crossings out.

Chapter Seventeen

It was very little compared with the letters Lily received from Jack, but the cards came often enough to remind her of Walter's existence, those and the threepence a day he had allocated to her out of his pay of one shilling and twopence a day, the shilling for being a soldier and the twopence for Brasso to polish his buttons. It added one shilling and ninepence to her income of Government money which, as a soldier's wife with a dependent, Lily collected every week from the Post Office, from the hands of Ma Morgan the Post or, if there was a crowd waiting, from Miss Edith herself. Funny, thought Lily, how Ma Morgan and Miss Edith never changed a bit. Even their clothes were the same she remembered them wearing when she had been their maid of all work so many years ago. Eight years ago, when she was young. It felt like a lifetime away.

Lily could not hide her feelings, and Jack marvelled how much marriage had changed Lily's nature. He could see that Walter would come back to an unwelcoming wife and a child who was already countering her mother's coldness by her own defiance. He was glad to turn to Dick Jenkins, for with Dick he was on safe and familiar ground, and so with Dick, as Charlotte had bitterly noticed, he spent most of his leave.

Dick had said to Annie May that he was afraid Jack would never recover from what he had been through in Flanders, but at least he had been able to divert Jack's thoughts, if only for the time being. He had tried, as bait, "Yes, bachgen, futile and wasteful this old war. And at home too, it's warfare. Class warfare, and a dirty fight."

Chapter Seventeen

Jack had taken the bait, even though his reply at first had been a mechanical "always has been, Dick, always been dirty, masters and men."

Dick had brought up the issue of strikes, particularly the strikes of 1915 and 1917. "All they've done for us is to bring condemnation for the miners for not supporting the nation at war."

To his relief, Jack had taken fire in almost the old way. "People outside the valleys don't realise how desperate the situation is before miners will strike. And they don't realise that when the miners see the coal owners making such profits and the armaments manufacturers making their millions then they're bound to see this war as a means of making money and not as a fight of Good against Evil. Though," he added, "it looks different again when you're in the front line."

He could see full well that Dick's attitude to strike action had not changed. Dick was still convinced of the power of talk and negotiation, was still a believer in the goodness of even coal owners. He felt himself slipping back easily into familiar attitudes.

"Dick, I know you're all for reasonable negotiation, talks round the table, the inescapable justice of the cause and all that. That's fine if you're dealing with reasonable men. But you're not. You're dealing with the coal owners and they are not reasonable men. They are bloody greedy men, greedy and callous. What the hell would we have gained without strikes? Bugger all. You can't deny it..."

Dick was shaking his head involuntarily but more in disapproval of Jack's language than of his sentiments. It was true that the latest strike had won from the coal owners an important concession. They had been forced to agree that membership of the union be compulsory for all miners.

"A bitter pill for them to swallow Dick, considering that they've been victimising men for years just for being union members. All these years they've been fighting tooth and nail to destroy the Fed because they know damn well that unless we band together we can do nothing. *Non*-unionism. That's been their policy, and very successful they've been up to now in imposing it. But now they've been forced into agreeing that every workman must join a union. Hundred percent membership Dick! They've been *forced* to make it policy. They wouldn't have come to it of their own sweet will, oh no."

"True enough, bach." Dick was rejoicing to see Jack looking and talking a bit more like the old Jack at last. "You're right of course. It was the Board of Trade that had to intervene in the end to get the owners to agree that men in the pits had to be members of a Trade Union. April 1916 that was. You had been away a year and more then, Jack. And then of course a few months later the Government took control, so it's all out of the coal owners' hands for the time being."

"For the time being, yes. But remember Dick that any agreement they made is "without prejudice to the position after the war". The Government's got control of the coalfield now, and as long as they are running the show, there'll be no more talk of non-unionism. But when this war is over, it'll be a different story. The coal owners'll come into their own again, so look out for fireworks."

"Well, we are riding the wave at the moment Jack. A hundred percent membership was an impossible dream when we founded the Fed so long ago. It was our hope and our aim of course! For twenty years we've had that same aim, that same hope..." He broke off. It was one thing to see men join in solidarity with their fellow workmen, but quite another to see them being compelled to join a union. He began again: "This idea, though, of compulsory membership. I can't go along with that. It can turn nasty when men refuse to go down the pit with any man who can't show a paid-up membership card, the yellow show-card, a "clean card" on his cap. Voluntary membership of the Fed, yes, but not this bigoted mess, this intolerance, this putting a white shirt on their back if they're not members, to mark them out, violence being offered them and all that, no,..."

Jack moved impatiently. Dick would be talking about the need to recognise the Brotherhood of Man and to treat all men as Ends and not as Means before you could say Jack Robinson.

"Look here Dick. Those who refuse to join a union are letting us all down. *Unity*, Dick, we got to have unity if we are to influence the owners at all. We got to stick together, and if that means outlawing those who won't join, then so be it." He warmed to his theme: "How else are we to get any lever against the owners? *They* know the advantages of unity. Nobody knows it better than they do. That's what the Combines are all about. That's why they've been joining together to form these Combines. They know the advantages of Being Big. Big Units, the mass instead of small individual pits. United they stand and divided we fall. That's the measure of it, Dick. What power do the small unions have? The colliers' unions, the surface men's unions, the hauliers' unions, general workers' unions? Answer me that. One union for all is the only way and yes, alright, if it must be, then compulsory membership. Why were the owners so keen for non-unionism? Why were they set on victimising committed union men and intimidating the others to stop such commitment? You know the answer as well as I do. A powerful Fed might force them to behave a bit less like slave owners. They won't do it of their own accord! Non-unionism is dead, Dick. It's gone by the board. It's a step forward, and you ought to be rejoicing."

"I'm uneasy about it Jack. Compulsory trade-unionism, whether of the Fed itself or of those other two big unions, no, I can't agree with it. Not to compel anybody I can't..."

Jack sighed. Would Dick ever lose his idealism, his belief that men left to themselves would see that the good of the individual was bound up with the good of all?

He tried again: "So you'd allow opting out. Fine. They opt out; they make our bargaining power weaker. So we all lose. Where's the sense in that? Alright. I know you're thinking that it's a case of forcing men to be free! But if you can bear to come down to reality Dick, do you see them refusing the benefits the Fed have got for us?

Chapter Seventeen

Show me the man who wants to opt out of union benefits and I'll grant you his right to opt out of union membership."

Dick smiled. Jack had made his point. When he came back after the war, if please God, he came back, the Fed would go from strength to strength. The industry needed men of Jack's intelligence and energy. With men like Jack, their aim of getting the pits out of private ownership would some time be achieved. It had to come. The time would come, when men worked in pits owned by the state. Petty victimisation, pittance wages, inhuman working conditions, all would be things of the past. Jack would be one of the key men when he came back. Time would heal his personal hurts; he would bend his energies into working for the betterment of his fellow men. He would have to become one of the bosses before he could do anything. They could talk big in Maerdy about the Russian Revolution and it being our turn next, but a revolution needs organisation, dedication to the cause, time, and energy to do it.

Workers may be disaffected, thought Dick, but the workers are not the revolutionaries. The middle classes are the ones to change things. The slaves will always be slaves. But they could be slaves in better conditions, and Jack would be one of the leaders in trying to bring about those conditions. Of course, he reasoned, Jack would be changed to some extent by what he had gone through, bound to be. He could see already that Jack had a different outlook. But the boy would have matured, be a loud voice in the Fed, be a spokesman...

Chapter Seventeen

Dick's faith in the will of a good Lord and in his fellow men never wavered, for it was a faith built on the Bible and on a belief in the power of love. "Pob peth yn cyd-weithio er daioni i'r rhai sydd yn caru Duw." St Paul's words he knew by heart, and they comforted him. "All things work together for good to them that love God."

But Jack had no faith in God, no consolation of religion. Men like Walter came back from the war eager to bring reality to their dreams of a better life. War had chastened them, had maimed them, but had left them with their hopes intact. Jack came back to take up a life which seemed to him to hold no hope of personal happiness. He was one of those, and there were many, who had escaped all outward injury, only to find their inner life destroyed. Dick was right in his belief that Jack would throw himself into the fight of the Union to take the pits out of private ownership. But he was mistaken in thinking that time would restore to Jack his belief in himself and his confidence in others. That was gone for ever, destroyed by the horror of the trenches.

PART FOUR

CHAPTER EIGHTEEN

PUBLIC PEACE PRIVATE WAR

1919

"What is our task? To make Britain a fit country
for heroes to live in."

Lloyd George, speech at Wolverhampton,

24 November 1918

Chapter Eighteen

Walter had given very little thought to his homecoming. It was enough for him that he had come through the war, the bloody war which had lasted four years and a hundred days and left twelve million dead. He had been one of the lucky ones, not like the twenty million who had been blinded, maimed, or shell-shocked. He had survived "without a scratch, mun", and he was coming home. To a land fit for heroes.

He knew things would be different of course. For one thing there would be no Bert, the best and only real pal he ever had. And there would be Lily his wife, and Ruth the baby he had never seen. Except that by the time Walter was demobbed in 1919 she wasn't a baby any longer but a little girl over three years old who clung to her mother and looked at him with hostile eyes. Walter never forgot how Ruth cried and struggled to push him away when he bent to lift her up, nor how she tried her best to shut the bedroom door against him, screaming for Lily to "send him away, send that man away". Lily tried to point out that it was only to be expected that Ruth would shrink from him at first, and that she felt threatened by him only because she didn't know him. She had begun a tentative "It's not *you*, Walter. It's, well, it's that she don't know you. You're a stranger to her."

Ruth was instinctively rejecting Walter, the stranger who had come into her world, not Walter, her father, but a stranger who did not belong in their room, who did not belong in the big bed she shared with her mother. He was a strange man she had never seen before, never seen Down Gran's or in Milly's back kitchen. But Walter had been thrown off balance by Ruth's rejection. He felt he had been let down. Of course she was still only a babby he supposed, but why couldn't she see he only wanted to love her?

"A stranger? Not my bloody fault if I be a stranger. Blame the bloody war for that, not I."

Lily tried again: "She'll come round in time Walter. Give her time to get to know you."

"Never will come round, kicking and screaming the place down. Damned if I stays to hear that lot all the bloody time."

Walter had meant to be gentle. He had no idea how to treat young children, but years of handling horses had taught him that the quieter you were with them, the better the animals would like you.

"You never shouts at your horse, mun," he would say. "Never, not even if 'e's in the wrong." Walter had learned to coax, and he had wanted to win Ruth over, but his feeling of disappointment had maddened him. In frustrated shame he heard himself cursing and raging, even though he knew that he was losing Lily's sympathy and rousing Ruth to an hysterical fury which matched his own. "A temper like a raving madman," thought Lily coolly, turning away from him.

Walter was exactly as she remembered him in the old days when he and Jack would start arguing. It would begin reasonably enough, but as soon as Walter felt himself defeated by the force of Jack's logic he would start to bluster and lose his temper. Bert would try to keep the peace by laughing him out of his frustration, Walter would storm out proclaiming his pride at not being "one of they buggers with the gift of the gab", and Lily would feel protective and wish that Jack could make allowances for Walter's slow thought and feeble words. "Er shows 'isself up." "A braggart." Always, before, Lily had hated Charlotte's unsympathetic verdict, but now that she was faced with the violence of his outburst, she could feel nothing but scorn for his lack of self control. She brushed aside any thought that his anger might be a plea for her compassion and understanding, and that he was asking for comfort rather than contempt.

Contempt for Walter came naturally to Lily. It was a useful emotion. Contempt served to swamp any guilt she might have felt about her failure to prepare Ruth for Walter's homecoming; contempt masked her sense of relief that Walter had not thought to accuse her of that failure. Lily had justified her silence by telling herself that Ruth was still only a baby, too young to understand anything about a father she had never seen, about a father she might never have to see. But she did wish that Ruth's first meeting with Walter could have been different.

Milly Wilkins was sure it could have been very different. She had been telling her sister how it would be: "I seen it all coming, Jinnie. Mind you, I didn't think there'd be all that rumpus, but I knew all along there'd be a fuss. I wasn't surprised. No, it didn't surprise me *one bit*. Oh no. Look at it this way, Jinnie my girl. She had *never*, well, not to my knowledge whatever, she had never to my knowledge showed that child his photograph even. No, never showed that kid a photograph nor nothing. She never said a *word* about him. Never mentioned his name that I know of, never a word about him coming back, nor nothing. A damn shame if you ask me, him coming home to *that* reception. The screaming and the crying and the kicking the door. You can't blame the child. And him shouting and swearing. Poor dab. Beside hisself. And whose fault was it, Jinnie? Jinnie, I ask you, whose fault was it?"

It was a rhetorical question. Jinnie had scarcely put in her murmured "aye, well..." before Milly was continuing, as if she had a jury to convince: "Look at it this way. It's not like as if she can't understand. The kid's not daft, mun. No, she do know every word you do say. And talk! Nineteen to the dozen and as sensible as you or me. Bright as a button. Damn shame. Lovely child like that. And not the only one was she? But other kids, see, Jinnie, they knew different. Other kids, only the same age as her but they knew they had fathers alright, they knew all about their fathers coming back and that. They remembered them at night in their little prayers isn't it? You know yourself, Jinnie, you can give a child some inkling whatever, young as they are. No, I can tell you, that child had no welcome put into her little mind, none whatsoever. Only natural she kicked up a fuss when she saw him in their room isn't it? Stands to reason, mun. What can you expect? It's the attitude it is, isn't it? I tell you this, Jinnie, it would break my heart if I thought our Idwal would come home to a welcome like that from any child of his. No, I feel sorry for that Walter. Poor dab. He do deserve something better than that, whatever."

Chapter Eighteen

Milly might feel pity for him, but it was not in Walter's nature to feel sorry for himself. "I never loses sleep over nothing," he would say, and this included not only other people's troubles but also his own. He had a gift for living almost entirely in the present, and for accepting whatever each day brought without seeking to probe into motives or attitudes or reactions. He was stoical, and a born optimist, so that he had little sympathy with "them buggers, and your Jack be one on 'em, always moaning and groaning over summat." He had not yet realised how alike were Jack and Lily in their agonised scrutiny of their inner life, nor would he ever understand their compulsive need for such scrutiny.

Walter had been with the Gloucesters in Flanders, one of the Runners taking messages to and from the Front Line, and he had survived enough brushes with death himself and seen enough of the slaughter of others to have harrowed his spirit. But Flanders had not maimed Walter. He had gained a reputation for being fearless which was well-earned, even if his lack of fear arose largely from his lack of imagination. Walter was the same in the trenches as he had been down the pit, reckless in word and deed, full of humour and generosity, tolerant of his fellows and liked by them in return. For Walter, as for Jack, war had been pitiful, cruel, obscene; but unlike Jack, Walter had been exhilarated by the daily challenge of danger and had revelled in the companionship of men who were rough-mannered and as good-hearted as he.

Walter had liked being amongst men, men of his own kind with whom he didn't have to mind his p's and q's.

Chapter Eighteen

He had enjoyed his reputation for being "a card", and had found the breed of sergeants and corporals more human and humane than any of the overmen and managers he had come across in the pit. He had been able to put at the back of his mind the scenes of horror he had witnessed, and to recall only the memory of comradeship and unacknowledged heroism of those with whom he had shared those scenes. Not that he ever spoke of them. In after years he was as silent as if he had never seen Flanders, never fought on the Western Front; in that, Walter was as reticent as Jack.

His daughters would have known nothing about his life before they were born if they had not asked him, and it was only the younger girl who heard any of it. His first-born, Ruth, never overcame her initial dislike of her father, and he in turn kept himself aloof from her. Lily saw it was better when they were kept apart, explaining to Charlotte that "they got the same nature, the both of them. The very same. They do flare up with each other in a minute. She got the same temper exactly. Not a bit afraid of him."

Ruth was not afraid of rousing Walter's temper but she associated him from the first with unhappiness. With Walter's coming, their lives had changed for the worse. She could see that Mam was miserable now that he had come to live with them, the man she had been told was her dad. He had come between Mam and her. Mam and him were nasty with each other. Mam sat at the table crying after he had gone out. They shouted at each other after she had gone to bed, the little bed on the other side of the room...   Down Gran's she heard half-understood conversations and saw more tears, while in Bopa Milly's she felt the hostility to her mother.

"For *you*, Walter," Milly would say, giving him a plate of her Welsh cakes. "Just off the bakestone they are. Only for *you* mind. Not for *her*."

It was a house of discord, and yet Walter had the temperament to be happy. He had never been given much in his life so far, and he expected so little that he was easily pleased. He knew himself to be "happy-go-lucky", and would have been contented if only Lily had shown him any sign of affection. He had been lucky in getting his old job as hostler in the stables underground in the Gelli Pit, and it was almost as if he had never been away except that he had had to overcome his objection to joining the union. Walter had always held out against paying his dues and becoming a member of the South Wales Miners' Federation. He had seen no good reason to join and "keep officials in clover", and besides he had an opposition to "them Federation buggers" based on his dislike of Jack, who was one of them.

But Walter had had to bow to the ruling that "the condition of employment of any workmen in or about the mines" was membership of the Miners' Federation. Like every other man, Walter had to show his paid-up membership card, his "clean card", on his cap every quarter when he reported for work. Men like Walter had never recognised that by refusing to join the union before the war they had been playing into the coal-owners' hands. The owners had done all they could to stop men joining the "Fed", a union which had as its declared objective "the total abolition of capital in the mining industry". It was hardly to be expected that the owners would look with favour on a movement dedicated to abolishing them as a class! Now, with a hundred per cent enforced membership, the Fed was at its strongest, and nowhere more obviously strong than in the Rhondda pits.

Walter had no opinion about the abolition of capital in the coalfield. He had never set eyes on a coal-owner; pit officials he did know, and these he despised. But it was a hatred based on their callous inhumanity more than on his political views. He had found the undermanager and fireman of his own pit to be "cruel devils", but they were the same in Bert's pit, the Bryn, the same in Jack's, the Garth. He had never forgotten the winter before the war when Jack's butty Dick Jenkins had stayed away from work with pneumonia. Bert had relayed to him Jack's condemnation of Roberts the undermanager who had snorted "*Ill* you say? That's a luxury I can never afford. I haven't got time to be ill."

As Jack had said, the managers were worthy of their masters. Walter found that nothing had changed in the Gelli as far as he could see. The job in the stables was the same, the pay as low as ever, but seeming to be much smaller than before. Prices had gone up, and now he had his family to keep. Not that Walter took any responsibility for managing the money. That was left to Lily, for Walter took pride in being carefree.

He would look at Lily's set face and demand to know "What bist worrying about now, mun?" and without waiting for an answer would add with a cheerful look which maddened her "Theest never sees I worrying about nothing, mun. Theest want to take a leaf out of my book, theest know."

Lily could have answered that she had everything to worry about. Just to have Walter back was unhappiness enough. He had returned when Lily had hardly reckoned on his coming back and when she had got used to being without him. Being without him had given Lily a freedom which Milly Wilkins had denounced as "too much damn freedom for any woman if you ask me, especially a married woman". Lily had been able to leave Ruth Down Gran's while she went to mid-week choir practice, and had left her with Ethel while she went to see Olive from Gelli Crossing or down to Tonypandy to visit Vi from Bowman's.

Vi came up to Hillside sometimes, boasting about her latest conquest and showing off her newest costume. She was proud of being "still single and fancy-free, with loads of gentlemen friends and plenty of the wherewithal". She was able to pick and choose her boyfriends and was having "ever such a good time" going down to the dances in the Judges Hall in Tonypandy every Saturday. Charlotte would have been scandalised to hear her. Lily couldn't help envying Vi her freedom, though she didn't think she would care to go Down the Judges with her. She envied her not being married to Walter, not having a child to look after. She envied her being able to please herself, to live almost as independent as if she were a man.

Vi had news of the Bowmans. She had seen them since Mr. Frederick had come home from where he had been interned on the Isle of Man and she had been saddened to see the change in them both: "Oh, they look so *old* Lily. This war have broke their hearts, like as if they lost their own sons. You'd hardly recognise them for the same people."

Lily thought that the war had changed nearly everybody she knew and that for the worse. Vi was an exception. Everybody else had suffered, but for Vi the war had been emancipating. Working in the munitions factory in Swansea had given Vi confidence, and a greater freedom than she had ever known. It had given her more money, and new friends. She was the only one Lily knew of these New Women people were talking and writing about. Lily could see Vi preening herself in the mirror of the over-mantel as she stood up just as unselfconsciously as she used to in the tiny looking-glass on the dressing-table when they shared a bedroom at Bowmans Dairy. But the reflection she was admiring was altogether more sophisticated and fashionable than in those days, the auburn hair brighter and redder, cut short and trained into a nestling kiss-curl on her pink cheek. She had lost all that horrible yellow colour, Lily noticed, and was looking more glowing and younger than when they had first met. Lily felt dowdy and old in comparison, but she was proud enough of her own long hair done up in two earphone plaits to ignore Vi's "Why don't you have your hair bobbed, Lily? Long hair went out years ago. Everybody's got short hair now."

Ethel always knew when Vi had been. "The stink o' that scent Lily! Like as if 'er emptied a whole bottle over 'er! Smell it a mile away."

Chapter Eighteen

Lily had never been allowed to forget the day Ethel had called in and seen Vi lighting up a cigarette. "A bad influence on you, Lily." And, suspiciously, "*You* ever been smoking? Always been a bad influence, that girl. You be as miserable as sin whenever you sees that girl. You mark my words, Lily, a thoroughly bad lot. And she ain't got nothing *you* want. That little maid there, she be all you wants. She be your pleasure, or ought to be."

Lily thought that our Eth was getting to sound more like Charlotte every day. A pity she couldn't mind her own business and let Lily have a life of her own. But no, she prided herself on having her say. As elder sister, it was her duty: "That there Louisa Pearce, worth ten of she, put together. And that Annie May Jenkins. Take up wi' the likes o' them, Lily, and you won't go far wrong."

"Not far wrong," thought Lily, "That's something, anyway." But all she said was: "Well, Eth, I do see one or other of them every day if that satisfies you."

Ethel had mounted her hobby horse. "Nothing but powder and paint with that Vi. And there be *nothing* to her, Lily, *nothing*. Nothing but outside show. All outside show, like a painted doll exactly."

Lily was barely listening. She had heard it all so many times before.

"That girl will rue the day she started smothering her face with all that muck. It do ruin their skin in no time, Lily. It ain't worth it. Skin like orange-peel under all them layers o' paint."

Chapter Eighteen

Lily began to lose patience: "Well, Eth, that's *her* look-out. Nothing to do with us. *She* do like it. And it do suit her."

Ethel had been tempted to add "And ten to one, no better than she ought to be", but a glance at Lily's face had decided her against it. Our Lily could flare up in a minute, over nothing at all, and it would be the little 'un who'd bear the brunt of her temper. But she couldn't resist the final fling of "wicked to spend all that money on clothes though, Lily. Must be costing her a fortune in blouses alone", before she turned to a safer topic. "Different from that Louisa Pearce, mind. Only one thing though. Pity she don't learn what colours do suit her. Them bottle greens, them dark browns, them don't suit her, that's a fact. Thems don't suit her complexion. Brighter, a lot brighter colours... Even a nice ecru or a beige now... Could be not a bad-featured woman... Brighter colours, and a bit o' curl put into that fringe and side pieces... How old you reckon she be, Lily?"

Lily was tired of Ethel's obsession with age and with everybody's appearance, and she only just resisted the temptation to add, or better still, to subtract, ten years to what she knew to be Louisa's age of thirty-three. Ethel was well pleased. "Thirty-three! Only two years older than I, Lily! I'd a given her a good ten year older. I'd a thought her years older than I. She do dress older. Too old by far for thirty-three! She do dress like an old woman, Lily - all them drab colours. Making herself old afore her time. A foolish thing to do Lily, and she a single woman, on the plain-featured side. But when all's said and done she must have a heart of gold, giving up her life to looking after they two motherless twin boys of her brother Alf's and keeping house for them all, always spotless by what you say, Lily. A good friend to have, she being Ruth's godmother and all."

Neither Charlotte nor Ethel ever gave Lily credit for having much sense or for making wise friendships, but for all their distrust, and for all Milly Wilkins' hinted suspicions, Lily's friends, like her pleasures, were innocent. They hardly seemed so to Walter. He resented Lily's going anywhere without him, and began to show a jealousy which, because it was unfounded, gave Lily spirit to fight. "I had plenty of spirit in those days, and I needed it too, with him" she would tell her sympathetic daughter in years to come.

"Why don't you come to choir practice with me then?" she would shout, only to get his answer, "Aye. I ought to. I ought to come and see thee making eyes at all they stuck-up buggers. Theest got work at home here to do, not gallivanting off till all hours." At first she would become hysterical with anger and scorn, not caring if the whole street heard them quarrelling, but as time went by Lily grew sick at heart, and so fearful of rousing Walter's suspicions that she was reluctant even to spend an afternoon with Louisa, knowing that Milly had hinted to Walter that there was "an attraction there in the shape of Louisa's brother Alf".

Lily was beginning to dread his coming home from work and to be glad of the times when he stayed out until after she had gone to bed, even though she knew he was spending money on drink, money he said he had won on the horses, his own money. He was so much rougher in his speech than she had remembered; he was suspicious; he was domineering. She had to admit that he had not changed in his feeling for her, and he was as good-looking as ever, so that in his own way he was both attractive and loving. But it was not a way she would ever appreciate. He was not the kind of man she could ever care for. He would always disappoint her, could never be what she wanted him to be. And yet, when in the bitterness of seeing that he was failing to please her he would fling the accusation "Theest never wanted I back. Theest wanted I to go West like poor Bert!" she would shake her head and cry out "Oh don't say such things, *don't*", in an agony of pity that she should have made him so unhappy.

But he was blind to the full measure of her distaste for him, certain as he was of his own love for her. He would blame their quarrels and her frantic outbursts of irritation on Ruth, "spoilt by them buggers down your mother's", or on short pay, or on living cramped up in two rooms of somebody else's house or, because he was afraid of losing her, he would accuse her of having "somebody else on a string". Lily could have made Walter happy if she had been happy herself. But Lily was wretched. She had made a mistake in marrying him and the knowledge made her feel desperate.

It was not that she disliked men or found their company disagreeable. Jack, Dick Jenkins, Louisa's brother Alf, even Our Arthur and Ethel's weakling husband Will Shepherd, there was something she could like and respect about most of the men she knew. And it was plain to her that there were plenty who were attracted by her. She had liked Walter himself before they were married. He was cheerful and good-natured and he had made her laugh. His hot temper and his slow understanding had been of no importance. She had been glad to have Walter as a friend. But not as a husband.

Lily sometimes wondered whether there was any man in the world for whom she would have happily given up her freedom, and as for having children, she had never craved children. Nothing attracted Lily to babies or to children. It was Ethel who had been the one to take charge of neighbours' babies, never noticing however smelly they were. It was Ethel who was pining for a child, and whose life was to be fulfilled by her own longed-for family.

Ethel petted little Ruth, and thought more of her than ever her mother did. She was maternal, and Lily was not. To Lily, Ruth represented loss of youth, of dreams, of aspirations, of self-fulfilment. It was because of Ruth that she had married Walter and tied herself to him for the rest of her life. Resentment was making Lily sharp-tongued and moody, and Charlotte showed little sympathy in her reproof:

"Lily, make the best on it. You be in no worse state, my girl, than many another woman. You be better off than I were at your age. You got just the one babby, and her a dear little maid as ever was. I were only nineteen, same age as you, when I got married. But I had three babbies in seven years. And then there was you to

Chapter Eighteen

come, and Our Arthur, poor little feller. No Lily, you be better off than many a crittur, and you must count your blessings and be thankful for what you got."

Lily had little sense of being blessed in her lot, but there *was* one thing she was thankful for. In years to come she spoke of Walter as having been "a very considerate husband" and her daughter recognised the description for the euphemism Lily had meant. She had not had to bear a houseful of unwanted babies. Both Lily's daughters had been conceived out of pity. But she could not forgive herself her folly in marrying Walter, and she made no secret of her bitterness to either of her daughters. They took their mother's part unthinkingly, and in ranging themselves so firmly on her side they never realised the isolation and frustration which Walter suffered throughout his married life. Lily was his unwilling partner who despised him because he was loud-mouthed and boastful, hot-tempered and unreasonable. He was uncouth, he was uncivilised, and he offended Lily every time he opened his mouth. "If only he was more gentle" she would say. Even at the end of her life, bed-ridden and relying on Walter to nurse her, she would complain with tears of weakness in her eyes, "Oh, if only he wasn't so rough."

All his care, all his goodness counted as nothing in her eyes because he had no words of sympathy and love to match his deeds. Walter distrusted words. He was fond of quoting "actions speak louder than words, mun", and actions for Walter took the place of words, whether they were spoken or, more alarmingly, written. He was suspicious of the letters Lily wrote and received, even though he knew they were always addressed to women.

"Who bist thee writing to now, mun?" he would ask, adding "Thee bist writing all the damn time, summat or other, allus wi' a pen in thee hand."

Lily felt stifled, but sometimes she would fight back: "You don't want me to go out to meet anybody. Now you don't want me to write to anybody. It's only my Aunt Iris in Bristol, and my cousin Mary. See anything wrong in that?"

Walter never wrote a letter in his life and felt impatient with Lily's urge to communicate in writing. He never understood, either, her craving for the nourishment of speech, and especially for the food of praise, praise for herself as a person, the praise she was denied in her family. Sometimes she would be like a child eager for approval, asking Walter if he had liked the meal she had cooked for him. He would look up surprised from his empty plate: "Like it? Course I liked it mun. I ate it didn't I? Wouldn't have etten it if I hadn't enjoyed it." Then seeing her downcast face he would mutter appeasingly: "Lovely, mun, aye, lovely." Or else impatiently, "What dost want I to say? What bist fishing for now, mun? Thee bist allus fishing for summat or other."

He could not tell what it was she wanted him to say, and even if he had known, he had no words to express what he felt. Walter could not reveal in words the sensitive side of his nature. He never spoke of his delight in the beauty of nature. Instead he would bring home the potted aspidistras and ferns which Lily cared nothing for, and later on when they had a garden, he would grow roses and borders of herbaceous plants rather than the vegetables which Lily would have used to feed the family.

He squandered his money. That was Lily's opinion of everything he bought. It was extravagance to buy the gramophone, "His Master's Voice", with the horn and all the records, the cylinders which he kept in their boxes but which he played over and over again. Sheer extravagance to buy the comedy turns whose patter he learned off by heart, the sentimental songs like *Home Sweet Home*, the sets of operatic arias from *Tosca* and *Aida*, sung by Gigli or as Walter called him, "Giggly". Lily was surprised that Walter should enjoy "opera"; she herself would always prefer "piano music", much as she liked singing herself.

She would never have bought the gramophone, and left to herself would never have had an animal in the house, much less the dog and cat which Walter brought home as soon as they moved from Milly Wilkins' into a rented house with a garden. "More expense" thought Lily "and he thinks more of them creatures than he do of his own children."

But in this Lily was mistaken. Walter felt deeply for his wife and wanted to be a good father to his children. His loyalty to Lily was complete. Never, to anybody inside or outside the family, did Walter speak of discontent with Lily or voice regret at having married her. If it did occur to him that he too would have been happier if he and Lily had never married, the thought remained hidden. From Walter his daughters heard no word of criticism of their mother. Whereas Lily told them more than they should have known about her emotional life, from Walter there was silence, a silence which they misconstrued as unfeeling. Walter felt their indifference to him, and was inwardly grieved by it. He had had little experience of family life, for his own mother had died when he had been too young to remember her, and his father was mostly away at sea. He had left his aunt's house when he was twelve and had not been in a proper family again until he came to lodge with the Callows.

Between Charlotte and Thomas even the least sensitive observer could have detected a state of suspended hostility, and Walter had judged, if he thought about it at all, that that was probably the usual thing between a man and his wife. Between him and Lily it seemed to be much the same though he couldn't help thinking that it would do something for a feller to see his missus glad to see him, and her eyes light up when he came into the room. But you couldn't have everything, and Lily put all the others in the shade for looks, and for cooking and cleaning too. All the same, Walter was never anxious to be home before Ruth was put to bed, and he had taken to stopping for a drink or two on his way home on payday, and to getting out of the house and down the pub whenever he could of an evening.

Charlotte could see her own unhappy pattern repeating itself, and she sorrowed for it, although she showed Lily little outward sympathy. Instead she made much of Ruth, so that "the little maid" could play the tyrant not only with her Gran and Grancher but with her Auntie Ethel and even at times with her Uncle Arthur.

Chapter Eighteen

But not with her Uncle Jack. He was not like Uncle Arthur, who would lift her on to his shoulder so that she could touch the ceiling, and then pretend, heart-stoppingly, to drop her. And he was not like Grancher who would sometimes sing and dance about the kitchen, holding his arms above his head and looking funny as he tried to kick his legs up. Usually Grancher was sitting, in fine weather on the front door step calling out to the people in the street, and in winter huddled over the fire, and then she would climb on his knee and listen while he told her stories about "Uppome", always "Uppome", never "Bristol".

It was fun to be Down Gran's except when Uncle Jack came home. It was not that he shouted and got angry like Dad did, but he looked so unsmiling and as if he didn't want to bother with any of them that she would run to Gran and sit on the edge of her bed. Ruth loved Gran and Auntie Ethel, Grancher and Uncle Arthur, and Uncle Will; she loved Mam of course; she even loved Dad when he was jokey and brought home surprise presents for her and Mam. But she didn't know what to think about Uncle Jack. He wasn't like anybody else. He never took much notice of her, hardly ever spoke to her. It was like as if he didn't notice she was there.

CHAPTER NINETEEN

A GAME OF BLUFF?

1919

"The relationship between the masters and workers of the coalfields of the United Kingdom is unfortunately of such a character that it seems impossible to better it under the present system of ownership."

Royal Commission on Coal 1919

Chapter Nineteen

Charlotte had been the first to remark on the change in him: "Our Jack be acting like as if 'er was living among strangers, not wi' 'er own kith and kin, he be that quiet."

But Jack was only one of Charlotte's anxieties. The war had brought heartache, but the peace had brought its own worries. As she lay on the bed in the middle kitchen, where now all her days and nights were spent, Charlotte's thoughts were unquiet.

"Family, allus family, family afore all, but other folk too... Lizzie Totterdale, never the same after they two lads was taken. Like Bert. Like Our Bert... Like that Captain Harry up at the Big House killed early on in the war, and now Miss Beatrice, allus been sickly according to our Lily, dead of that Spanish Flu. So many folk down wi' it...like Maud Denmer, one of the first to fall...people dropping in the street... Vanw-next-door so bad, Fairyfeet looking like a ghost hisself, saying about soaking the sheets in cold water and Vanw her temperature that high that they were dry again in no time and Vanw delirious...please God our little Ruth be spared...

"Our Arthur poor little feller...three years' apprentice cabinet maker, a good trade in his hands if only er'll stick at it. Wanting to gi' it all up and go down the pit...no I said. Over my dead body I told 'un. Theest want to look at thee father I told 'un. Lucky to be here at sixty three but no breath in 'is body some days...no, never down any pit, I begged on 'un...

Our Lily a good worker...but a cat and dog life with him...and he looking to be going the same way as

Chapter Nineteen

Thomas... A thousand pities our Lily ever took up wi' him. She be neglecting that dear little soul right enough. If only our Eth had the care on it...our Eth, like a pin in paper and never a hair out o' place, but o my Lord as miserable as sin. No babby, like as if a judgement on 'er. 'Er'd be a good mother and she weren't the first to make away wi' summat unwanted... 'Er would 'a made up for it...would 'a been a good mother, not like our Lily, fly-be-night. Our Jack back wi' us safe and sound, but not like hisself, not the same, no, never the same wi'out Bert, our Bert. Jack saw it all. Shot through the heart. Thank God 'er didn't suffer. Died instantly, shot through the heart. Thomas took it as bad as any on us, took it as bad, nearly, as our Jack. Allus together when they was little, like Jack's shadow he was. Bert, our Bert, buried somewhere out there, we none on us knows where. No chance to close his eyes and kiss his forehead. Oh my boy, my boy, we never said goodbye to 'ee."

And at that thought Charlotte would reach in her apron pocket for her handkerchief and let the tears fall.

So many others had borne the same loss. Ewart and Elsie Denmer had seen their daughter widowed. Ewart had written in the summer of 1916 to tell Charlotte that Julie's husband was missing, believed drowned, after the Battle of Jutland. Familiarity had not yet dulled Charlotte's grief over Bert, and she realised that shared sorrow had brought her closer in spirit to the Denmers than she had ever been, closer to Ewart than she had ever felt when all three of them, Ewart and Charlotte and her brother Richard, had been growing up together as children in Wells.

All through the years when Ewart had been prospering and his haulage business expanding, his letters had been filled with pride in his own achievements, leaving Elsie to give news of Maud and of Julie, of their accomplishments ("a piano! Dancing lessons!") and finally of their well-to-do husbands ("Such good choices, both girls so very fortunate..."). "Not like our poor Lily," Charlotte would think as she read the letters aloud to Thomas.

"Nothing but braggarts," Thomas would mutter. "Allus have been, allus blowing their own trumpets. I wouldn't gie them the time o' day." But that had been in the old days, when Ewart still dreamed of the grandson who would one day reap the benefit of his hard work and make the name of Denmer famous throughout Somerset, not just as the name of a big haulage firm with scarlet and cream vans based in Bristol but as Lord Mayor of Bristol founding "The Denmer Hall"!

The war was over, and Ewart's hopes had faded. Elsie wrote in bitter sadness for the loss of their first-born, and Charlotte sensed an envy in her letters, an envy of Lily, whose husband had come back safe, and of Charlotte herself who had a grandchild. The Denmers had only money and the widowed Julie sharing their heartache.

"But they don't know the half on it" thought Charlotte. "Childer be a blessing, but only to them that wants 'em. To them that don't crave 'em they be like a millstone round their necks. Like with our Lily and that dear little soul. No sense in brooding. What's done's done. No childer wi' Julie but she be only our Lily's age. Time enough for she, time enough for another man, time enough for an 'ouseful of childer..."

Charlotte's thoughts turned, as they so often did, to her dead brother Richard and his widow Iris. "Richard dead this ten year and more, Iris thank God with her Mary for comfort. She be close to our Lily, allus writing to each other. They be close, for all they baint seed one another this many years. Richard's name'll die. No more Milsoms, no boy to carry on the name. They had no boy, no boy to lose, no boy to grieve over. Funny to think how hard we prays when we be in labour. 'Dear Lord' we prays, 'let the babby be a boy, not for him to go through all this pain.' And that's why you welcomes it more when it turns out it's a boy, a different sort of crittur than you, and one that'll be spared that pain. But to lose your boy when he be a man, that be worse pain. To lose your son do hurt worse. Bodily pain be bad. Lord knows how sharp that bodily pain can be, pain in me insides that stabbing, some days there be hardly any standing it. But then there's other times, when there's ease from it all, days when you hardly feels it. Not like the ache you feels in your heart, the yearning to see your boy again. There's no ease from that pain in your heart."

Charlotte had become housebound, and with her increasing frailty and almost constant physical discomfort she was retreating into a world within herself. She would rouse herself when Thomas came in, but only to voice her anxieties about Jack and the added fear of the Workhouse:

"Jack be the only breadwinner now that our Bert be taken...us'll be paupers when Jack leaves us...nothing for it but the workhouse...us'll have to go on the parish...whatever's to become on us Thomas?"

Thomas was well used to hearing Charlotte worry about Our Arthur and about Jack. His soothing replies had become as automatic as they were futile. But this fear of having to end her days as a pauper in the workhouse had only newly come to the surface, and seemed to be gaining a hold on her imagination. The workhouse, where husbands and wives were lodged in separate quarters, where the old, the ill, and the destitute were herded together, where the sanitation was primitive and food unsavoury, no wonder that the very name of workhouse had a ring of dread about it.

Thomas knew that Charlotte would never survive a move to such a place. "It 'ud be the end on 'er" he thought. "In double quick time it ud be the end on 'er. In pain so much o' the time...er lives on Bengers Food, there'd be no Bengers in them places...she wi' that pain..." He tried to reassure her that it would never happen. "The Lloyd George," he said. "Us'll manage on the Lloyd George. It'll pay the rent and keep us out o' the workhouse."

The Lloyd George, the national pension which after ten years of campaign and debate had finally reached the statute book in 1909 under Lloyd George as Chancellor of the Exchequer. To Lloyd George had gone the glory of giving every seventy year old in the land the sum of five shillings a week as of right, with seven shillings and sixpence for a married couple. Thomas put from his mind the knowledge that he would have to wait seven more years before he could draw his pension, and tried not to think how hard it would be to find clothes and food as well as rent out of that seven and six a week. "We'll manage," he repeated. "Theest be fretting about nothing."

Charlotte's fears of the workhouse were real, but vague; her anxiety about Jack was well defined: "Summat be preying on that boy's mind. 'Er don't stir outside the door except for 'is work and yet er don't seem to want to bother wi' any of us, only with that Dick Jenkins."

Thomas had never observed Jack's comings and goings with Charlotte's eagle eye, but he had noticed that Jack seemed less likely to pick a quarrel over nothing. Some spark had gone out of the boy, that was for sure. But they was all missing Bert in the house. There was a dullness about them all. Jack was the one who took everything to heart.

Jack had come home feeling contaminated in soul and isolated in spirit. He shrank from contact with a world of people who had not witnessed the horrors he had seen and who could not know what he had been through; he had found in the family a place to hide. If Bert had come through it would have been different. Bert with his boisterous laughter and sturdy unimaginative common sense could have swept away Jack's morbid thoughts and been a bulwark against outsiders. Bert had been there with him; Bert had been through it all with him; Bert would have been his salvation. But he and Bert would never meet again this side of the grave, a thought which brought the sharp pang of loss whenever it came into his mind.

Although as the weeks and months passed, the thought had come to him less and less often. Bert's death was a wound which was healing only slowly.

Jack now described to Dick Jenkins, and only to Dick, the horror of Bert's death. With Charlotte and Thomas he kept up the fiction that Bert had died instantly, shot by a single sniper's bullet, a clean and painless death.

With Dick there was no need of concealment, and in his company Jack could hope to regain some of his old spirits. It was Dick who was despondent at the beginning of the year when the Miners Federation had voted to strike for what seemed impossible demands.

"The moon we are asking for. As good as the moon, whatever. Thirty per cent more money, two hours off our working day and, wait for it, nationalisation!"

Dick had never believed in strike action and he was relieved when the Government, to avert the strike, set up a Royal Commission to look into working conditions in the mines.

Jack was scornful: "A delaying tactic, Dick that's all it is. It's like when you think a dog is going to turn nasty. You throw him a bone to keep him quiet. The Royal Commission is our bone. The Government can see us baring our teeth. We got one hundred percent compulsory union membership now, and we got the backing of the Transport men and the Railwaymen. We could win a strike."

Dick smiled. "The Triple Alliance. A lovely thing and we were the prime movers in setting it up, before the war of course. Yes, they are behind us but I put my faith in the Commission, whatever."

His faith was justified when the Interim Report was published on 20th March. Under the chairmanship of Sir John Sankey, the Commission proved sympathetic to the miners. It recommended an increase of two shillings per shift, and a seven hour instead of the eight hour working day "subject to the economic position of the industry at the end of 1920." It also accepted the principle of state ownership: "The present system of ownership and working in the coal industry stands condemned, and some other system must be substituted for it...we are prepared to report now that it is in the interests of the country that the colliery workers shall in the future have an effective voice in the direction of the mines."

"So far so good, Jack. And you know that Lloyd George has expressed the intention of His Majesty's Government to carry out 'in the spirit and in the letter the recommendations of Sir John Sankey's Report.' Peaceful means. Jack..."

Jack was still distrustful. "The intention is one thing; carrying it out quite another. It's peace only because we were ready for war. And the battle isn't over yet. What about the question of local wage settlements?"

"Let's hope we are strong enough to get national settlements, holding across the whole country," said Dick.

"Yes," said Jack. "No more individual Lodges bargaining separately, not only for wages but for our allowances of coal and blocks. There's some very weak districts – the Garth for one – and no hope of getting support from any stranger. Just your bad luck if your pit pays poor rates. You could be getting a sight less than somebody else in a better pit, and you'll be working the same kind of seam exactly."

The Interim Report had elated Dick, and had raised even Jack's hopes. But when the Final Report of the Sankey Commission came out on the 23rd June with its proposals for nationalisation of the mines, the Government rejected them all as being impracticable. The cause of ownership by the State had been lost for the foreseeable future, while the question of a national wage rate was still unresolved.

"The whole thing was a game of bluff by the Government," said Jack bitterly. "They never thought that Sankey would side with us, mind. They made a bloomer there alright. But they never intended to desert their friends the coal owners."

"Well, we didn't gain all we were asking for," Dick agreed. "But that's not to say we gained nothing. We did. We gained a moral victory over the coal owners. And as well, Sankey gave us more money every shift and a seven-hour day instead of eight. I call all that gain, whatever."

It was a gain which was short-lived.

CHAPTER TWENTY

MANAGERS AND MEN

1921

"I never had any illusion that we'd get anything out of the owners because of kindness of heart - I knew that we'd get what we were strong enough to take."

Arthur Horner (President, South Wales Miners' Federation 1936-46)

Chapter Twenty

There was nobody who looked cheerful these days, not even Dick Jenkins, who could usually see some good in everything, even though he had to admit that you sometimes had to hunt pretty hard to find it. Jack thought he had never heard people sound more down-hearted, not even during the grim weeks of the Cambrian Strike, not even in the dark days of the war. 1921 was proving to be disastrous for the miners, marking the beginning of the long decline of the coal industry and foreshadowing the years of the Great Depression.

"We're finished now, Dick. We've gone right downhill this last couple of years, steadily downhill ever since 1919..."

He fell silent, thinking of what had happened since he beginning of the year. In March 1921 the Government had suddenly announced that as from the end of the month the coal fields, which they had controlled since 1916, were to be taken over again by the owners. Parliament was still debating the Decontrol Bill when the owners announced sweeping wage reductions and posted Lock-Out notices at all the pits. The lock-out began on the first of April, and on the eighth the leaders of the Triple Alliance called for a protest strike involving all the members of the three unions. It was the first real test of the Triple Alliance, for in the confrontation in 1919, there had been no trial.

As Jack had put it, "In 1919 the Royal Commission had drawn the teeth of the Triple Alliance." It was only in 1921 that its strength was tried. And in that test it failed. The miners struck against the lock-out and for three months they stayed out without the support of either the Railwaymen or the Transport workers.

"'Work for less pay or you don't work at all!' That was it, Jack, in a nutshell. How could we agree to a cut in our wages, when prices were going sky-high...?"

Jack nodded. He was thinking that like every other man he knew he never did any of the shopping for food, but all the same he knew very well how high prices had risen. You couldn't live in a house where Charlotte managed the money without knowing how much had to be spent on feeding a family.

Charlotte could calculate to the half-penny the cost of the week's groceries from the Maypole in Pentre. A loaf of bread had risen to nearly three times its price since 1914, and she could and often did, quote all the new prices in between. The biggest jump had been in the first year of the war ("Eight pence farthing! Somebody be making summat out of this war") and the price had risen steadily to elevenpence farthing. That had been in June 1917, but in the October the price had come down to ninepence owing to Government subsidy. ("About time too. Baint much else for poor folk to eat.") But by 1920 a loaf was costing a shilling, and with other prices rising almost as fast, families like Vanw-next-door were living on potatoes instead of the meat, the eggs and the milk which would have put back the colour into Vanw's face. She had "never picked up after the Spanish flu'" and had never lost "that peaky look".

"But all on 'em peaky in that house" said Charlotte. "Too many mouths to feed."

Chapter Twenty

But such families were invisible to the coal-owners, comfortably far-off in their houses in Brecon and in Cardiff. Jack was convinced that they would have stared in the faces of the locked out miners and still cut the wages and still imposed the lock-out, for the demands of Profit were the first consideration.

"We don't exist as human beings, only as bodies to be used like machines," he thought. Aloud he said "Of course we had to take a stand. But a fat lot of good it did us to strike. We had to go back on their terms in the end. We couldn't expect to do anything else once the railwaymen and the transport men left us in the lurch. If they had kept faith with us, it would have been a different story. Maybe." Jack's tone was resigned.

Dick could only agree. "Yes, bach" he said. "We had high hopes of the alliance at first - a pit strike, a railway strike, a transport strike."

"It was enough to scare the Government," said Jack, "and panic them into declaring a State of Emergency, call the reservists to the colours and all that, post machine guns at pit heads, troops in battle order, all set up for an all-out fight, the Triple Alliance challenging the Government. They needn't have worried though. The transport men called off their strike the day before it was due to begin, and then after a couple of weeks the railwaymen pulled out as well. And that did it. Triple Alliance? No, more like a Cripple Alliance"

"Mind you, Jack, I do believe the bulk of the railwaymen were behind us. I think their leader, that

Chapter Twenty

Jimmy Thomas, betrayed his own men as well as us when he called off their strike..."

Jack could not share Dick's idealism. "Dick Jenkins! I despair of you sometimes! The railwaymen didn't care a damn about us. Think they lost any sleep about deserting us? It wasn't their fight and they didn't see much reason to support us at their expense. Stupid and short-sighted, that's what they were. They didn't have the sense to see that our only hope, and *their* only hope, lay in solidarity. Jimmy Thomas sold us down the river the day he called off the railwaymen's strike, yes. But he did more than that. He destroyed any hope we had that workers could win anything. If we had stood united, we could have won something. Divided, we failed."

"Yes, indeed. A black day for us, that day, and a black day for unionism. Black Friday, 15th of April 1921."

Jack smiled grimly. Trust Dick Jenkins to give the day its rightful place in the calendar!

"If only we had that spirit of unity" said Dick. "But instead of that, everything is falling apart. That breakaway union of the enginemen and other craftsmen isn't strong enough on its own. All it does is to take power away from the Fed. The Fed's losing ground, Jack. Men are having second thoughts about paying their dues. You can't blame them. They can see that none of it seems to make a haporth of difference whether they're members of the union or not. We still lose out. The owners win in the end. They won this time, they've always won. We've gone back to work on their terms. Lower pay, same hours. We tried for better working conditions, a national wage rate and

State ownership, and we failed. We had to back down. Three months is a long time to live on parish relief. It would have been like the Cambrian Strike all over again if we'd stayed out any longer..."

The same thoughts were in both their minds. Soup kitchens set up in chapel vestries to give everybody one hot meal a day, boot-repairing centres in the Workmans' Hall, men and women going digging for ribblings on the tips, scraping a living selling them for sixpence a bag...

"Even as it is, families are in want, Jack, and deep in debt for food and clothes."

"No wonder so many are going Communist, Dick, thinking we'd do better to join up with the Red International. Our own union can't seem to do much for us anyway."

Jack had too much respect for Dick's commitment to Christianity to dwell on the support in the Rhondda for the newly-formed Communist Party of Great Britain, and he knew how strongly Dick had opposed the Conference resolution in July which had urged the Miners' Federation of Great Britain to affiliate with the Red International of Labour Unions. Revolutionary trade unionism would never win Dick's vote. His faith was in a loving God and in a Divine Plan, but even Dick wondered sometimes what the Good Lord was up to when, contrary to what was promised in the Bible, you watched the righteous begging their bread, and when every day you noticed the thin legs of ten year olds who looked like six year olds and saw the gaunt faces and hunched shoulders of their parents. You were bound to say "How long, O Lord?" He sighed.

It's always the same" said Jack. "Heads they win, tails we lose. There was a time when you could almost guarantee a pound a shift, on the good days. And now we're all of us hard put to it to make ten shillings..."

"But at least we got jobs" said Dick. "Not like the poor dabs you see any day of the week in Cardiff, holding out their trays of matches, their cheap toys, their strings of balloons. They're all ex-servicemen wearing their khaki greatcoats with their medals pinned to them, trying to sell something to the people hurrying past, looking the other way so as not to see the misery in their faces. A million without jobs now by all accounts. A bitter thing, men begging for the wherewithal to live, trying to sell brushes door to door, or standing outside the queues for the theatres and picture palaces in all the big towns and singing *Roses of Picardy* or playing *Tipperary* on tin whistles..."

"It would be laughable, grown men playing with toys, if it wasn't so bloody tragic, said Jack. "And that's just the tip of the iceberg Dick. Like the appeals for work in the Personal Columns of the newspapers, the local ones and the national ones. They're still carrying columns of advertisements like they were in 1919, a lot of them from ex-officers "seeking position, any capacity", that's how they usually put it. Officers and men, all in the same boat competing for jobs that aren't there."

He caught up last week's *Rhondda Gazette* that Our Arthur had left lying on the couch in the back-kitchen and began looking down the inner pages. "Here's one that's been in before. Somebody called Lewis from Pontypridd 'ex-serviceman (26) wants employment, anything...unfortunately deaf'. And there's a Cox from Treherbert...Oh and this one I recognise again. 'Discharged soldier wants work. Handyman as Sheeter, Boiler, Sealer or Fitter's Helper. Colliery preferred Rhondda Valley.' That's from some chap in Coed-Ely in the Vale. And here's one from somebody you must know Dick, a Tawe Thomas from Treherbert, describing himself as 'Demobilised', advertising for 'pupils in the organ or piano, singing and theory, open to receive engagements as adjudicator accompanist, conductor'..."

"Tawe Thomas?" said Dick. "Organist at Bethania Congregational? Of course I know Tawe Thomas, know him well. A fine musician, an eisteddfodwr, a local winner many times. Sadly come of it now though, like so many."

"Yes," said Jack. "Everywhere you look, it's the same. Up in England with the cotton mills closing, the shipbuilders out of work...And it looks as if we're going the same way, fast. Pits are closing already, more being threatened. Only last week they were talking about the Ferndale Collieries, output being so low that unless there's an improvement the pits'll have to stop."

"The slump has come with us already." said Dick. "They are not buying our coal, people abroad aren't..."

"Can't blame them for that," said Jack, "not when our coal is the price it is. We can't compete with the Germans and the Poles. They got modern machinery, not pick and shovel like us. You don't catch the owners putting money into our pits! They're too damn used to taking money out. No, our coal is priced too dear, and in any case they don't want our coal. The Germans are supplying the French."

"That's true" said Dick. "They got to anyway, to make up for the coalfields they destroyed in the war. Years they'll be, making Reparations..."

"Not only that," said Jack, "but here at home, ever since the Navy went over to oil and stopped using our steam coal, that was our best customer gone, and it's played havoc with us."

"There's the Navy, yes," said Dick, "and that hydro-electric business, that's another thing taking the place of coal. So there's no need to bring it up out of the ground. Jobs gone and nothing to take their place. The Bryn and the Garth on short time, but like Roberts the undermanager keeps bawling at us, we are lucky to be in a job. Funny thing," he added with a twinkle in his eye, "funny thing, but I never met a manager, no, nor an undermanager either, that I felt I could take to. Their families might love them, could be, but in the pit, oh, you can't trust them."

"You can trust them to be bullies," said Jack, "vindictive bullies. Like Evans the manager last week with poor old Mouthy Matthews."

Harry Matthews, 'Mouthy' because he never kept quiet, had had the foolhardiness to contradict Evans the manager publicly, at one of the men's Friday Night Bible Classes in the vestry of Jerusalem Chapel. On the following Monday morning Evans had come down the pit to see Mouthy, asking him if he felt as clever that morning as he had on Friday evening, and if so, could he explain why his timber props were set out of distance. Evans measured the distance with his tape and found the props to be a couple of inches too wide apart. "Perhaps you're clever enough to tell me why I shouldn't fine you ten shillings for breach of regulations?" That was his revenge.

"Poor old Mouthy" said Jack. "Had to pay up of course, dare not do otherwise. And there's never any question of an appeal against it. You don't contradict the bosses. That's one of the first rules you learn isn't it? And it applies equally well above ground as in the pit. I'm damn glad I don't belong to any chapel with a Bible Class, or Band of Hope, or Christian Endeavour, or Prayer meeting, because I might forget myself and treat a pit official as an equal."

Managers and undermanagers used fines and threats of dismissal to keep the men in their place. Their wives asserted their superiority over other women by equally effective means, even though they were only small acts of unkindness performed as it were accidentally.

Jack was remembering how Lily had told Charlotte of the time she found herself sitting next to Mrs Josh Griffiths the undermanager's wife at the weekly Sewing Guild in the Church Hall of St. David's, and how Mrs. Griffiths had let her scissors fall to the floor for Lily to pick up, not once but four or five times during the afternoon. Lily had retrieved the scissors each time, feeling more and more humiliated as Mrs Josh received them in silence. Lily never went back to the Guild again, but didn't dare tell Walter the reason. She knew that he would have stormed up to the Griffiths' house in Ton to confront the pair of them, and that would have meant Walter losing his job and being black-listed. Lily couldn't let Walter risk his job and their livelihood, though she knew it was a risk he would have considered well worth taking. Walter prided himself on kowtowing to nobody and if a woman had made Lily look small, he would have given her the rough edge of his tongue, and to hell with the consequences.

"There *are* some good uns" said Dick.

"Maybe" said Jack. "But the good uns don't seem to keep their jobs for very long. You got to say it yourself Dick, it's hard to find a good word to say about most of the pit officials you ever knew. They can be decent enough when they are still ordinary colliers working alongside their butties, but you let them get a bit of power, and it all goes to their heads. Bosses' men, and they behave like the worst type of boss. They suck up to Management by getting as much work out of us as they can, and diddling us out of as much money as they can. The worst ones are those two-faced devils. When you go to them to complain about not getting paid for a job, they're all sympathy, saying they knew nothing about it, and they'll see to it straightaway. When you go again the next week, they'll sound surprised – 'No money come through for you again this week? What's the matter with those fools in the office? You just leave it to me, my man, I'll put a stop to it', and sometimes the money never comes through. You can't blame the manager of course, - you think he's been doing all he can, and all the time they've done nothing."

Chapter Twenty

Jack paused and looked straight at Dick. Dick had been urging Jack for months past to take the Firemen's Examination.

"Try for Fireman. You got the necessary years of work underground. You can pass that old exam of theirs; pass it standing on your head. It's only the English and the mathematics isn't it, and you're alright there. And their gas test is simple, simple. It's something that we all ought to take anyway, for our own safety."

But Dick knew that it wasn't the thought of the Qualifying Examination for Colliery Fireman which was making Jack so hesitant.

A Fireman was an official, a Company man, one of the Bosses. In exchange for more pay, a guaranteed job every week and a holiday with pay, Jack would have to see that the men got out as much coal as possible. And that meant cutting corners, ignoring the danger signals given out from the pit itself. He would have to be one of the slave drivers or else soon find his job forfeit. It was not a prospect he relished.

"You wouldn't want to see me join that gang, would you Dick? I'd have to be one of them if I went in for Fireman. Some of the Firemen we've known have been the worst of the lot, responsible for safety, so-say, but turning a blind eye to every safety regulation, signing the Report Book religiously every day as per Regulations, but opposite 'Gas?' they put 'None', and opposite 'Timber' they put 'Plentiful', even though they know damn well that there's every danger of fire damp building up in that seam and that we been crying out for days for more pit props."

Chapter Twenty

"Aye" said Dick. "They do fill it in without thinking." He smiled. "Remember what they used to say about Davies the Fireman in the Lady Lewis? How he slipped up one day and put 'Plentiful' opposite 'Gas' and 'None' opposite 'Timber'! He didn't make that same mistake twice!"

He became serious again. "All the same, Jack, you could be the leaven in the lump, my boy."

Jack had learned that when Dick called him 'my boy' instead of his usual 'bach' or 'bachgen' the issue was a grave one. Dick had recognised that ever since he came back from France Jack had lost all his *hwyl*. He had been saying to Annie May only the other evening that "the dark night of the soul is upon Jack, but please God he'll come out of it." For Jack to pass the examination and become a Colliery Fireman seemed to him to be the way for Jack to get back his spirit again. Jack could not help but be efficient, and Dick trusted that he would also be fair-minded, two commodities very rarely to be found in one Overman. Such a combination was bound to be a force for good.

"Don't hide your light Jack - let it shine in the darkness of this world - 'a hi a oleua i bawb sydd yn y tŷ' and give light to everybody around you. We are bidden to do it, Jack, to glorify your Father who is in heaven. 'Llewyrched eich goleuni ger bron dynion fel y gwelont eich gweithredoedd da chwi, ac y gogoneddont eich Tad yr hwn sydd yn y nefoedd'. Wonderful words Jack, a challenge and an injunction on us. It's all there in Saint Matthew, the chance to do good in the world...and it's a warning too –

that light inside a man can turn to darkness... Take care that our light is kept shining - 'edrychwch rhag i'r goleuni sydd ynot fod yn dywyllwch'? Woe to us if we choose the dark..."

Jack had heard him out almost without imterruption, although it was only his affection for Dick which kept him silent. He would have lost patience with any other man who spoke to him of glorifying God. Like Dick's Welsh, he heard the sound of the words without understanding their meaning. But he could tolerate Dick's talk of a Heavenly Father. Dick was not like any other man. Who else, thought Jack, who else but Dick would challenge you to increase the sum of goodness in the world? Who else could remove each individual act of choice from the here-and-now and place it so firmly in the context of eternity?

"It's like this, Jack. There's the Treforest School of Mines, there's our own Cambrian Mining School, only down in Porth there, you pay your half a crown a lesson, you pass the exams. Better still, do it by post and study at home. They can give you all the training you need to make you competent, oh yes. But it isn't good enough to be competent - although that's a help, mind, and we haven't seen too many of them, either! There's got to be the attitude behind it, the caring, the sense of responsibility. And all the training in the world isn't going to give a man that if he hasn't got it in him. Now Jack, you know the situation as well as I do. There's a desperate need for men who'll carry out the Regulations and use some honesty in their inspecting. You are not like the usual run, my boy. Are you going to turn your back and betray yourself and others by hiding your light? Think again Jack."

He made it sound as if Jack would be a coward if he kept on refusing to take the examination, and only Jack himself knew how keenly that accusation stung. In his working life he could not refuse the challenge. With Dick's urging, Jack was tempted to feel that he could indeed be one of the decent officials, one the men could trust to see that their lives were not put at unnecessary risk. He knew only too well how vital was the job of Fireman. Like all miners, he knew of many an accident and still more near-misses which had been caused by a Fireman's neglect or his deliberately blind eye, and he knew too, the cover-ups which went with them. How often had he and Dick heard the blustering "no need to say anything about this, then, right?" or sometimes, "Get your cards and don't show your face here again". Black-listing was the automatic penalty for opening your mouth too wide.

"And mind you, Jack, you got the Mackworth Recommendations behind you. Got to enforce *some* safety regulations, by *law*."

"Oh yes." Jack's voice was dry. "We've had Mackworth for seventy years, and a fat lot of good it's done us. It's notorious, isn't it - when men are killed in the pit, it comes out at the inquest that somehow its always their own fault that they got themselves blown up or burnt alive or buried under a roof fall. They can't be there to defend themselves, and there's nobody with any self-preservation that will stand up and say any different. Even when a verdict of manslaughter is returned, and negligence has been shown, even then the Manager, the Overman, the Fireman, they all come out so-say without a stain on their character, 'no personal default, no legal blame'. It's notorious, mun."

"True enough, Jack. Any dispute and it's always the officials who are believed, never the eye-witnesses on the spot. They dare not stand up and point the finger of blame where it should be directed. Neglect, negligence, all done to save time, it's the old story. Coal must be cut, and got out quick. But see, bach, even just one official, acting like a man with human feeling, even just one can bring about change..."

"I very much doubt that," said Jack to himself. "All very well for Dick to talk about teaching by example, about the power of love, about turning the other cheek. He's preaching to the converted, to those who were forced to turn the other cheek; his sermons never reach Bailey the Overman nor James the Fireman. Officials in the pit will always be on the side of the owners. Fat chance of the system ever changing. The coal owners have got one aim. Profit. And it unites them. Not like us miners, a bunch of individuals. Ironic, really, that below ground in the pit we work in fellowship, united in mutual trust. Above ground, there's no solidarity. The Fed is splintering, members falling away. Can't blame them. It's become a broken reed. We have no weapons to fight the system, no power to change things for the better; strike action has failed, negotiation laughable. Fine just after the war, with good money being earned, but that's finished. In 1919 we were near to revolution. But not now. There'll never be a Russian Revolution here, not even in that little Moscow called Maerdy... Everything is too firmly entrenched for that. The war has changed nothing. Power and influence still with the same men, the same institutions. The pits back again in the hands of the owners and it's their greed that's dictating all our lives..."

Dick's voice was urging: "Change has got to start somewhere bach, and it could be with you. I'm fifty four now, and I won't be going on much longer. It'll be up to the young ones, men like you, Jack, to carry on the fight for those who have no voice, to show compassion in a brutal world."

"I'm nearly thirty-three, Dick, hardly one of the young ones. But perhaps you're right."

Every man's life was significant, not only for himself, but also for those whose lives he touched, particularly in a job where life itself was held so cheap and where the effect of one man's actions showed up all too clearly. In a job like theirs the pattern of interdependence was not hidden. He would follow Dick's advice and "try for Fireman". If he succeeded, he would at least be giving Charlotte the satisfaction of seeing him "make something" of himself. It could be, he told himself, that his salvation lay in work. If he could work for the owners as an official without becoming their tool, he might regain some integrity and enjoy some self-respect. He had seen the waste of too many lives in the war to be able to neglect the chance of using his own in honour. He had none of Dick's faith, but he could act as if he shared Dick's convictions. And

Chapter Twenty

besides, he felt he owed it to his brother Bert to justify his being alive when so many others had fallen beside him.

He was not to know how soon all debts were to be paid, how soon he too, like Bert, was to lay down his life for others, "a human sacrifice, merchi" Dick was to say to Annie May "not to war, but to Mammon. But a sacrifice all the same."

That sacrifice was not very many years away.

CHAPTER TWENTY ONE

NOTHING BUT A GAMBLE

1922-1923

"We are on a perilous margin when we begin to look passively at our future selves, and see our own figures led with dull consent into shabby achievement."

George Eliot, Middlemarch, chapter 79

Chapter Twenty One

From where she stood at their front room window in Hillside, Lily could see across the road right through the great open doors of the Smithy, to where the fire lit up the anvil and the workbench, casting on the wall the huge dark shadow of Old Pearce the Forge.

Walter liked Alf Pearce. "Theest can bet on it, when Alf have done the shoeing, that horse'll never go lame, no, not he. And another thing, whatever be wrong with an horse, Alf do know what be the matter wi' it and can do summat about it. Except for one thing, that there grass sickness, and there's nobody that knows much about that. Up in Scotland it have very near wiped out the whole damn lot of them. Nobody got no remedy for it. They be trying all sorts to get summat as'll do the trick. Alf and me have seen 'em trying opening medicines, black oil with turps, vitriol and myrrh, olive oil, jalops, the lot. But it aint grass sickness, whatever it be. 'Taint got nothing whatever to do wi' the grass. I got pit ponies, mun, that have never been up for grass, and yet they still gets it and dies on it. It be summat that came over with they horses from France that was in the camp down in Barry. They none on 'em gets cured, mun. Damn shame to see 'em when they keels over. They falls and they never gets up again. And there aint no cure for it. They never gets up. Like as if there be a spell put on 'em. There won't hardly be none on 'em left afore long, not in the pit nor anywhere else, thee canst mark my words."

Walter's prophecy came true, though their disappearance owed more to the spread of the motor car than to disease, and even then for many years horses continued to be used throughout the Rhondda. They pulled the brewery drays, the coal carts, the bakers' vans, the milk carts and especially the big vans in which Watkins the Flannel Merchants took their bolts of flannel, calico and cotton round the streets to undercut the Co-op Drapery. Underground, they were used right up to the day the pits closed for good. Above ground, change had already begun. The horse-drawn double-decker trams owned by Solomon Andrews had given way to the electric tramcars of Rhondda Transport Company; farmers were beginning to use tractors instead of shire horses, and private people were buying motor cars. There were a few motor cars in the Rhondda, but so few that everybody recognised them and knew their owners, the long white Napier belonging to T.R. Evans the Auctioneer and Furniture Dealer, the open-topped Rover parked outside Sidoli's cafe, the black Ford owned by the Rayners of Penmaen.

Lily sometimes caught sight of Frank and Beatrice Rayner, and she would recognise the chauffeur as John Jones who used to bully the stable lads and look after the horses in the days when she had been one of the housemaids in Penmaen.

"I do feel sorry for them, mother," she said. "All that money, and what have they got?"

"Aye," said Charlotte. "Money won't bring back their boy nor their girl neither..."

"Kicked you out for laughing didn't they, our Lily? I wouldn't waste my sympathy on that uppity lot. Like those precious Denmers our Ethel's always writing to," said Our Arthur.

Chapter Twenty One

"You know nothing whatever about the Denmers," said Ethel. "You're too young to remember them when we left Bristol."

"I know enough about them to know they write you drivel. Catch me reading rubbish like that. I go to the library and get a book out if I want to read anything. *You* ought to be improving your mind, our Eth."

"And you ought to be smartening yourself up, Our Arthur, instead of looking like a tramp all the time. And I thought you were supposed to be going in for a good trade in your hands? I only see you lolling about at home whenever I come, your nose stuck in a book."

"Better than parading about looking like a dog's dinner though..."

"Mother! *Speak* to him."

But Charlotte was deaf to any such appeal and it was left to Lily to change the subject: "There's dirty and noisy it is in Hillside these days, mother," she said. "Nothing but the steamrollers now, all day and every day except Sunday."

They were building a new road to link Tonypandy with Treorchy, and Hillside lay at right angles only a matter of yards distant, so that the noise of men with pick and shovel and the rattle of the steamroller over the tarmacadam made it impossible for Dick Jenkins and for Walter on nights to sleep during the day. "Thee cassn't get a wink with that bloody racket going on under thee nose - thank God I be on days next week mun."

Walter was not alone in complaining about the noise, but there was no doubt about the need to duplicate the one and only road running north from Llwynypia through Ystrad, Pentre and Treorchy and ending at Blaenrhondda, the dead end at the top of the Rhondda Fawr. This was Ystrad Road, a low-lying road stretching alongside both the railway line and the River Taff, and liable to flood after heavy rain, bringing drainage water into peoples' houses.

When they came first to the Rhondda, Charlotte had been appalled at what she saw, and indignant at the way it seemed to be taken for granted that winter after winter there would be subsidence on Ystrad Road, so that people would have to spend the worst weeks of the year drying out their wet walls and floor-boards and trying to rid their homes of slime and stench. She knew nothing of the schemes for raising the level of the highway which were periodically considered by the Roads Committee of the Council, but she would read in the *Rhondda Gazette* accounts of the damage caused to kitchens and cellars, and later reports of the Council's decision to refuse compensation.

"Poor souls" she would say. "It's a crying shame the way they got to put up with it. Council ought to be made to do summat about it, not wriggling out of it all. Never would be like it Up Home. I never seed such things Uppome, no never."

Jack was never impatient with his mother ("O no, 'er saves all 'er black looks for I" said Thomas), but he was quick to point out "Up Home? Mother, it's the same Up Home as down here, the very same. It's no different in Bristol, no different in any of the big cities. It's two nations everywhere in the country, the rich and the poor, and nobody in authority cares a fig about the underdogs."

For those unlucky underdogs living on Ystrad Road, the floods continued to be part of life, though they could console themselves with the knowledge that there were others worse off than themselves, for in Ynyshir, in the Rhondda Fach, the flood water rose so deep that permanent pumping stations had to be set up to pump it back into the river.

Railway Terrace was built on a bend away from the river, and so kept "dry as a bone, thank God." And it was far enough away from Pentre to be safe from the landslide which in 1916 demolished houses and shops and wrecked the roller-skating rink where Walter had made good to Bert his boast that he was "game to try any damnfool thing once." Nobody had been killed or injured in the landslide, but the road had been blocked for a time, isolating the head of the valley. The need for a road to bypass Ystrad and Pentre need was obvious, but it took more than five years after the landslide for the contractors to move in and start to build on the other side of the river.

The new road was built in two stages. The first section started from Tonypandy and cut through the bluebell wood where Walter or Bert used to escort Lily when she walked home from Bowmans Dairy on Tonypandy Square; it sliced the Lady's Field in two and ended at the top of Hillside where the rows of streets making up Gelli and Ton Pentre began. After Ton Pentre, the second part of the road carved through Pentwyn woods and skirted the streets of Cwmparc, before bridging the river Taff and joining up with the main road, the old road, at Treorchy.

The old road was lined with blackened terraced houses, with occasional shops, public houses and chapels. It was an ugly narrow road, choked with vans and carts, noisy with tramcars, its grimy pavements thronged with people. But the new road ran nearly the whole of its length through open country. On its western side it met bare hills and greening tips; on the east, thick woodland sloping down to the river where courting couples flattened the ferns. In summer the riverside was a favourite spot for gangs of children and for families, and although Lily refused to make jam sandwiches and carry bottles of pop just to please a child, Ruth had only to ask her Auntie Ethel to be sure of a picnic outing.

Lily was glad to see them go, but she couldn't help feeling angry when she thought of the way Ethel had spoilt the child, "running about after her, giving her everything she asked for. That pink teddy bear... she had found a pink teddy bear in Pontypridd market of all places, just when anybody had managed to get it into the child's head that they didn't make such things...no sense in running about searching for something like that just to satisfy the whim of a child. You got to punish a child sometimes, not to be cruel of course, not like that awful Mr. Murdstone to that poor little David Copperfield, but firm all the same. For their own good you got to be firm and show them who's master. Otherwise kids would rule you, and there's no sense in that..."

Lily would try and keep such thoughts to herself, but every now and then she would complain to Charlotte. "I can't do nothing with her, mother. Defiant and stubborn, and worse when she do come from our Eth's. The rows she do make with Walter, it's awful. They got the same high temper, the both of them, and she got to have all her own way. Well, she do try to. I won't give in to her though, mother, no, I won't. She got to learn to knuckle under, like we all got to do. I'm not going to give in to a child, no, not likely. But you know, we do have more rows and upsets about that child than about anything else."

That was only partly true, and Lily knew it. There were certainly rows caused by Ruth, and about Ruth, but there were other rows too.

"What bist doing all the damn time, slaving for them Down There?"

"I got to give mother a hand, Walter."

"What for? What's wrong with your bloody Ethel? She can do summat can't she? She got no kid to look after."

"She *do* go down home,'" said Lily defensively. "But," she thought, "with all her tidy clothes on all the time how can she wash the skirting boards or put a drop of paraffin on a cloth to clean the windows?"

"Your Arthur don't do nothing, lazy bugger. Waited on hand and foot."

"He's got a heart murmur. You know he had to give up that cabinet-making 'prenticeship."

"Oh, aye. Good excuse."

"Well, he don't smoke his head off and he don't take a drop to drink. Nor do Jack."

"No, course 'e don't. Bloody perfect, both on 'em. Too damn perfect to live."

"And they don't waste their money on the horses like you do. It's always 'down the course again' with you."

"Good reason for why, mun. They been and put a spell on I".

"Oh don't talk so soft, Walter. A thousand pities somebody didn't put a spell on you. I'd pay somebody to put a spell on you if I thought it would stop you."

Gambling was a wicked waste of money. Of less importance to Lily was the knowledge that gambling on horse races was legally permitted only on the race course or through a recognised-and-for-the-rich Commission Agent, so that Walter ran the risk of being arrested every time he handed to the bookie's runner on the corner the slip of paper with his instructions painstakingly written in pencil:

"3d each way Mushroom King

If cash a shilling to win Best Boy."

The risk was slight for Walter, greater for the runner, and greatest for the bookie himself who took home the money and slips of paper, except that a looker-out ensured that no policeman on the beat or on his bicycle was in sight.

Lily would have been tolerant of his gambling if Walter had won more often. Just as she would have felt more respect for his superstitious belief in omens and "signs" if it had helped him place successful bets. But so far from winning any money, Walter's trust in The Stars in Their Courses only involved the spending of more. He had noticed the *Gazette* advertisement for "Faustina's Astrological Readings", and had not been satisfied until he had sent off to 8 Working Street, Cardiff, a postal order for one and sixpence, together with his name, address and date of birth. By return of post he got back a sheet of paper headed *Characteristics of the Scorpio Subject* and a sealed envelope containing notes on *Your Personal Prediction for the Year Ahead*.

Both items contained so many unfamiliar words that Lily, not sure of the exact meaning of all of them herself, took pity and read them out aloud.

"Impulsive, aggressive, the most possessive of all the signs in the Zodiac." Lily had to admit that some of it rang true, but she found it laughable when Walter laid claim to 'Business Acumen out of the ordinary'.

"All down there, in black and white for thee to see".

"And that do make it all true," said Lily sarcastically. "You believe in that rubbish more than you do the Bible. I don't think you even believe in God."

"Believe in God? I aint telling thee what I believes in. I aint stopping thee believing in God. Theest can believe it. I never stops thee going to church and believing what the 'ell theest like. 'Live and let live's my motto."

"It's useless to talk to you," said Lily. He would never understand her interest in the unanswerable questions, like whether the stories in the Bible were really true, or how a good God could allow terrible things to happen like war and strikes and pit accidents. Walter thought such questions were "morbid".

"What bist being morbid about now, mun? There baint no need on it. Theest know I can't abide anything morbid. You be getting exactly the same as your Jack, mun."

It was because Lily did share Jack's inward-looking character and his questioning mind, that in the old days she had been able to talk to him. In the old days Jack would insist: "Think of it Lily. Bishops in palaces. In Palaces, and preaching the gospel of one who was homeless. Something ludicrous about that!"

Lily would nod her head as if she agreed but her acceptance of the hierarchy of the church remained untouched by what she dismissed as Jack's socialism. The vicar she could see was clearly a cut above his congregation. He lived in a better house and spoke in an accent very different from the miners and their families. And the bishop would certainly be above him again. No, Lily was not prepared to question the organisation of the church, even though Jack urged it.

More disturbing was Jack's rejection of Christianity. "It's founded on sacrifice, isn't it? The cruel death of God's only son. What kind of a god is it who needed that sacrificial killing? Blood of the lamb indeed. It's a cruel religion, Lily, cruel and barbaric."

Lily would try to say something about God's love of the world which lay behind that sacrifice, and the everlasting life for believers.

"Redeemed from our sins by sacrifice. I can't accept it I'm afraid, any more than I can accept original sin. Adam and Eve and Fall in the Garden of Eden? No. And if there's no Fall, then there's no need for redemption. As for Eternal Life, all we know is *this* life, and it's here and now, Lily, that we see the consequences of what we do, not in the world that may be to come. Yes we get our rewards and punishments but never mind about the final Judgement Day. Every day is judgement day."

"That's just what it says in the Bible," thought Lily. "As ye sow, so shall ye reap." That was a text Lily had learned from Charlotte's lips long before she read it for herself, just like that other awful warning about sowing the wind and reaping the whirlwind. Ruth, and her marriage to Walter. Those were the consequences of sin, her punishment in this life. But not her punishment alone; Ruth and Walter were both being punished. They were all three suffering, a family in a love-less home. But Ruth had done nothing wrong. Of course she was conceived in sin, but that was hardly her fault. It was a clear case of "the sins of the fathers being visited upon the children".

It seemed to Lily that Jack was accepting and yet at the same time rejecting what was written in the Bible. Perhaps he was right about it being a cruel religion, despite what we are told about the love of God which brought the peace which passeth understanding. Certainly it didn't do to think too much about that awful death on the cross. The idea of those dreadful nails being hammered into soft flesh was unbearable, and all so very far removed from the handsome solid church of St. David where only the most respectable people in Gelli went of a Sunday, and where they spoke to each other in a reverent whisper if at all. Lily couldn't help wondering sometimes whether they thought about the violence and the brutality of that central event, the reason they were all there, or whether for most people as for her, Sunday worship was an event divorced from everyday life, more appealing than everyday life.

For Lily it meant escape from the cramped front room in Hillside where she never felt free from the hostile presence of Milly Wilkins. She liked to sit with idle hands in the high-ceilinged church, knowing that Ruth was going to have Dinner Down Gran's, and that Walter was at home busy reading his *John Bull* and puzzling over the weekly "Bullets" competition. She was happy to let the familiar words of the First and Second Lessons flow over her head while her gaze wandered along the polished pews and rested on the stained glass above the altar, conscious that she was wearing her "bit of best clothes and looking tidy for a change", although of course she realised that looking tidy had nothing to do with religion, and that pride in your appearance was really a sin. But not, she thought, as bad a sin as the feelings of hatred, envy, anger and despair, which she harboured and which made her so unhappy.

"Have mercy on us, miserable sinners." Lily's awareness of wrong within made her cling to the promise of Salvation, no matter what Jack thought, no matter what Walter said. Lily was determined to keep her faith in a God who loved her however bad she had been, and in an Eternal Life better than this earthly life. Lily desperately hoped that at Judgement Day she would be found among the sheep and not the goats, so as to enjoy an everlasting Sunday with no Monday to follow.

Jack dismissed the ritual of the church as irrelevant, never recognising that Lily needed the comfort not only of her Faith but also of her sharing in the ritual. In the solemnity of the service and in the singing of the chants and hymns, Lily could forget the wretchedness of her life with Walter. She could forget herself in merging with the rest of the choir, the women who sat in the pews on the right hand side of the church under the all-seeing eye of Mr. Rowe the choir-master, sopranos in the front row, altos behind them in the second. Some of the women wanted to wear surplices like the men, and file out behind the vicar from the vestry, walk in procession round the church and sit in the choir stalls in the chancel.

But Lily felt noticeable enough when they stood up at the same time as the vicar and the choirboys, at the first notes of the organ. She had no wish to be more conspicuous, even though when Mr. Rowe singled her out for the solo parts Lily had no hesitation in letting her voice ring out alone. Mr. Rowe had assured Lily that her singing was equal to the soloist May John from Ystrad who sang with the Welsh Ladies Choir, and that she should get her voice professionally trained. He had spoken about her to Madame Clara Novello-Davies who conducted the choir, and she had agreed to audition Lily.

Mr. Rowe was pleased. "Now then merchi, a chance for you isn't it, a chance for you to use to the full your God-given gift, a gift not to be wasted, no indeed."

Chapter Twenty One

It was a chance which Lily knew she could never take. The Welsh Ladies Choir was based in Cardiff, and it held its rehearsals in Cardiff. There was no possibility of Lily's joining that choir. Everybody was agreed on that. Jack would have encouraged her to make the most of her voice, but he was realistic. He knew as well as Lily that Walter would never allow her to "gallivant off to Cardiff for any so-say choir practice", even if she could have afforded the train fare. Lily would have to be content with singing in the choir at St. David's, where Walter was prepared to allow the Wednesday evening practices. Lily alone knew the bad grace with which permission was granted, and the subtle coaxing which made Walter willing for the extra practices before the Christmas and Easter services.

Charlotte too was discouraging. To her mind, it was unnatural for a married woman with a child to seek any un-called for activity outside her home. "What be so special about that choir, Lily? Thee can sing up here, just as well as in any Cardiff that I knows on."

Lily could have given Charlotte a full account of the Welsh Ladies Choir. They were famous throughout Wales, but only, as Lily realised, to those who took any interest in choral singing. Charlotte was not one, and she would not have been impressed by Mr. Rowe's repeated account of Welsh triumphs gained at the world International Eisteddfod held in Chicago in 1893.

"Thirty years ago, but I remember it as if it was yesterday. Organised by the many Welsh men and women throughout America and still speaking their mother tongue, isn't it. In the Rhondda Glee Society, I was, competing against seven other male voice choirs. First Prize we carried away that day. There was nobody to touch us, nor the Welsh Ladies Choir. The singing of the Rhondda men and the girls from Cardiff was heavenly. That's what it said in *Y Drych*, the Welsh paper published over there. *Heavenly*. That's the sound I know I can get from you contraltos. Are you ready now? Take it from the top of the page - come in on the beat - 'He was despised and rejected of men'."

He would go on: "And after the Chicago Eisteddfod, nine years after, another honour was paid to the Ladies Choir when they were invited to sing in Westminster at a dinner in thanksgiving for King Edward's recovery from appendicitis! Madame Novello-Davies has shown me the menu of the feast... A wonderful occasion, and the King paying out thousands of pounds out of his own pocket towards the cost... Now I know that in this very choir here I've got the equal of any in the land, so it's back to work now. 'Lo! at noon 'tis sudden night! Darkness covers all the sky! Earth is quaking...land is shaking...' Watch those quavers in the fifth bar now, not too soon with the crescendo, draw it out, give every note its full value. Now then! '*Lo!* at *noon*'...".

In the twinkling of an eye Mr. Rowe had swept his mind clear of Chicago and Westminster. His voice and appearance changed as he spoke. He had entered the world of sacred music, and was drawing the choir after him. They were all at Golgotha. Christ had been crucified. Darkness covered the land...

Chapter Twenty One

If singing in St. David's choir was fulfilling, then to be one of the Welsh Ladies choir must, thought Lily, bring pure joy. But Charlotte would never understand Mr. Rowe's pride in the Welsh Ladies or Lily's longing to join it.

"I never heard tell on it, Lily. But no question about it, thee'll have to draw thee horns in. None of that traipsing off to Cardiff. And aint that where that Vi of yourn be living? In that teashop baint it? I aint blind, Lily, theest be wanting to take up wi' she again. The least thee has to do wi' she the better, my girl."

Lily had got into the habit of not mentioning Vi's name, but she must have let it slip that Vi had moved to Cardiff and was working as a waitress in the Excelsior Cafe in Queen Street. The pay was poor but the uniform of brown dress and cream apron and cap was becoming, and some of the gentlemen regulars left good tips. She had become engaged but was in no hurry, as she told Lily, to tie the knot. There was too much fun to be had "keeping John Henry dangling".

Vi was still free, still to be envied. Lily had no freedom. Not only was she tied to Walter, but she was held back too by the thought of what Jack would say, of what Charlotte would say. Lily was a rebel only in thought, not in deed. Mr. Rowe's advice was well-meaning but futile. To join the Welsh Ladies choir was impossible; to become a 'real' singer was only a dream. And it would always be the same.

Lily could see that she would never achieve anything worthwhile, by her singing, or by her writing. Those were her gifts, her God-given gifts, just like our

Chapter Twenty One

Ethel was given the gift of loving children. But Ethel was using her gift; Lily's talents would be wasted, and some day, she thought, like it said in the parable of the talents, she would be called to give an account of what she had done to develop them. At the Day of Judgement she would be condemned. No verdict of "well done thou good and faithful servant". Oh, if only she had been born a heathen knowing nothing about an after-life of judgement, or could be strong like Jack and throw away such beliefs...

If only she could put the clock back... If only she were single again and not have to worry about Walter's drinking and his gambling or whether he would be called out on strike again, like they were in the lock-out last year, when she had gone hungry because she had been too proud to go down to the soup kitchen set up in the vestry of Bethesda Chapel. If only Walter had never come to lodge with them in Railway Terrace... If only he hadn't known Bert in Long Ashton and been friendly with him... Bert was out of it all now, nothing could touch him now...but life could be very long...life that stretches out hateful and empty of everything that makes the heart glad.

CHAPTER TWENTY TWO

TO SEE SOMETHING OF THE WORLD

1923

"Things and actions are what they are, and the consequences of them will be what they will be"

Bishop Butler, Sermon No. 7

Lily came close to despair during the first few years after Walter's return. She had not learned to savour those times of contentment which come even to unhappy men and women if they are not in physical pain; she was not by temperament suited to exaggerating all her small pleasures and making them last; she was not good at following the advice which Charlotte was always giving, that she should count her blessings.

There were blessings she could have counted. There were friends, not only close at hand like her neighbours Annie May Jenkins and Louisa Pearce, but further away like Vi and Olive from Gelli Crossing. In Bristol there was her Aunt Iris and her Cousin Mary, even Elsie and Julie Denmer. And there was her mother and Jack. Never in her life did Lily need to feel lonely, friendless or isolated. She never had to face a strange environment or make a new life among strangers. There were doors which were always open to her, friends and neighbours she was glad to see. In Hillside Lily felt herself surrounded by good will if not affection, for Milly Wilkins was the exception in not liking Lily.

As a child Lily had been in and out of the neighbours' houses, and she took for granted the rich communal life of Hillside, which included the Street Outings. Lily loved these trips, and was sorry that Charlotte was never well enough to join any of them. "I'd a dearly loved an outing, Lily, but me insides 'ud never stand it, theest know that as well as I."

Charlotte would never have borne the discomfort of the "Rhondda Butterfly" or the "Lily of the Valley", the charabancs with their open tops and solid tyres taking thirty seated passengers on Evening Mystery Tours. Even though the Unknown Destination nearly always turned out to be the same, Ewenny or Cowbridge in the Vale of Glamorgan, the Mystery Tours were so popular that there was often a waiting list of people from streets other than Hillside and the neighbouring Bronllwyn Road.

Walter was never one of the passengers for he was such a poor traveller that even a ride on the tramcar as far as Pentre could make him feel queasy. As long as Lily took Ruth with her, he was glad to stay at home. Lily knew exactly how he would spend his time. He would first of all sit in their room studying Racing Form and working his System, getting to know where and when the horses in any particular race had had a good run out. His knowledge never seemed to help him to place winning bets, but it was information which he found absorbing for its own sake. When he had gone through the racing cards he would make his way into Milly Wilkins' back kitchen, where she always "just happened" to be baking bara brith or Welsh cakes on the evenings that Lily was out. Lily recognised that it was one more sign of Milly's hostility towards her, however much Walter might urge her "not to be so fanciful mun".

One place Lily could be sure Walter would never visit was Railway Terrace. With Bert gone, Walter had no wish to see any of the Callows, and he would have been glad to see Lily cutting herself off from the family who had "treated her like dirt, mun" before her marriage. He was resentful of the hold they seemed to have over Lily and their influence over Ruth, forgetting that all the years he had been away it was Charlotte and Ethel who had helped Lily to bring her up. He wanted to forbid Ruth to go near the place, but there was "blue murder mun" if he said a word against her going. Charlotte's influence was not as great as Walter feared. She disapproved of Lily taking Ruth on the Evening Trips. "Out in the hours of darkness and losing her rest", even though, as Lily pointed out, it was hardly the darkness of night at half past nine of a summer's evening, and there were plenty of children younger than Ruth, sitting on their mothers' laps on the way home and sleeping sound.

It was only the young who were able to sleep through all the noise of the singing. Charlotte would have sympathised with Angharad-next-door, who was so near her time that Vanw her mother thought she was taking a risk to set off on foot up the road for a packet of tea, much less go down the Vale for the whole evening in a contraption which threatened to rattle the insides out of your body. Angharad herself felt a bit anxious, but she bore it pretty well through the gentle old favourites like "Just like the Ivy on the Old Garden Wall" and "When you wore a Tulip". It was only when "Stop yer Tickling, Jock" and "Keep Right on To the End of the Road" reached their crescendo that she started moaning from the back of the charabanc: "Oh, the noise, the noise...my poor head...why don't they give it a rest?"

But there was more to come. "Oh, Mr. Porter, what shall I do?", "Daisy Daisy, give me your answer do", "Any old Iron, Any old Iron?", "Henery the Eighth I am, I am", "Boiled Beef and Carrots", the rollicking words had to be sung over and over again, until the more staid element of chapel-goers, who shook their heads over the Harry Champion lyrics, decided it was time for hymns and Welsh folk songs. But *Calon Lan*, *Dafydd y Garreg Wen* and *Codiad yr Ehedydd* were sung with such fervour and *hwyl* that, if there had been a roof to the charabanc it would have been raised a few inches if not blown away completely.

Lily would sing with gusto, but Ethel, who hardly ever joined them on the street outings, felt out of place amongst the songsters. Unlike Lily, Ethel had been too old for school when she came to Gelli, so that she had never learnt the words of the Welsh songs. And although she knew the English, the idea of joining in the raucous choruses, of linking arms and swaying about in her seat, offended her sense of what was lady-like. Besides, with all the jogging and jostling, her hat-pins might have worked loose and sent her hat awry. Ethel preferred the more decorous day trips in the autumn to Miskin or Llantrisant or Taffs Well to gather blackberries, when after an exhausting day there was more dozing than singing. The return home, through the dusk, always made Lily feel melancholy. The peaceful Vale of Glamorgan with its lanes and its hedgerows was so much more attractive than the noise and dirt of the coal-mining valley, the laughter and companionship of friends so much more enjoyable than the continual strain of living with her husband and her child. Away from Walter, Lily was a happier and a nicer person.

Chapter Twenty Two

The Evening Trips meant a few hours of freedom from Hillside, but the yearly Sunday School Outing to the seaside gave her a glimpse into a different world. It was always the second Saturday in July, the Saturday after the Anniversary Service, and it was always Barry Island, for of the other two possible seaside places near the valley, Porthcawl was too genteel and Aberavon too dreary. Porthcawl was nothing but big houses, posh little shops, empty promenade and pebble beach, Aberavon, nothing but windswept sand dunes. Barry Island had the best of both. It had the select Cold Knap, which attracted the lady teachers of the Sunday School, and the families of the vicar, the church-wardens and those few who put a silver coin, or maybe a golden guinea, on the collection plate even when it wasn't Christmas or Easter. Cold Knap was, as Vanw-next-door was fond of saying, only for the *Crachach*, those above the common run. But on Barry Island there was the funfair too, with the Dodgem Cars and Gipsy Petrulengo, and the golden stretch of sand where most of the women settled for the day. The children could paddle or build sand-castles under their mothers' watchful eyes, or they could have donkey rides, gather round the Salvation Army Open Air meeting, to join in or to jeer according to their nature, or stand watching the sand artists make realistic models of forts, palaces and ships which would all be washed away at the next high tide.

By tradition, very few husbands or brothers came near the beach. It was accepted that they would spend the day in the hotels and pubs, leaving the town only when it was time to join their families at the railway station. Walter never once went to Barry Island with The Church, so that Lily never had the worry of wondering whether the Special Excursion Train which left Platform Three sharp at half past six would have to leave without her man.

It was when they were going away from the beach in the late afternoon that Lily would notice the little groups of people who were coming out of their boarding-houses on the sea-front. In twos and threes, the elderly ladies dressed in walking costumes and holding parasols would be taking the air with their menfolk before going back for their evening meal. Lily could smell the roasts, and if she looked down the area steps she could see into the kitchens where the cooks and the kitchen maids would be working against the clock, as Lily well remembered from her days in Penmaen. The ladies would return a little weary from their walk, and ready for a rest before changing for dinner. They would be summoned by a gong, and would drift elegantly downstairs, agreeing that the sea-air did give one such an unladylike appetite. The kitchen maids would be hot and tired, their hair damp with the steam of the basement kitchen and their long white aprons soiled and greasy. Lily knew exactly how *they* would be feeling, but she could only imagine what it must be like to be one of those ladies with a parasol. She longed to be one of them, and not one of the unwashed stragglers from the sands.

Most enviable of all were those other groups she could see making for the bathing huts on the beach against the promenade wall. They were young women, women about her own age, wearing sleeveless summer dresses and carrying their bathing costumes and towels brazenly over their arms, in full view of everybody. "Hussies" Charlotte would have called them, "forward hussies". They looked carefree, they looked beautiful. They belonged to a different class, and they lived different lives. They were on holiday, staying not just for the day, but for the week, maybe the fortnight. They could go in the sea in the evening when the day-trippers had gone. There would be no troops of children making sand-castles and moats at the water's edge or splashing in the shallows. They had the sea to themselves. And when their holiday was over, they would go back, not to the blackened terraced houses of the coal-mining valleys, but to the stone-built cottages in the villages dotted about the Vale or to big semi-detached villas in the suburbs of Cardiff, for they were not living on the edge of poverty, knowing only Sundays and Bank Holidays free from work. Their husbands had clean jobs, not work in the pits, clean, safe jobs where even your everyday clothes were good clothes, jobs where you had to have schooling.

Lily envied people like that, though she knew Charlotte's sermons off by heart: "Only the few are so fortunate, Lily. Happiness don't depend on having money. Nobody escapes sorrow in this world, be they high or low, and theest know that envy be a sin. Be thankful you be free from pain. You got your health and strength whatever else you aint got. When that be gone, Lily, it be a sad look-out." They were words which Lily was to bring to mind often in years to come when Charlotte had long gone, and when Lily herself was lying bedridden and needing help even to turn over on her other side.

Chapter Twenty Two

Charlotte was in almost constant pain and had become resigned to being unable to step outside the door. "Can't say as how I misses going up the road, Lily, but now and then I craves to go up 'Ome again. I don't say as how I'd walk a mile to see Ewart and Elsie and their Julie, they thinks that much of theirselves." Charlotte's memories of her childhood were unfaded "but they maybe have changed their tune a bit. Life aint been all honey for 'em, money or no money. But to see poor Richard's widow and their little maid, that's summat else again..."

Ethel cut her short. "Little maid indeed! Time don't stand still mother. Mary's gone thirty!"

Ethel had decided to go to Bristol, on the cheap Evening Excursion train, and had paid for Lily to go with her. Ruth was glad to stay Down Gran's; Walter had made no objection and even joked: "If theest see any of my family there, tell 'em I be still in the land of the living. I aint heard nothing from any of 'em since I were twelve, theest know."

Ethel still had friends in Bedminster and was anxious to see them. If she spent the rest of the time with Aunt and Uncle Denmer and Julie, Lily could go see Aunt Iris Milsom. That way they could better satisfy Charlotte's craving for the details of their visit.

Ethel had high hopes that she would equal, if not outshine, Julie. "Time was, Lily, when anybody had to go down to Cardiff to get anything decent. There'd be nothing fit to put on your back in the Co-op, nothing in Howells' really stylish, and nothing with Miss Jenkins in Avon House that wasn't made in the year dot. Nothing ready-made anywhere in the valley that didn't look like it had come straight out of the Ark. Mind you, there still baint a lot of choice but them paper patterns be a godsend when we be so handy wi' our needles. They be bang up to the minute wi' their styling."

Ethel was not so handy with her needle, but Lily had fathomed the mystery of the Butterick paper patterns which had at last appeared in the Haberdashery Department of Howells and she had successfully cut out the material. She had sewn the tiny stitches round the neckline and wherever it showed, and left Ethel with only the side seams to sew.

"I been a good customer for Evans the packman, and for Watkins the Flannel this last year, and they be generally on the generous side wi' their measuring. Not like that red-headed mommock in the Co-op drapers. Talk about exact in her measurements! To the quarter-inch, she be, and theest know Lily, if she don't cut it straight all along, it be the devil's dream to get the pattern cut out of the stuff." Lily did know, by experience, and she knew too why Ethel had a reason for wanting to impress. Ethel had been married for eleven years, and was pregnant at last. She was only a couple of months gone and so was not showing at all, but even her delight at "expecting" would hardly have reconciled her to the need for wearing such loose-fitting garments if they had been out of fashion.

"No need for a woman in my condition to let myself go Lily. Lucky the fashions have changed. They be just my dap-off."

Chapter Twenty Two

Fashions *had* certainly changed. Influenced by the opening of Tutankhamen's tomb in November, the Egyptian Look had come in, and Ethel had adopted the style with enthusiasm. The loose slip-over dresses hanging from shoulder to hem with no shapings, belts or fastenings were even more suitable for an expanding figure than for a slim, the draped sleeves made of two large squares of material the perfect camouflage for plump upper arms.

For the Bristol trip Ethel had chosen the coffee-coloured dress with the brilliant bead embroidery which had first led Our Arthur to invent his stupid song, "Tootin', rootin', high-falutin', Tootin' Khamen's tomb."

"Tuneless caterwauling," said Ethel in irritation. "If only you didn't encourage him mother. So childish and unnecessary. You wouldn't catch him doing anything like that in the Denmer family, no fear. There's a different mentality there altogether. Nobody *there* to make fun of anybody, trying to make theirselves look decent. Nobody there poking fun at what Julie was wearing."

Ethel had taken in every detail, from her cropped hairstyle to her bar shoes and "flesh-colour stockings Mother! You'd a sworn she had none on at all!"

It was the one and only irritation. Ethel and Lily had worn the black silk stockings they kept for best, with the black kid shoes Ethel had got cheap from Evans-the-Shoes where she had served behind the counter before she was married. They had not reckoned on the flesh-coloured stockings. It looked as if black was going right out of fashion. Not that there was much stocking leg to be seen, since the hem of Ethel's coffee-colour was only six inches from the ankle, very much the same length, she was pleased to note, as Julie's grey-green.

"Plenty of money there, Mother. Gold-thread embroidery and tassels on her bodice and sleeves! Uncle Ewart must have sold that there haulage concern for a pretty penny. They be right out of our league."

"They allus was, Eth. Elsie's bit of money, and his head for business, oh aye, they was well off afore us ever left Bristol."

"Still a lot of style about them, and Julie like to be wed again before long, a feller she were at school with years ago. They be all on 'em pleased enough about it, by all accounts. I didn't see Uncle Ewart saying much about it. Didn't see him saying much about nothing, seemed to have no life in him. Like an old man he looked, Mother. Years older than you and Dad. They both on 'em have aged something terrible."

Charlotte sighed. "Money aint everything, and that's a fact. Money don't bring back nobody. We be all on us getting old theest know, Eth. Fifty-six. That be Elsie Denmer's age. I be a year younger than she. A year between us, that be all. Iris be the same as she. I'll wager *her* girl won't go off and leave *her*. Mary as like as not'll be one of they old maids, past the marrying age."

But Lily has news for Charlotte.

"Mary told me she was engaged, mother, and Aunt Milsom will live with them."

"I'd never a thought it Lily, would you? Such a delicate little critter and kept so close, never a fly-be-night."

Chapter Twenty Two

To Lily it came as no surprise. It had been clear that the John Beer mentioned so often in Mary's letters was no casual friend.

She had been glad to see her aunt and cousin, and to feel the loving warmth they had shown in their letters, but the trip had not cheered her. It had served to bring home to her the lack of hope in her own life. Compared with Mary, with Julie and now lately, Our Eth, Lily's future seemed to hold no promise of happiness.

The only bright spot in her world was that Jack seemed to be shaking off that awful cloud ever since he had passed the Fireman's exams. Dick Jenkins had been saying only the other day that Jack was showing what it was like to be "honourable, and you can't say much better of a human being than that, merchi, especially underground and in his position too, where everything is against honour".

But she could look forward to no widening of her horizons, no escape for herself from the narrow world to which she had condemned herself. One thing she had determined on. No more babies. One was enough, and thank God that one was getting up out of the way a bit now, though going to be more of a handful by and by.

The present could have been more bearable for Lily if she had had a temperament like Walter's, to make light of everything, or if she had been able to overcome the sick feeling of resentment at being trapped in a marriage from which she had no escape. But it was her nature to brood, so that for Lily the mistakes and misjudgements of the past threatened to blight the present.

Chapter Twenty Two

The present was difficult, but the year ahead was to bring disaster; the blow which fell on Walter cast a long shadow on all their lives, on Lily, on Ruth and on the daughter yet to be conceived.

CHAPTER TWENTY THREE

A NEW BEGINNING

1924-1925

"The number of coal mines at work was 356...persons employed 180,082...the total number of accidents reported during the year was 997. The number of fatal accidents was 209, the number of persons killed was 213... *The fact that with one doubtful exception, no accident of a serious nature has occurred with the winding arrangements* goes to show that the machinery...is of sound construction and is maintained to a state of high efficiency. Great credit is I think due to those responsible for ensuring the safety of the very great number of persons who are raised and lowered at the collieries."

Reports of H.M. Inspector of Mines for 1924.

Cardiff and Newport Division.

Chapter Twenty Three

Lily had kept very quiet about Vi's coming up from Cardiff to see her, so that she was hoping that Ethel would stay away that afternoon. Ethel was convinced that Vi was A Rotter. Her clothes alone betrayed her: "Them cost too damn much for any ordinary working girl to afford. Summat fishy there, our Lily."

If Ethel had opened the door to Vi she would have recognised immediately that the blue silk coat with the beaver lamb collar was Dear Stuff. The beige georgette dress Vi was wearing beneath it with its dark blue piping and hand embroidery was elegant enough to grace the upright figure of Queen Mary herself. The clothes were faultless; even the shoulder-length earrings and the double string of coloured beads dangling to the waist were fashionable, though to a conservative eye, "common". But Ethel's verdict would have been: "All that pink stuff on her face, and that purple muck on her mouth, like a regular strumpet."

No, thought Lily, it would never do for Ethel to catch sight of Vi. Now that she was expecting, she seemed to go off the deep end over nothing at all. It was partly the morning sickness to blame. It had started up again and seemed to go on most of the day, so that even Lily couldn't help feeling sorry to see her "crawling about limp as a rag, mother, and looking like as if her face had been dipped in the flour-bag".

Lily had been sympathetic at first, but with the prospect of having to "put up with our Ethel being hysterical for six more months" she had begun to lose patience.

Chapter Twenty Three

Ethel had been offended at Lily's sharp tongue: "Our Lily always been hard, mother, hard as nails. Hard and unfeeling, even to her own sister. She don't know when she be well off and that's a fact. Going about with a face as long as a fiddle."

It was only too obvious how unhappy Lily was becoming. Vi could see at a glance that Lily was in A Right Old State. She took off her blue felt cloche hat and placed it carefully on the chair beside her. Her shining auburn hair was cut short and shaped close to her head, tapering to a vee at the nape of her neck, and it looked so smooth and sleek that Lily had instinctively put up a hand to her own head to check that the hair-pins holding her loosely-coiled bun were not allowing too many long wavy strands to escape.

Vi was more lively than ever. "I'm going to be an old man's darling Lily! Three weeks from now, in the Registry Office in Cardiff. The last but one Saturday in September. The 20th at 11. You and Walter. Ruth can be down her Gran's for the day?"

Lily nodded. Walter wouldn't go to the wedding, "I never goes to weddings, and I never goes to funerals. Theest know that."

She would go on her own. She would like to go. Ethel would lend her something decent to wear. There were plenty of nice blouses and skirts gathering dust in Ethel's wardrobe. Lily knew that she would think a wedding in a Registry Office was hardly a proper wedding at all, and that if Vi and her feller weren't going to get married in church they must have something to hide, but she surely wouldn't want to see Lily shown up, especially in front of Vi of all people...

Vi was going on: "Upstairs room in the Excelsior for the wedding breakfast after. Special rates. I've given in my notice. John Henry's orders! No wife of his will wait at tables he says. Not other people's tables anyway. He'll have another think coming if he thinks I'm going to be at his beck and call though, Lily, I can tell you. But I won't be sorry to give up that job for a bit. Just till I set the house to rights. It's in Albany Road, Lily. A big house though, with attics and all. It ought to be big with all the rent they're charging! Not all that far from Roath Park but easy enough to get into the centre. A tram from the bottom of the street and you're by all the shops in Queen Street and St. Mary Street... no furniture, no curtains nor nothing. We been looking in the Times Furnishing... John Henry do always say you get what you pay for, and we got to..."

Lily had stopped listening. She had heard Milly Wilkins going out and slamming the front door, and had seen her pass the window, walking a lot more quickly than she usually did, and not staring in through the window but looking straight ahead, just to show Madam Lily that she knew how to behave when there was Company in the front room, and Company with a bit of money behind them too, to judge by what she had managed to see from the back kitchen when Lily opened the front door.

It was Milly's day for shopping in Pentre. She would have to be gone some time even if she took the tram home as far as Carter's Corner. Now was Lily's chance to talk to Vi, and be certain of not being overheard.

"Oh, Vi," she blurted out. "That Milly Wilkins can't bear me. She do know how jealous Walter is, and she do drop hints all the time... Walter do go mad... Never wants me to go outside the door. And it's awful with Ruth, there's never a minute's peace when the both of them are in..."

Vi stirred her tea thoughtfully. No point now in saying "I told you so", though she had warned Lily against encouraging Walter when they were at Bowmans, and even afterwards she had been against her marrying him just because of the baby, "there's ways and means of dealing with those things...".

"Well, Lily," she said, "If he's jealous it's only because he's dull on you. You can twist him round your little finger if you want to. And there's no roving eye there. He's a good enough chap. I know I'll have to watch John Henry. You know what travelling salesmen are like!"

Lily shrugged impatiently. "Oh I'm not worried about that. But it's the drink too, Vi. He's getting like my father used to be."

"Well he do still give you all his money don't he? I'll never know what John Henry's kept for his pocket."

"Money? What money, Vi? They all been on short time lately, all the pits, the Bryn, the Garth, the Gelli."

One glance at the dress Lily was wearing had told Vi they must be living on the poverty line. Pity really. Lily could have had her pick years back. Now with the shortage of fellers you had to take what you could get.

Vi put her spoon firmly back in the saucer. "It's all a gamble Lily and you got to take the rough with the smooth. You got your family round you. You're lucky there, Lily."

Lily looked up. "Lucky?" It had never occurred to her that Vi's envied independence was not so much chosen as forced upon her. Vi had neither parents, brothers, or sisters, only John Henry.

"You ought to hear Walter going on about my family! Our Jack, too stuck up to see us now he's one of the bosses he says. It's not that, Vi. The pit's his life now. And he's well-liked there according to Dick Jenkins. One less thing for mother to worry about. The both of them so frail now. They never go outside the door. Awful to see dad some days, breathing so bad. Our Arthur's home all the time now, bad heart or something. Our Eth's expecting."

Vi was still smiling at the look of distaste on Lily's face as she made her way towards Ystrad station.

After she had gone, Lily was thoughtful. She accepted that Jack and Charlotte were the foundations of her life, and that on their approval rested her emotional security. For Ethel and Our Arthur she felt indifference, or envy, or impatience, or dislike, nothing as simple as affection. But the bonds of these emotions were as powerful as the ties of love, though it was only when she was left as the last survivor that Lily recognised how vital it had been to see and hear that irritating family every day of her life.

Lily found herself remembering the old days, when she had liked Walter and felt protective towards him, accepting him for what he was, and taking for granted his uncritical love for her. He had no family now that he had lost touch with everybody he had known in Bristol. He had only boyhood memories of what it was like to live surrounded by a close family. He had been alone. He had had to fend for himself, to look for friendship. Walter had lost his best friend when Bert was killed. In all the world he had only Ruth and Lily and she had to admit herself that that wasn't saying much.

"Walter hasn't changed," she thought, "not in anything. The war has altered Jack. He's like the men Vi said came into the cafe with their wives or girl-friends. 'You can always tell the ex-servicemen,' she said. 'They're not like John Henry. It's in their expression, a look you see in their eyes, as if they had seen more than they wanted to remember.'

"But Walter's been right through the war too, and he's really just the same. He's still the same rough and superstitious Walter going on searching for his Lucky Clover, missing for over a week now. Like a child over that clover, so downcast over something so trivial. Silly, just silly. A grown man behaving in that way, so sure something awful will happen because he can't find it. And yet you can't help feeling a bit sorry for him, especially when it means so much to him. You can't be hard all the time, but all the same it's dangerous to be soft, too. It's like Vi used to say, you give a man an inch and he takes a mile..."

The Lucky Clover with the Cornish Pisky and the Touchwood Imp were Walter's talismans. His Cornish Pisky he kept in his purse, in the 'secret' compartment of the pigskin purse he carried with him "when I be dressed up". When he was at work, the purse stayed in the back pocket of his Good Trousers.

His Touchwood Imp was kept with the Lucky Clover in the middle drawer of the chest crammed between their double bed and Ruth's truckle bed.

The Lucky Clover was a real four-leaved clover Walter had found in the Lady's Field soon after he came back home in 1919. He had regarded it as a Good Omen, and even after five years of indifferent or downright bad luck, he still trusted to its beneficent power. Browned and brittle now, it was enveloped in a fold of paper on which he had written out his Lucky Numbers, 2 and 7 ("lest you should forget" said Lily sarcastically), and his Lucky Birth Stone, Topaz. It was this fold of paper which had disappeared. Walter was inclined to blame Ruth, though he had to agree that a disintegrating clover leaf was of no value or use to her.

Milly Wilkins too could hardly be thought guilty of theft of something she knew belonged to Walter. No, it was a mystery, and Walter was prepared to see in it an omen of disaster.

He had expected Lily to be unsympathetic about the Lucky Clover. He was ready to see her laugh in his face, tell him he was off his head to make such a fuss about an old clover leaf, and that they didn't need the loss of an old clover leaf to bring them bad luck because they had enough of it already. He wouldn't have been surprised if she had brought Jack's name into it. Instead, she had turned out everything in the chest of drawers, even the bottom drawer just in case it had slipped down the back, and not in an angry or a scornful kind of way either. He was sure bad luck would come, but all the same it had lifted his spirits to see her acting as if she were concerned.

Walter had got used to Lily's indifference when he came home from work, although the place was always clean and tidy, with the kettle and the two iron saucepans full of hot water ready for him to wash, and his dinner keeping warm on the hob.

"And that's summat to be thankful for," he thought, "especially with all them slummocky women about. Milly Wilkins could take a leaf out of our Lily's book. Our room neat as a pin in paper, and *her* place looking and smelling like a pig sty. Making them Welsh cakes be all she be fit for. No wonder she don't like Lily. Our Lily do show her up too damn much, that's the truth on it. Lily can knock spots off 'em all. Deserves summat better than she got. No wonder she do get them black moods at times, only natural mun, stuck in the one room. Not much of a life for her. All the women wants a place of their own, , and a bedroom for the kid, not all cooped up day and night. That kid be a fly in the ointment, thanks to them Down There, spoiling her. Going to be a handful afore long. Better if she'd a been a boy. A boy can look out for hisself. A boy has a better life on it. Mostly anyway. Except for that lot in France. Pity Bert had to cop it. A good sort, and he gone west. Like a lot on 'em. I come through it somehow. Touchwood Imp brought I through it. Still got that. But no Lucky Clover. That be gone. Summat'll happen. Summat be bound to happen."

Chapter Twenty Three

But it was the third week in October before something did happen. Ethel's first daughter Harriet had been born, Vi's wedding had been and gone, and Walter was beginning to think that the dreaded bad luck would pass them by, clover or no clover. But as Charlotte was fond of saying, "What is to be, is to be".

In years to come Lily used to say that she felt sure something was going to happen to Walter that night. "I didn't want him to go out of the house that night" she would say.

Lily had wanted to be free from Walter, but she had never wished him harm, and lately she had been full of foreboding. "It would be so awful," she thought, "an accident now, if...although it's time enough to start worrying about *that* in another month."

"I had an awful feeling about him" she said, "and as soon as I heard the Gelli hooter going at half past four in the morning, I knew it was for Walter."

There was nowhere in the Rhondda to escape from the sound of the colliery hooters. They blasted at regular intervals throughout the day and night, to signal the start of the eight-hour-long shifts, the day shift at seven in the morning, the afternoon shift at three o'clock and the night shift at eleven p.m. These were the familiar time signals, so familiar that they could pass without being consciously noted. Charlotte, lying hour after hour on her bed in the middle kitchen, had sometimes heard Vanw-next-door call across the back yard to her neighbour getting in the washing at the same time: "Gwenno! Have the three o'clock gone yet?" and she would wonder how anybody could miss hearing a noise so brutal and insistent.

But when the blast of a hooter sounded outside the expected times, it never went unheeded, for it blew then to announce Accident, and people would run to the pit head and gather there. They would quickly learn the nature of the accident, but not how bad it was until they saw how many bodies were being brought out. And, in the too-familiar words of the *Rhondda Gazette*, it could take hours for the rescue party to recover them all.

Charlotte, Ethel, Jack, all encouraged Lily to talk to re-live that night: "I waited in the house" said Lily. "I got up and I dressed. Ruth was still sleeping. She could sleep through anything. I came downstairs and I put on my big coat because the room was so cold. I never thought to start the fire going. I just sat in the chair and waited. I was expecting Mr. Rees the Overman to knock on the door and tell me Walter had been killed. Then they would bring Walter home on a stretcher with his face covered over, the men who knew him and who'd been working by him. Then one of the neighbours would go to fetch old Granny Thomas to wash and lay out his body. Milly would let him lie in her middle kitchen, I thought. But they didn't bring Walter home. Mr. Richards the under manager came to tell me that he had been in a cage accident with four others, and that none of them had been killed. One of them, he said, was in a more critical condition than the others, but they were all badly hurt. He needn't have told me that about Walter. I knew it. He said they were taking Walter straightaway to Bristol Infirmary and that I could go with him if I could make arrangements to stay somewhere. He said Walter had internal injuries and his left leg was crushed. The cage was overwound he said. He asked me if Walter had taken out any insurance against death or injury. I said 'no'. He said that was a pity. I could tell that he thought there wasn't much hope for Walter."

Walter had been against joining any insurance scheme. "Don't agree with any on it" he had said "that be tempting fate, that be. One of the most unluckiest things thee canst do. Worse than making thee will, that be."

"I thought to myself, how strange they should be taking him to Bristol Infirmary," said Lily. "Not to Cardiff, but to Bristol. Walter was going to see Bristol again. He's going Up Home to die, I thought. And then I thought, if he don't die straightaway I can go up there to see him and stay with my Aunt Iris. I won't be much expense to her. I can leave Ruth with our Ethel."

Walter was lying with his pelvis fractured and his left leg bent beneath him, so distorted that it seemed unlikely it could be saved. He had been knocked unconscious by the impact, and Dr. Williams the colliery doctor could see that unless he received immediate treatment there was little hope of his surviving.

Pentwyn hospital in Treorchy was newly built specifically to deal with men injured in local pit accidents, but Walter needed specialised treatment. Bristol Royal Infirmary had the experience and resources, gained during the war, of treating men with shattered limbs, and it was there that Walter spent most of the next year of his life while Lily lived out at Knowle with her Aunt Iris, seeing at first hand the pattern of her cousin Mary's happy marriage.

"It's an accident that should never have happened," said Jack. "The overwinder automatically stops the cage in an emergency. What happened to the 'dead man's pin'?"

The explanation was simple; the consequences, tragic. The overwinder had been removed earlier that night to allow timber to be loaded into the cage, and the engineers had forgotten to put it back into its working position. So when at 4.15 in the morning, the sixth hour of the shift, Walter and the three other men stepped into the cage to be lowered to the pit bottom, their lives were totally in the hands of the winding engineman.

It was bad luck that he had not reset the safety mechanism. It was worse luck that just as the cage was nearing the end of the wind he noticed that the winding drum was striking against one of the eccentric rods. He had looked away from his depth indicator on the wall of the winding room, and when he looked back at the arrow it was too late to apply the brake. The cage hurtled down out of control to overshoot the bottom and bump heavily on to the sump beams yards below. The man in the ascending cage was unhurt, for it stopped before it could be flung over the big wheel. But Walter and his companions were badly injured.

"There aint much about it in the paper here," said Charlotte. She was looking at the brief paragraph in the *Rhondda Gazette* for October 25th, headed "Accident".

Chapter Twenty Three

"An accident which proved fatal to at least one took place at the Gelli Colliery early on Thursday morning last. Some men were being lowered when it occurred. Mr. Cyril Morgan who was in the ascending cage miraculously escaped."

She laid the paper aside. "That's all it gives" she said. "'Some men'. It don't even bother to give their names. No, it don't even give all their names. You'd a thought they'd give out all their names in the paper. And it don't say what happened, and it don't say who was responsible for it neither. Fatal to at least one. Aye, and Walter be like to be another by what they told our Lily."

Jack looked up from the day's *Western Mail*. His face was grim. "You can't expect details, mother. You can't expect them to go into every little detail like names. They're not important enough to be named. And what happened on Thursday is happening all the time to somebody. It's not news when 'some men' are killed or injured."

He turned the page. "Now this is something like news! This is the kind of thing that makes interesting reading. Listen to this, mother! 'Prince on the Ocean on board the Olympic. Tired out after his strenuous holiday in America the Prince of Wales is resting, mostly in seclusion, on his way home.' Just the kind of news we were all eager to hear about! Much more interesting than this other at the bottom of the page - 'Fatal Roof Fall. Two killed at Glyneath Colliery.'"

Charlotte shook her head. "Perhaps the funeral account in next week's will be fuller," she said. "That poor

Jimmy Stadden. They say he took nearly two days to die. A widow and three children..."

"I know what'll come out at the inquest." said Jack. "Accidental Death, no blame attached to anyone. Nobody's fault. Just bad luck."

"Aye," said Lily, "Bad luck. Walter like he is and me expecting. How will I manage with two children? One's bad enough. He might never come from there. And if he do, he'll be on crutches for the rest of his life. It's a poor look out, mother."

"Summat'll come," said Charlotte. "Walter baint no weakling, and that child be sent for a purpose, born to put bread in our Lily's mouth."

"Walter'll be back," said Jack. "He's come through so far. He's a survivor, Lily. It's just a matter of time now."

Walter proved their words were well-founded. His spirit was uncrushed by the accident. He had seen his workmates killed, and he counted himself lucky to be alive. He was stoical. Lily could tell only by the drawn look on his face when he was most in pain, never by any complaint he made. And the last thing he ever wanted was pity. He made light of the weary months he had spent in Bristol Infirmary, and bringing out a well-thumbed postcard of the long surgical ward he would point to the bed at the far end:

"See that cheeky face there, mun? That be I, poking me head out from they curtains. I tickled them all up there, I can tell thee, all on 'em, they doctors and they nurses alike. I tormented the life out of they nurses. Matron told I she was never so glad in all her life as to see the back of I. She never seed anybody make the place look so untidy."

Because Walter showed so little resentment or self-pity, Lily felt herself softening towards him.

"Now that I got him home, mother," she said, "he's a changed man. Well, as regards the drink he is anyhow. Never touches a drop now."

"Er's making the best of a bad job, Lily. A blessing in disguise, could be. And 'er do fair dote on the babby don't 'er?"

"Oh, he's dull on her," said Lily. "He'll sit for hours nursing her in our room or else out on the step showing her off to everybody. So different from what he was like with Ruth."

"I see Madam has changed her tune a bit," said Milly Wilkins, "and about time too. I was getting, before his accident, that I couldn't stand having her in the house. But they seem to be shaping a bit now. They might manage."

Walter was sure they would do better than 'manage'. "I been looking at Old Moore's Almanack. He baint never far out in his predictions, Old Moore baint. By the end of the year we be going to see big changes. Come the new year, Saturn be moved away from Scorpio and Jupiter be taking his place. So us Scorpios'll be under the planet of Good Fortune 'sknow. 1926 be bound to be a lucky year, mun, stands to reason."

"I don't see much reason about Jupiter or Saturn," said Lily. "Here, take this baby from me. I got better things to do than stand here listening to you all day, you and your nonsense."

Chapter Twenty Three

Walter took the baby in his arms and began singing softly "If you were the only girl in the world…"

When Lily looked in at them a little while later they had both fallen asleep.

AFTERWORD

"...that things are not so ill with you and me as they might have been, is half owing to the number who lived faithfully a hidden life, and rest in unvisited tombs"

George Eliot, Middlemarch Finale

Afterword

Her funeral was magnificent. Emrys Davies the Undertaker had brought a metal stand, a sort of three-tiered clothes horse with projecting hooks, and had placed it against the wall opposite the coffin "so as to accommodate the floral tributes, like, see", and there they hung displayed, the wreaths of daffodil and narcissi, the sprays of irises, the florists' arrangements of freesias all jostling each other and threatening to overflow the stand. There were hardly enough vases for all the tulips "for the house" brought by the neighbours, and no room on the front room alcove shelves for the mixed bunches sent Interflora from Bristol and Swansea. My sister Ruth brought them to put on the side-board in the middle-kitchen, their unfamiliar sight and insistent scent constantly reminding us that they, like us, were there because our mother was lying dead in the next room.

Ruth read aloud all the sympathy cards, especially those with verses, and noted the names of the senders on a piece of paper. "For the *Rhondda Leader* see, kid. I'll write it out." She looked at all the flowers. "Duw, there's a marvellous send-off for you. It do show you she was well-liked, though, don't it?"

I nodded. But, I thought, it showed more than that. It showed a respect for the dead and that compassion for the living which I had so much taken for granted while I was growing up in the Rhondda and which I had scarcely realised had almost gone out of my life. The funeral rites of an English suburb, private and attenuated, serve but to guard the anonymity which shrouds the living. No obscure private person ever commands the public attention which in her death my mother received as her right. She had spent seventy of her eighty years of life in the Rhondda, the last forty of them in the same house. She belonged to the Rhondda, not to the Bristol of her birth, and the strength of that attachment was never revealed more clearly than when death had severed every link.

The new curate at St. David's opened his Book of Common Prayer at The Order for the Burial of the Dead, conducting the service for the benefit of the family gathered unfamiliarly in the middle kitchen. He cleared his throat and lowered his eyes: "I am the Resurrection and the Life saith the Lord..." My father began to sob, untidy gulping sobs without dignity, just the sort of unrestrained display which would have embarrassed my mother most. "Making a real exhibition of himself." How often, in her eyes as in ours, had he made a real exhibition of himself. Never then, or now, was he aware of it. "He don't care a bit." She was right. He had an enviable unselfconsciousness.

"He that believeth in Me, though he were dead, yet shall he live..." The words carried a more confident promise than Mr. Lane's tentative delivery of them would ever have suggested. "I know that my Redeemer liveth and that He shall stand..." Lily's solo, sung to Handel's music, the anthem she so often used to tell us she sang in church one Easter Day, long before I was born, long before my sister was born. I thought of the Lily we had never known, the Lily who was young and beautiful and gifted, and who only didn't become a great singer or a famous writer because we had prevented her.

Afterword

"We brought nothing into this world, and it is certain we can carry nothing out..." She had become a miser by the end. "I don't save in ones. I do save in fivers." Transparent plastic envelopes full of notes, crammed into jumble-sale handbags, never put into a banking account because that would have meant not being able to see and handle the money. "I couldn't count it then. I do like to count it." Molière's Harpagon, The Miser, a figure of fun; my mother, misguided, pathetic, terrifying in her greed for money.

The notes had at first represented security, freedom from the poverty which had wasted her youth and her middle age, but they had become precious for themselves, to be collected, amassed, hoarded and increased. She found it difficult to part with any of her money, and when some of it had to go on birthday or Christmas presents, she would stint herself until she had made up the loss and added to the original sum. While Jack and her mother were alive, Lily could give. She gave unselfish love which, although it was largely unreturned, served to enrich her emotional life. But after their deaths she found no others to cherish, so that her affections had no outlet. Her great-grandson she felt for, but the years before he was born were barren. He came only at the end of her life, and by that time, love of money had made her poor in spirit.

Love of money made my mother bitter against me.

I had not recognised her need to keep her money and increase it, nor had I foreseen the disastrous consequences of my own casual attitude, little short of sinful in her eyes.

Eighteen months before she died, when she had already become bedridden, she had given me as an interest-free loan the £400 'dry money up front' to help with the expense of moving house. That loan we repaid in agreed instalments, and paid back all the sooner because instead of sending birthday money she deducted £25 from the sum still owing.

When I handed her the last instalment she took the notes so hesitantly that I wondered whether she was thinking of giving some of them back. Later, much later, I realised that she was remembering a second loan, also of £400, which she reminded me she had advanced us. She had been waiting for me to arrange the repayments. But I had not mentioned any repayment, not mentioned the second loan at all. It had gone from my mind.

But Lily would never believe that anybody could forget such a loan. It was unthinkable that personal concerns could have been important enough to blot out such a memory. Convenient amnesia. It had to be either pretence or else malice.

She had to be right. She was too meticulous to be wrong about the number of notes she could count. I was at fault, not deliberately, but heedlessly. Either way, Lily did not forgive my guilt. The second loan, still not fully recognised though accepted as such, was promptly repaid. "Too damn quick for my liking," according to Ruth's report of my father's reaction. Guilt it had to be.

Afterword

The rift remained unhealed. She had chosen to believe that the daughter who had never failed in love for her would try to cheat her out of her most cherished possession.

"You couldn't have done anything worse to her."

Ruth's words echoed through the final months while I found it hard to accept that my mother had not known me well enough to realise that her suspicions were groundless.

Looking back, I should have made allowance for the insecurity of the invalid and not taken the hurt so much to heart. It would have helped if she had accepted my regret for what had happened. But the letter I sent with its passionately worded attempt at explanation and pleas for her forgiveness never reached her.

It was the only letter, out of the hundreds sent over the years ever since I left home for university, which ever went astray. It happened that they were staying with Ruth at the time, and it was to Ruth's address the letter was sent. Ruth was not prepared to be peacemaker. It was more interesting and profitable to keep me as black sheep

And Ruth was with her when she died. "There was nothing in mam's handbag, not a thing. And there was nothing mam wanted you to have. She told me."

I didn't care. I couldn't lament the lack of a mourning ring, the symbol of a love which had been forfeited. Only later came "pity like a new born babe" to bring me healing peace, though not with Ruth.

Mr. Lane's voice sank.

Afterword

"...world without end. Amen." The service was over. We stood silent in the narrow passage-way, waiting until her sons-in-law and her nephews between them shouldered her coffin and carried it from its place under the front room window where Lily had lain for the past four days. It slid into the hearse surrounded by wreaths, a discreet directive from Davies Undertaker ensuring that "only family flowers please" were piled on the coffin lid; the mourners began to form the slow procession of funeral cars, the sleek black hired cars which stretched the whole length of the short street. Emrys Davies was known to be "always very good, fair play. Nothing out of place. Very nice, always", but to see to it that the mourners filled their rightful places in the cortège was nothing but routine. Husband to the deceased, sons, brothers, sons of sisters, sons of brothers, uncles, cousins, all had a position in the established hierarchy, and that hierarchy was exclusively masculine. Only the men attended the coffin to the cemetery, stood at the graveside, heard the words of committal, joined in the prayers, and sang the hymns. Only the men returned in the cars, at a homeward pace, to be dropped off at the Club, where the Family by tradition paid for every round of drink.

The women stayed at home. After the funeral service, and when the cortège had left for the cemetery, they would prepare The Tea, cold meat sandwiches, slices of sponge cake and fruit cake, "shop" unless a neighbour had baked them. No-one expected home-made; grief was held to suspend and prevent such a normal household activity as cake-making. The Tea was never judged by ordinary standards, for it was properly an extra-ordinary meal.

That women did not "follow funerals" was tradition, and if my sister and I had stayed in the Rhondda, we would have bowed to that tradition. We would not have accompanied the funeral procession to the cemetery. We would have thought it unseemly to try and break into a male conclave. It would have been unwomanly, an insult to the deceased. But we had come from afar. Emrys Davies had nodded at Ruth's "we'll be going to the cemetery with the men" as if he had been expecting such a statement. Perhaps he had, for our reputation as being different because "away" was long-standing. We went in the first car with my father, my father who had so much offended my mother by refusing to make one of the official mourners for any of her family: "Theest know damn well I don't go to funerals mun...they don't want I there..." He had kept up his antagonism to her family even to their graves. Hers was the only Callow funeral he could not shun. I had awakened that morning to hear him downstairs in the middle kitchen where he had spent the night on the settee. He was moving about, folding the blankets and piling them in the corner, covering them over with an old piece of curtain. I could hear him moaning, repeating over and over again "Oh, whatever be I going to do..." in all the anguish of a man who had been well acquainted with pain but who had never before known grief.

At the cemetery the only other women were the two district nurses who had tended Lily with such thankless devotion. But even though their office and their uniforms might have given them the status of honorary men, they would not have been at the graveside had not Ruth and I been there. They would have stayed behind with Lily's granddaughters and the women neighbours. She had outlived all her friends except Olive from Gelli Crossing. Those who came to the house to visit her in her long-drawn-out illness were mostly neighbours. And it was neighbours who came, in ones and in twos, to "pay their respects" and "to view the body". The unlined floral curtains hanging on their plastic-covered expanding wire had been closed together, as had the curtains in all the front rooms in the street, and the room was cold and shadowy. Emrys Davies had supplied the coffin. Oak, with chrome handles and name plate, as good as silver. "Like you ordered, Mr. Besant. The best quality casket and lining." He had closed and weighted the eyes which my father had remorsefully insisted were staring at him in reproach. He had bound up the chin and come back the following day prepared to find that her mouth had dropped open again. "At her age you see, Mr. Besant, it is only to be expected..." But her mouth had not dropped open, though the lips were ever so slightly parted. Emrys Davies was well satisfied that she was "seemly". My father would not allow her body to leave the house. He was distraught with the release from the tension of nursing her for the last two bed-ridden years, and had become hysterical at the thought of her being taken into any Chapel of Rest. So Emrys Davies had arranged the casket on his trestles, and the widow who had performed the same service of Laying

Afterword

Out for so many neighbours over the years had washed and dressed her. The coffin was in the exact place where her bed had been.

She was dressed in the pale pink cotton nightdress I had given her that last Christmas and which she had told me she was keeping unwrapped and unworn for her to be buried in, and over the nightdress she was wearing a full-length white satin dressing-gown tied with a tasselled cord. It was more 1930's-Hollywood style than I had expected for a shroud, but my mother would have loved it. Looking at her lying in her silk-lined oak coffin with its silver-look handles, I realised that I had never given her the gifts she had wanted. I should have given her extravagant useless presents, like satin negligees and low-cut blouses, and not the unadventurous cardigans or the practical long-johns which she had accepted with so little grace. She would not have worn the garments, but she could have shown them to the neighbours, and been pleased that I could have imagined such flamboyance to be suitable for her. She would have disclaimed them, but they would have reminded her of youth and frivolity. They would have represented another sort of life, a free, a desirable life.

My mother Lily was as unhappy in her life as had been her own mother, Charlotte and, like Charlotte, she could find a fleeting escape from it in material objects. For Charlotte, her early happier days in Bristol were represented by The Heirloom, the set of miniature goblets and decanter given her as a wedding present by the Denmers and held up to scorn by her husband Thomas. For Lily, something supremely impractical would have

398

allowed her the illusion of glamour. I had offered her only presents relating to ordinary life, such as a daughter gives to a woman who is content to be reminded of her lot. Realising as I did her deep unhappiness, I should have recognised her need for gifts which were not serviceable but symbolic. I had not been the kind of daughter she wanted, and there was little comfort in knowing that there was no kind of daughter Lily would have wanted. But since she had had daughters, she wanted to keep them close to her, just as she and her sister had lived all their lives in daily touch with their mother. It would have been an acknowledgement of her importance. She never became reconciled to the fact that both Ruth and I went away to lead our own lives. Years before she died, and long before the rift opened between us, she said "I feel as if I've never had any children." It was a reproach for having left her, and I felt it as such.

Now she had left us. She lay with her hands folded across her breast in the unnatural and accepted pose of an effigy on a marble tomb. They were blue-ish white with dark shadowed veins, hard-working hands with fingers which had worn no ring except the wedding-band, nails which had never known polish or varnish. They were hands I had known all my life but now barely recognised in their unfamiliar stillness. Beyond the edge of her dressing-gown her feet looked small and thin, very clean and smooth but grey against the matt white silk of the coffin lining. I had not realised that they were so well-shaped with such straight uncalloused toes, for I had not often seen them uncovered. I felt it an intrusion now that they should be exposed for all to see, and wrong that she should go barefoot on her final journey to the grave. Surely at the Laying Out there could have been white nylon stockings? But Ruth saw nothing inappropriate, and she was our accepted, even if self-appointed, arbiter of taste.

One of the neighbours had placed a single red carnation at her side, looking at first startled glance like a stain of blood against the stark white satin. "The cheeky flamer! Taken from that bunch in the middle kitchen by damn!" said Ruth as she removed it. "*So* gaudy isn't it" she went on. "And quite uncalled-for. They ought to know it's only family that puts any flowers in the coffin. I know who done it though. Mrs. Williams. She was here a *very* long time this morning, on her own in here with mam. And *that's* what she was up to. Damn cheek. Mam wouldn't have wanted that carnation in any case. No way would she have wanted *that*." Then she hesitated. "Mrs. Williams was very good to Mam though. Very good, in many ways. Especially at the end, see. And it's the *thought* it is, isn't it?" She leaned over the coffin. "*I* don't like the carnation, mam, no I don't. I can't say I like that carnation, because I don't. *No.* Very gaudy. But there, p'raps after all..." She looked consideringly at the body, biting her lower lip and putting her head on one side. "Would *you* like the carnation Mam? If you want it, back it shall go. It's gaudy, mind, but..." She straightened up. "Well, never mind. Better put it back. Mrs. Williams will be in and out again before that lid is screwed down. She'd see it gone, and she'd ask about it. I know her. Only too well. She wouldn't let it rest. Be awkward, isn't it, with our dad in the state he is." She laughed. "Oh, anything for a quiet life. That's what I say, whatever. We better not make a fuss. Not worth it, is it?"

She was like my father in looks, with his bright eyes and ready laughter, and she was like him in temperament too. Lively and good company, she was theatrical when she was telling any tale, which like my father she couldn't help exaggerating and embroidering. And she had always been even more superstitious than he, attracted by mysticism, by fortune-telling, by Tarot-cards, by all the manifestations of The Occult. But her interest had gone far beyond his, and had developed into something more than a spectator-sport. She had been claiming for some time to be a white witch, saying that she could predict the future and see the colour of people's auras, and more definite than all, that she had been given as her spirit guide an elderly Eskimo with auburn hair who had put her in touch with "the other side".

She had not, as far as I knew, been any kind of witch during our childhood, and I couldn't help feeling it an improbable attribute to have acquired in middle age. But it was clear that our mother's death was holding a quasi-professional interest for her. Even so, it seemed at first unlikely that there could be any special significance in her saying that she "fancied she could see our mam sitting in the chair by the window". My mother often sat in that very chair, and it was not a difficult feat of imagination to picture her sitting there. But by the following day, fancy or imagination had been overtaken by reality, at least in Ruth's mind.

Afterword

From the kitchen I could hear her voice as she confided to the first of the day's callers: "I saw mam last night, Mary. Sitting in that chair she was, plain as anything. I saw her like in life. Sitting there peaceful as anything."

But she had chosen the wrong neighbour. Mary Caradog was also psychic. No church-goer, she belonged to The Spiritualists, and could hardly let Ruth's claim go unchallenged, especially since Ruth had got in first. I could hear the cross-examination.

"What was your mother wearing then, Ruth?"

My sister was ready with her answer: "Oh, her nightie, you know, her nightie."

Mary Caradog gave Ruth time to reconsider. "Sitting in that chair in her nightie. You're sure of that Ruth?"

"Oh yes. Quite sure. Positive. Last night. I saw her. Our mam, sitting in that chair in her nightie. Just like life."

Mary Caradog smiled forgivingly. "Well Ruth my dear, I'm sorry, but I've got to contradict you there." She became more authoritative. "Your mother would *not* be sitting there in her nightdress. Oh no. Certainly not. Only head and shoulders would appear in any case. *And*," with quiet emphasis, "she would, of course, be *fully clothed*."

Our mother, said Mary Caradog, would stay with us, unseen, until her funeral. She would be present at her own funeral. Then she would leave the house for ever. Her husband would follow her into the next world, probably within the month. Ruth said nothing beyond an appeal, to nobody in particular, as to the likelihood of a daughter's knowing whether she had seen her own mother or not. There was no empirical ground for argument, and the sad occasion prevented open dispute. Ruth had given in over the carnation with a good grace, but Mary Caradog's contradiction had irritated her. She would not forgive Mary Caradog.

They were all in their element, the neighbours with their assurance and sense of decorum, friends with instinctive tact, my sister with her knowledge, wherever she had gained it, of the etiquette proper to the occasion. It was she who opened the door and acted as escort to those who had come "to see your mam"; she who looked with critical gaze to observe any changes in the body day by day; she who lingered over the coffin, smoothing the immaculate pillow, fingering the folds of the undisturbed dressing-gown. When Ruth had left the Rhondda, it was to live in Cardiff, and not as I had done, "somewhere up England way", and so she still Knew Everybody. She knew which of the visitors would kiss the icy forehead, which of them would murmur words of prayer, which of them had come only as busy-bodies. She knew them all, and she knew my father too. It was she, and not I, who could judge when he should be coaxed from the front room, before his vigil gave way to wild distress. She took charge as a professional nurse might have done, with competent sympathy but no emotional involvement.

I was the outsider. To me, the cold front-room was awesome, especially after dark, so that if I had to fetch china from the cupboard, I would try not to look towards

403

the coffined shape, but childishly hurry back to the warmth, light and companionship of the back kitchen. We never switched on the electric light in the front room, so that any errand would have to be accomplished by the light which shone from the passage through the half-open door. It was strange, I thought, that although we prayed for "light perpetual to shine upon her", yet our reverence for the dead forbade us to subject the body to the full glare of artificial light. 'Her' part of the room lay hidden in the deep shadow of the open door, so that I need not have averted my eyes. And however much I tried not to see, I still could not escape the images of my inner vision. The first long glance had told me there was no detail of her face or form I would ever forget.

In death my mother looked almost young, her skin hardly wrinkled, her brow calm. Her expression was benign, for closed lids hid the hostility in the grey eyes which in life had been magnified behind the thick glasses she wore to correct cataracts. She had been stooping in old age, and bent with illness, so that she had looked tiny. Now, lying full length, straight, everybody said how tall she seemed, how long the coffin looked. Death had given grace and dignity to her body, and serenity to her face. It was not my mother. It was a corpse which bore but little resemblance to the woman I had known, or thought I had known.

She was buried in the windswept cemetery high on the bleak Penrhys mountain. It was a sunlit day in early March, a day which carried all the promise of spring, a day she would have been sorry to leave. I felt her to be as much a stranger to me as my grandmother Charlotte and my uncle Jack, who lay in unmarked graves close by. The week before her death Lily said she had seen her mother and Jack standing at the foot of her bed. My father had never lost his superstitious belief in omens, but his dread of losing her made him vehement to deny: "It wasn't they. It couldn't have been they, mun. It was a dream. Must have been a dream. One of they vivid dreams you had." Lily had insisted. Her voice, once so clear and sharp had become a hoarse whisper, but she had persisted: "No, Walter. Not a dream. It was my mother and Jack. I saw them. They wanted me to go with them." The thought of death had always terrified her. But with her mother and with Jack both beside her, death could no longer be feared. They had gone on ahead and were waiting for her in an eternity of love.

I had no tears. Our recent estrangement and her long illness had exhausted my grief before she died. I had grieved about her life and about the cause for our separation, the coolness so skilfully fostered by Ruth that I was hardly aware of its extent. But my grieving for her death was long in coming, not until my father's removal from my life, not until I came across her last letters which I had thought lost, a thick bundle all written in her last two years, in reply to my own. Never any punctuation or paragraphing, the handwriting becoming smaller and smaller and illegible at the end, in her own words "like a spider crawling across the page".

The earliest letters were before what my father had called the Bust-Up, the latest a record of what it felt like to be old, in permanent pain and totally dependent on others. These were the letters which were to make me grow up in grief and bring forgiveness and reconciliation beyond her reach.

In September I had hurt my foot and had a tetanus injection. In reply she wrote:

"it took me back about 74 years ago when we lived in Bristol my brother Jack kept pigeons and I climbed up a short ladder to the loft he was making boxes for baby birds and I trod on a nail which went into my big toe but I don't remember any hospital treatment I sometimes doubt if I will ever go out Nurse English took me in the wheelchair to the middle room and I haven't moved from the front room since."

In May of the following year, 1976, after thanking me for her birthday present

"Now how are you I have an awful feeling that you are worried about something can I share it with you whatever it is or am I dwelling on nothing in particular as dad says."

But these were <u>before.</u>

In her last letters reminiscences and news about her Bristol cousins give way to references to the nurses who came every day, Nurse English, Sister Davies, and to the sameness of her days.

In October 1977

"it's a nice day out today and how I wish I could go out if only for a little while but I doubt if ever I will walk again I spend all day and every day in the front room."

In November 1977

Afterword

"if only I could stand alone I suffer a lot of pain rather than ask dad for help if only he was gentler."

In January, her last January 1978

"nothing but rain and high winds and only about two hours of real light every day but I console myself with thinking the weather doesn't make any difference to me if it was warm and sunny I should be still sat in the room facing the window I haven't been out of the room since we came back from Cardiff."

And, one of the very last, so difficult to decipher, with a postscript

"please forget all that has been said" which made me wonder exactly what had been said. Certainly very little had passed between us on the 'phone.

Ruth and I never quarrelled. She had simply not made anything easier, and had ensured by her seeing to the selling of the family house that all the money from the sale was hers. But then, she did take my father to live with her, and no doubt allowed him enough spending money for him to pay his way down the club. She had been a dutiful daughter and had reaped a just reward. I think his last years with her were as happy as his own cheerful temperament and freedom from the care of his invalid wife could make him. His was the gift of living for the day; I never shared a single hour of those final years except by report and postal contact.

They lie, all the Callows except one, in the same cemetery high above the valley floor. And with them now, though nine years later than Mary Caradog had predicted, my father. He was buried on the last Friday in March

1987, a day of thick cloud, sleeting rain and blustery wind, more like winter than spring. I had not seen him for six years, not since he had gone to live with Ruth, and although I had no wish to meet her again, some primitive urge dictated that I should be at my father's funeral. I had gone early to the cemetery, for I had driven down the day before and stayed overnight. It was easy to find the opened grave, although my mother's headstone lay hidden beneath the newly-turned pile of clayey soil, and standing on the path beside it, I waited for the funeral cars.

The icy wind was robbing graves of their legitimate wreaths, sending them bowling across the sloping ground and piling them up behind strangers' tombstones. On this exposed hill-top it kept threatening to blow inside out the black umbrella which was being held over the professional figure intoning the words of committal, a figure whose biretta showed him to be Roman Catholic. A Roman Catholic priest for my father who had always insisted that he believed in "none on it".

For me it emphasised that the arrangements Ruth had made were for a ceremony unrelated to any part of my father's life. She had phoned to let me know that he had "not wanted any fuss" and that he had not wanted me to be told about his death until the funeral was over. He had wanted to exclude me from his dying as completely as he had from the last years of his living. My mother had been our only link, and with that broken, contact between us gradually ceased. In the first year or two of his lonely unwelcoming widower-hood, we would go to visit him, staying the night, trying to make conversation. He would stand at the door and wave us off, small, shrunken, withdrawn. I had wanted to write to him, the same kind of letter I had sent every Sunday to them both ever since I had left home, letters which my mother would keep in the pocket of her "pinny" and read aloud to him.

He was firmly against it. "I can't see to read any letters, mun. Theest know I gets a pension from The Blind." I was not going to give up straightaway. Duty and pity made me persist. "But Mrs. Lewis opposite would read them to you. And you could dictate letters back." He shook his head and became irritable. "I don't want she to know all my bloody business, mun."

This was the neighbour who had helped him nurse my mother during her last dreadful bedridden year and a half. This was the neighbour who had taken the place of the daughters who had chosen to live away and be detained by husband and children, the neighbour of whom my mother had said that it was "like having an angel in the house." It could not be that he objected to her reading any letters. She had become too intimately knowledgeable about their affairs for that. He did not want me to write. And because he was so hard of hearing, 'phone conversations were irksome to us both. It was his and Ruth's decision to sell up and go and live with her which finally destroyed whatever relationship there had been between us. I never saw him once he had moved. I would 'phone to ask how he was. Ruth would answer and in her high-pitched eager voice would assure me he was "fine", "bright as a button", "just gone down the club with our Terry" or "up the road with our Alun". She would promise to let him know that I had been "asking after him". She phoned me only once, one Monday morning, to say that he had died. He had come home from the club on Sunday evening, had sat in the chair, complained of feeling "a bit funny" and ten minutes later he had gone, peacefully, without pain, without any illness. "I've made all the arrangements. It's up to you whether you want to come to the funeral. Twelve o'clock. Friday. Penrhys."

It was no weather to be lingering, but I saw the three or four old men whom I presumed to be some of "dad's pals from down the Club" stay behind to throw their handfuls of wet clay on the coffin lid. "So long, old buddy." They had known him better than I had, they had given him friendship and companionship in his last years.

The earth spattered on the shining engraved plate, so that his name was obliterated even before the gravediggers in their shiny yellow oilskins had cast the first shovelful. It was all over. I felt grief at my heart, not for his death but for all the years I had taken no part in his life, futile grief which had kept me dry-eyed. Ruth had shed tears throughout the ceremony and I could hear her now saying over and over again how much she would miss him. I left her at the cemetery gates for she had not asked me back to the house. I had not wanted or expected her to; this was not the time or the place to begin to heal the estrangement between us. I was hurrying back to my own life, leaving the Rhondda never to return, except in imagination.

But when I close my eyes, the picture I see is not the Rhondda of today, where there are no more pits, where the river runs clean of coal dust; where tips have been levelled and houses re-roofed; where churches have been demolished and chapels become centres of DIY. The Rhondda I see is the Rhondda of my childhood, where the streets still echoed the tramp of colliers' working boots and where the blaring of the colliery hooter signalled the hours of the day; where grass grew in the cracked paving stones in front of the shabby terraced houses; where men became unemployed and families knew poverty.

To be poor was commonplace, taken for granted. But we kept up appearances. "To be poor and show poor" was the disgrace. "Soap and water's cheap enough." It was still the same kind of community to which Charlotte and Thomas Callow brought their family in 1907, and it was in that narrow enclosed society, in the shadow of the mountains, that the living spent their days.

But on the topmost slopes of those mountains the dead are handsomely housed, in detached plots. Above their graves the earth blooms with shrubs and flowers, the well-raked gravel paths and the close-shaved grass proclaiming the hand of the paid municipal gardener. In this Eden are laid to rest those who lived in squalor on earth's surface and those who toiled in danger beneath it. They are the meek who have inherited the earth.

But it is a gift of which they have no need, and for which they can feel no gratitude.

THE END